GENERAL SYSTEM OF SYMMETRICAL LOCOMOTION OF TERRESTRIAL VERTEBRATES AND SOME FEATURES OF MOVEMENT OF LOWER TETRAPODS

TT 71-58006

ACADEMY OF SCIENCES, USSR—Institute of Paleontology
Scientific Council on the Problem: "Biological Principles of Mastering, Reconstruction and Protection of the Animal World"

GENERAL SYSTEM OF SYMMETRICAL LOCOMOTION OF TERRESTRIAL VERTEBRATES AND SOME FEATURES OF MOVEMENT OF LOWER TETRAPODS

(Obshchaya sistema simmetricheskoi lokomotsii nazemnykh pozvonochnykh i osobennosti peredvizheniya nizshikh tetrapod)

V. B. SUKHANOV

Nauka Publishers, Leningrad Division
Leningrad 1968

Translated from Russian

Published for the Smithsonian Institution
and the National Science Foundation, Washington, D.C.
by Amerind Publishing Co. Pvt. Ltd., New Delhi

1974

*Translated and Published for the Smithsonian Institution,
pursuant to an agreement with
the National Science Foundation, Washington, D.C.
by Amerind Publishing Co. Pvt. Ltd.,
66 Janpath, New Delhi 110001*

*Translator : Dr. M.M. Haque
General Editor : Dr. V.S. Kothekar*

*Available from the U.S. Department of Commerce
National Technical Information Service,
Springfield, Virginia 22151*

Printed at Navchetan Press Pvt. Ltd., Delhi, India

CONTENTS

IN MEMORY OF MY TEACHERS,
Alexander Nikolaevich Druzhinin
and *Nikolai Vladimirovich Shibanov*

INTRODUCTION

Progressive movement or locomotion in animals takes place in different ways. Among the better known types are, for example, quadrupodal and bipodal locomotion, swimming, and flight. Allures or gaits form another category and include such types of locomotion as the trot, amble, walk, and gallop. Some animals use a wide variety of gaits, ranging from fast to slow, which can be more "economical" and extremely effective in a particular situation, even though requiring large expenditures of energy. Other animals have a limited choice of locomotory types. While a horse is capable of changing gaits, this is not so with a lizard; a lizard is like a car driver who cannot change the order of cylinder function although he may start or stop the engine, go fast or slow, straight or sideways (Howell, 1944). Unfortunately, we are far from understanding the evolutionary cause of such limitations. Morphologists do not differentiate between the methods and forms of locomotion and only explain the organizational features directly through the movement, such as walk or trot. There is no generally accepted classification of gaits which could be applied to all animals. There is no clear understanding of the biological phenomena reflected in these gaits. And until recently, zoologists did not realize the importance of different modes of locomotion in mammals characterizing the biomechanical aspect of animal locomotion.

Man's centuries-old interest in animal locomotion is not accidental.

Hundreds of years ago, it was important to study thoroughly the possibilities of using the horse as the main mode of transport. Much later, it was realized that the forms of locomotion (gaits or allures) could be useful in assessing the individual qualities of horses and other agricultural animals during their employment (Yakovlev, 1951). Medicine and sport demanded the study of locomotion in man.

The success of the theory of evolution, and accordingly, the realization of the great role of movement in animal evolution (Osborn's "adaptive radiation") resulted in a number of great morphologists and paleontologists (A. N. Severtsov, W. K. Gregory, D. M. Watson, A. S. Romer, and others) giving importance to the study of the evolutionary development of the locomotory apparatus in vertebrates in order to reconstruct the peculiarities of locomotion in different groups. This branch of study—evolutionary morphology—attained its full development in the twenties and thirties of the present century (Watson, 1917; Gregory and Camp, 1918; Romer, 1922; and others) and they achieved a number of more or less successful reconstructions of the locomotory apparatus including their musculature in extinct animals. However, further advances in this direction first demanded a solution to a purely morphological problem: to establish a homology of limb muscles in the vertebrates. It is not by chance that Romer and his colleagues later published papers on the embryology of the musculature of the locomotory apparatus in the hen, newt, lizard, turtle, and oppossum; these works were specially meant to explain homology. The most significant contribution of this approach was the development of a phylogeny of the locomotory apparatus as a whole together with details. For example, Gregory has published many papers in which he traces the evolution of the pelvis, humerus, femur, etc., from fish to man. However, until recently, zoologists paid attention only to the morphology of the locomotory apparatus. The study of its function and locomotion was beyond their reach. There is no doubt that the wellknown works of Abel (1912), Gessen (1913), and Böker (1935) on morphological adaptation in animals had an adverse effect on zoological studies of the locomotory apparatus and its functions. It has become a rule to infer the peculiarities of animal movements (even in extant animals) from their morphology, ignoring a direct study of locomotion in natural surroundings. The general enthusiasm aroused by applying the concept of "convergence" to extant animals and the "theory of uniformitarianism" to extinct animals, formed the basis for substituting these methods for the study of functions in the organism (in a broad sense, i.e., locomotion) because of the ideas arising from the concept of "adaptation types." This resulted in a separation of morphologists from experimental biologists studying locomotion isolated from morphology. The concept of gaits developed for the horses was not accepted by the majority of zoologists. At the same time, locomotion in man was successfully studied in the Soviet Union by N. A. Bernstein's School and became more and more physiological in nature and gave "construction of movement" to special problems of a physiological nature. Achievements of this type quickly found their uses in the biomechanics of physical exercises and in medicine (prosthesis). But, as a result, the zoologists working in this field lost interest in the study of locomotion owing to a lack of proper instruments for recording it, lack of methods, and lack of clearly defined aims, particularly because they were engaged in specific problems of ecology, etc. Field observations on animal behavior were considered obsolete. Without establishing any quantitative method for the evaluation of animal movements and behavior, zoologists found it convenient to ignore the simplest "visual" observations. As a result, the centuries-old experience of hunters and naturalists was lost within a few years. Under such conditions, the study of the vertebrate locomotory apparatus was confined to morphologists.

The development of bionics led to an increased world-wide attention to the biomechanics of animal movement. It is enough to say that two of the biggest zoological organizations in the world—The Zoological Society of London and the Zoological Society of America—organized special Symposia (1961 and 1962) on the problems relating solely to vertebrate locomotion. Much attention was paid to the traditional methods of locomotion, i.e., swimming and flight. But the need for a detailed study of terrestrial locomotion of tetrapods is realized more and more, especially in view of the need for developing improved machine designs. Here, nature is considerably ahead of technology.

Animal locomotion has two aspects: Firstly, it is a subject relating to biomechanics—a science, the early historical development of which is associated with the wellknown mathematician and naturalist, Borelli (1681) who was the first to make a consistent study of man and animal as objects of the laws of mechanics. The physiological aspect of the process of movement is linked with problems relating to the forms of locomotion, although it is not fully explained by the latter. Similarly, the study of the latter has a long history. For example, Newcastle (1657) had already given a detailed description of gaits in horses.

Subsequent studies concerned with locomotion in man and animals continued in different ways. Locomotion in man which is limited to only a very few forms (walking and running) compelled scientists initially to make deeper studies to explain the internal peculiarities of movement, and to develop still more accurate methods explaining the speciality of locomotion itself. The main investigations along this line are the works of the brothers, A. Weber and V. Weber (1836); Marey (1873, 1878, 1884, 1894, 1901); Muybridge (1887); Braune and Fischer (1898-1903); the Moscow School of Human Biomechanics (Bernstein, 1926, 1927, 1935, 1940, 1947).

Locomotion in animals as a whole, and even in the most frequently studied, the horse, varies much.[1] Constant attention was given at first to gaits: the peculiarities of each gait were studied separately, together with the possibilities of a change from one gait to another. Detailed classifications, etc., were given for these gaits, mainly those meeting the requirements of the horse—for sports and horse-breeding in general. Here, the main stages of study are associated with the names of Goiffon and Vincent (1779), Marey and Muybridge, and Howell (1944), and most recently, Hildebrand (1962 and 1963).

Other researchers gave much importance to the "general principles" of the animal mechanics. Gray (1939a) pointed out two closely related aspects of animal locomotion which attracted the attention of students for many years. These aspects are an explanation of the mechanical or kinetic principle of animal locomotion and the physiological nature of the locomotory mechanism. As early as 1873, Haughton published a book which is still useful today. Gregory's article (1912) on the principle of tetrapod locomotion showed the importance of animal weight on movement for the first time and was a great step forward. Experimental studies on the mechanics of the action of forces on animal limbs were carried out by Manter (1938) and Barclay (1946, 1953). The main principles of their research were formulated by Gray (1944) in his work on the general problems of the mechanics of the tetrapod skeleton. The purpose of these studies is analogous to those on human locomotion at the beginning of the last century. However, the great complexity of the subject (movement not on two but on four legs whch often move not in one, but in many planes at a time), does not allow us to place the results of these studies at the same level with the findings of N. A. Bernstein. It is still important to search ways of connecting these results with "normal" biomechanics and the morphology of the locomotory apparatus.

In spite of the fact that definite progress has been made,[2] studies on animal biomechanics are made without any reference to the specific forms and modes of locomotion. In the first instance, gaits must be combined in an acceptable form in biomechanics. On the other hand, the necessity for distinguishing particular modes of terrestrial locomotion as categories dealing with the biomechanical aspect of locomotion in its development along certain specific lines of tetrapod evolution has actually only begun to be realized (Gambaryan, 1968; Sukhanov, 1968a). Still more work is needed to eliminate the gaps in the different trends of studies on animal locomotion and the morphology of their locomotory apparatus, so that a morpho-functional

[1]Incorrect thinking prevails that, as a result of domestication, the horse occupies a unique position among the animals due to its ability to use almost all the known gaits. But the same is true of tapir, camel, and many other animals with specialization.

[2]The present level of the study of animal locomotion was summarized up by Hatt (1932), Howell (1944), Slijper (1946), Gray (1950 and 1953), S. V. Ottovei (1959) and Hildebrand (1960).

analysis of the apparatus becomes functional not in words but in practice.

The present work is designed to answer only a few of the above-mentioned problems. Symmetrical locomotion encompasses almost all the forms of locomotion in the lower tetrapods and a number of gaits characteristic of mammals; undoubtedly, it represents the first and primitive type of terrestrial locomotion, the knowledge of which should serve as a basis for further studies on all types without exception to form and mode of movement in terrestrial vertebrates. This work consists of two portions: a general one which proposes a new system of symmetrical locomotion, and a second, more specific part which suggests methods of utilizing the new system for specific animal groups.

Animal locomotion studies were carried out by the author for almost ten years (with intervals) both in the field and in the laboratory, simultaneously with studies on some other topics. The completion of this work is largely due to the sincere interest and collaboration of Academician Y. A. Orlov, Prof. K. K. Flerov, K. A. Yudin (Doctor of Biological Sciences), P. P. Gambaryan, I. S. Darevskii, and L. P. Tatarinov (Kandidat of Biological Sciences), and also, to the hospitality of my colleagues at the Repeteks sandy-desert station of the Turkmenian Academy of Sciences, USSR. I wish to express my special thanks to my teachers, A. N. Druzhinin and N. V. Shibanov, Docents at the Moscow State University, to whose everlasting memory this book is dedicated.

Much help was received in the formulation of results from B. F. Sukhanov (Artist), A. V. Umrikhina (Kandidat of Biological Sciences), N. V. Kalandadze (Trainee at the Paleontological Institute of the USSR Academy of Sciences, and the Directorate of the Paleontological Institute.

PART I

GENERAL SYSTEM OF SYMMETRICAL LOCOMOTION OF TERRESTRIAL VERTEBRATES

Chapter I

DEVELOPMENT OF THE CONCEPT OF GAITS IN TERRESTRIAL TETRAPODS AND METHODS FOR THEIR GRAPHIC REPRESENTATION

In spite of the absence of an exact definition of allures or gaits,[1] hippologists have a more or less clear idea of what phenomena should come under their purview. Since attention has been primarily paid to the locomotion of the horse, and to a lesser extent, other domestic tetrapods, scientists are not disturbed by the ambiguity of the self-evident definition: "...gait—a mode of progressive movement of animals" (Drasnikov, 1957, p. 56), a definition which occurs almost unchanged in textbooks on the animal morphology. It is true that recently, attempts have been made to improve this definition. For example, V. D. Uspenskii (1953) defines gait in another way, in full accordance with the present state of science (and terminology). "Gait is a comp-

[1]Both the terms are synonymous. The horse-breeders in the Soviet Union prefer to follow the French terminology on allures of the horse aud other farm-land animals. All the zoologists, as a rule, use the English term "gait" corresponding to the term "Pakhodka." Americans also call the various forms of locomotion in horses, "gaits" (Grogan, 1951).

lex, strictly coordinated, rhythmic movement of the entire body of the animal treated as an integral complex of reflex acts that occur in accordance with the conditions of the environment and which are capable of producing progressive movements of different types inherent in each animal species" (Uspenskii, 1953, pp. 109-110, 115). As a whole, of course, this can be applicable to a gait but does not take us nearer to the concept of gaits. The latter should provide the means for classifying, generally and specifically, those locomotory phenomena which hippologists have, for a long time, combined under the general term "allure" or "gait" in their dynamics, interrelations, etc.

Newcastle (1657) mentions five types of locomotion in horses: walk, trot, amble, gallop, and running. Naturally, the definitions given by Newcastle do not conform to our present understanding of these gaits, but one can guess what he meant by them. Thus, according to him, a walk is the form of movement when two of the horse's legs are always held in the air and the other two legs are on the ground, all the legs move in different ways, unlike the trot in which the diagonally placed limbs function simultaneously. In this way, Newcastle's definition of the *walk* applies only to the rapid part of the walk of the current usage. A literal description of gaits in Newcastle's day would not have been accurate. Often, the quick movement of a horse's legs resulted in a wrong representation of the whole movement, and attention focuses only on the relatively prolonged acts in the movement. Until the second half of the 19th century, observation "by hearing" remained the principal method for studying movements. One can only wonder at the volume of knowledge which was acquired by hippologists prior to the application of the first objective methods of motion.

However incomplete, the nature of literal description was clear right from the beginning. Already in the second half of the 18th century, the first method of graphically representing gaits appeared. This was done in relation to the ten wellknown gaits. Order of raising and advancing of hoofs, mode of combining acts of limbs, number, sequence, and rhythm of thuds, the arrangement of steps, length of stride, the form, extent and direction of the area of support (Goubaux and Barrier, 1901, p. 429). Of these elements, the important ones which define the gait proper (or the one in question) were incorporated in the "notation" system of recording by Goiffon and Vincent (1779). The duration of contact of each limb with the ground is marked on four lines (Figure 1, A) situated one under the other in the natural sequence in which the hoofs of the horse strike the ground while walking: Right front (*RF*), left hind (*LH*), left front (*LF*), and right hind (*RH*)—hoof time is recorded for the duration of contact of each limb with the ground. Time was determined from the sound: for example, in "walk," thuds are heard at uniform intervals. This determines the ratio of the segments marked on the straight lines, i.e., by this method, recording is fixed for only a relative time of support.

Here also, inaccuracies in descriptions of gaits existed. The walk was described as the gait when only two legs were always on the ground. It was almost a century later that the walk was accurately shown (Lenoble du Teil, 1877; Goubaux and Barrier, 1884); as in the walk of a man in which a period of "single" support on one leg alternates with periods of "double" support on both legs (Weber and Weber, 1836), so also in the walk of a horse there ought to be periods of support on more than two legs (i.e., three or four legs). The earlier mistake is easily explained: sound relates only to the thud of hoofs on the ground and not to the acts when the hoofs are raised; three or four-limbed support periods in the ordinary walk of a horse are of comparatively short duration (according to Goubaux and Barrier, they constitute only 1/7 of the total support period of each limb and are two times shorter than the "main supports," i.e., two-limbed support periods).

Several other methods of diagrammatically representing gaits are now of historical importance (Lecoq, 1843; Lenoble du Teil, 1877). On the whole, from the end of the 17th through the first three-quarters of the 19th century, there were many important hypotheses: Certain concepts were established such as, two phases in the action of each limb—support and hanging—jointly constitute a "full walk" (which is what we now describe as the locomotory cycle); the "four-pace" movement in which the four thuds of hoofs are heard in the cycle; and the "two-pace" movement wherein the thuds of two limbs fuse so that only two thuds for the four limbs are heard. Such types of gaits as the four-pace (*pas* or walk), the two-paced trot, the amble, and "irregular" rhythmically different forms of movement such as gallop, were clearly defined. Gaits and their various forms were early distinguished, but even the best experts could not describe properly how the horse's limbs function in one or the other fast gaits. The representation of horses by past artists are full of mistakes. Therefore, for a long time, one of the most important services of photographic snapshots was to help artists in studying them before practice.

A revolution in the study of animal locomotion came about through the use of special recording equipment—in the beginning, pneumatic and automatic (Marey, 1873), and later, electrical (Marey, 1878)—and the start of snapshot photography (Marey, 1884, 1894, 1901; Muybridge, 1887). For the first time man noticed the locomotion of animals and had the opportunity to pay special attention to each gait. The entire signs of animal locomotion virtually changed within a few years; to see this, one need only compare Pettigrew's brilliant work, *Animal Locomotion* (1873) with Marey's works: *La machine animale: Locomotion terrestre et aerienne* (1873) and *Le Mouvement* (1894). The scientific achievements of the world also had widespread effects in Russia. In this regard credit must be given to the Russian horse-breeders and equestrian sport fans (S. Uruso, and others). Marey's first book was translated into Russian in 1875, just two years after its publi-

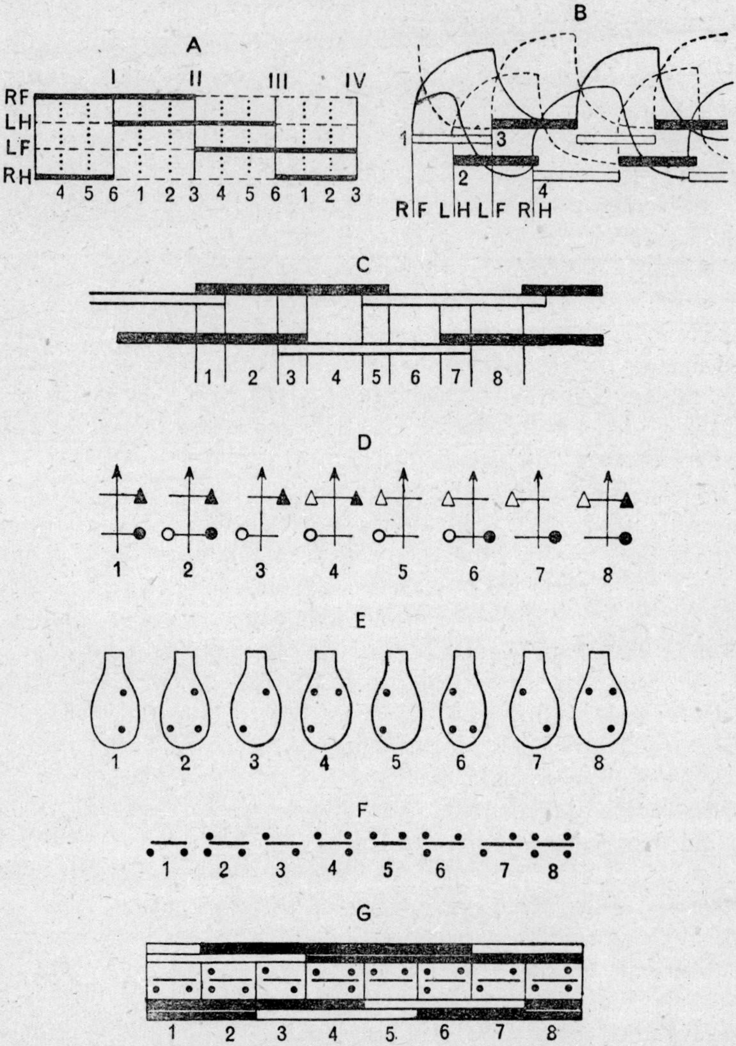

Figure 1. Methods of diagrammatically presenting gaits.

A—according to Goiffon and Vincent; B—according to Marey; C—according to Goubaux and Barrier; D—according to Muybridge; E—according to Smith; F—according to Howell; G—method recommended by the author. In all instances, the same gait is shown—normal walk. A and G—black portions on the horizontal scales show the time during which the limb is on the substratum; white portions, the time when the foot is in air. B and C—black portions correspond to the support of the left limbs; white, to the right; horizontal intervals between the portions, to the proportions of limbs. D—circles show hind support of limbs; white represents left, black represents right; triangles, also white and black, show front support of limbs. E, F and G—dots represent support limbs; standing from above, left, right; at the end of the horizontal lines, front. Paces shown A—by Roman numerals; B—by Arabic numbers; in the remaining cases, Arabic numbers show the order number of stages. Limbs in A and B represent : LH—left hind, LF—left front, RH—right hind, RF—right front.

cation. The first photographs by Marey were reprinted in Russian journals on horse-breeding and even in newspapers.

It would be a mistake to consider this early period as one of an uncontrolled desire to photograph only moving animals without giving importance to the results obtained by Bernstein (1935). Marey is responsible for not only introducing several methods for recording specific movements in man and animals (self-recording apparatuses, chronophotography, chronophotocyclography) but also, and more important, a method of graphically representing gaits which is practical to this day in a simplified form (Bourdelle, 1934; Faber, 1956; Hildebrand, 1959, 1960, 1963). By these contributions, Marey advanced the concept of gaits and attempted to give a "synthetic" analysis of all known gaits.

Marey's graphical method (see Figure 1, B) envisages the same "notation" scales as suggested by Goiffon and Vincent, but is admittedly arranged in a somewhat different and less successful order: The two upper lines were intended for the front limbs and the two lower lines for the hind limbs; the right and left limbs are characterized by different striations (in Figure 1, B, the black segments relate to the left limbs, the white, to the right). Marey's method has a specific combination of "notation" scales on which the support time for each limb is plotted with the curves characterizing the moments of touching and lifting of limbs. The curves can be obtained with the help of self-recording devices. Thus, not only is the relative support time and transport time recorded here, but absolute time as well. Marey's followers gave his method a modern appearance (Figure 1, C) by discarding the curves as they did not carry any additional information.

Marey's technique was not just to record the real time (instrumental defects made it difficult for him to ascertain three or four-support periods in the walk cycle) but also to compare different gaits since his diagram is a synoptic table of gaits in horses (Marey, 1873). The main disadvantage of Marey's method is the underscoring of what is now known as the "support plan": The spatial arrangement of the supporting limbs at different stages of the cycle is not represented diagrammatically; hence, the comparison of gaits demands distracting attention from some important features of movement.

On the other hand, the method graphically representing gaits through photography by another pioneer (Muybridge, 1887) in the study of movement, focuses attention mainly on the support sequence (Figure 1, D). Based on the fact that the limbs of an animal may be found only in two states, support or transport, Muybridge subdivides each cycle into eight successive stages on the number of combinations occurring in two different phases for the four limbs. Each stage is represented by a vertical arrow, the point of which corresponds to the position of the head. He characterizes the limbs under a particular stage of contact with the substratum through some special symbols.

The absence of any sign shows free movement in the air. Hence, one is struck by the idea of the support sequence, that is, which limbs in each stage rest on the ground and how subsequent stages of the cycle are distinguished from each other. Thus, it is considered that the duration of these stages may be different.

Muybridge's method gives a terser characterization of each walk than Marey's method; it brings closer the "literal description" in the diagram of gaits, but it completely ignores the absolute time of support and transport, and somewhat schematizes relative time. For example, in walk as depicted in Figure 1, D, the right front limb is in contact with the ground in five stages out of eight, i.e., in equality of stages, the relative support time is 5/8 of the total duration of the cycle. The walk recorded by Marey's method modified by Goubaux and Barrier (1901) as shown in Figure 1, C where the support time is shown in relation to the absolute time, the relative time is estimated to be 7/12 of the total duration of the cycle. As seen, the figures are quite close. It must be mentioned that neither Muybridge nor subsequent workers employing the modification of Marey's method (Smith, 1912; Howell, 1944; Snyder, 1952, 1962; Urban, 1965) confirmed that all the stages of the cycle are alike. Yet none of them (except perhaps Howell) even attempted to indicate the relative support and transport time, considering such as perhaps too strenuous. However, experience has shown that because of this neglect, the potential possibilities of Muybridge's methods were not fully realized.

Nevertheless, Muybridge continued to work on developing the concept of gaits in animals and distinguished new forms of locomotion after proper characterization. Marey differentiated the lower and higher forms of the trot and interrupted trot,[2] amble, walk with variations depending on the relative duration of some stages of the cycle, and the gallop of two-, three-, and four-paces. Muybridge classified gaits in the following categories: Walk with a modification in the form of "creeping" (amble),[3] synchronized and non-synchronized forms of trot and amble, slow and fast canter, two forms of the transversal (diagonal) and two rotational (lateral) gallops, each of these being in two-, three-, and four-paces, and finally the ricochet of the kangaroo.

Muybridge's main contribution is his compilation of photo albums of moving persons, horses, different domestic animals, and a few wild animals (1887), since he had developed a special photographic technique with 24 cameras in sequence on the side, 12 in front, and 12 behind. It was possible for him to show the locomotory cycle through a series of successive snaps

[2]In the case of the interrupted trot, the synchrony of the diagonal limbs is disturbed. Low or slow trot is characterized by the presence of certain stages in the cycle which have support on all four legs; the high or fast trot, on the other hand, is characterized by stages in which the foelimbs move in the air independently.

[3]This is a running gait rather than an amble as defined by Newcastle.

indicating the relative portion of limbs and of the animal itself with regard to the substratum at various moments in the cycle. Unfortunately, his analysis of these photographs is incomplete, and the definition of gaits is not always correct. Nevertheless, even now, Muybridge's photographs provide invaluable material for further studies as he captured innumerable animal forms and the quality of his photography is excellent.

The achievements of this period in the study of gaits were in general, detailed by Goubaux and Barrier (1884) who compiled a manual on the morphology of horses; this manual was reprinted many times and translated into Russian (Goubaux and Barrier, 1901) and is significant even today. However, the nature of the manual is such that a theoretical comprehension of the rich material it contains is difficult. Only from a sequel which would rediscover the facts presented in this manual, could a correct approach be made to the problem of gaits. Another monumental work of this period is *A Manual of Veterinary Physiology* by F. Smith (1912), but it does not give any substantial information on the study of movement. However, it suggests some modifications of Muybridge's method of diagrammatically representing gaits (Figure 1, E).

On the whole, an historical approach to the phenomenon of locomotion was lacking during this period, although since the last quarter of the 19th century, the role of motion in the evolution of animals was clearly understood. The problem of a correlation between various gaits was tackled only in one direction: how the conversion of gaits from one form to another is accomplished in the movement of the same animal. Marey's synoptic table of gaits constitutes a major generalization which shows how beginning from amble, a gradual retardation in the functioning of the hind limbs gives rise to walk and subsequently, to trot.

The first investigations on the origin of gaits appeared in a series of works by Croix (1927-1940). But his somewhat scholastic approach, modified terminology, and disregard of the traditional methods in the study of locomotion resulted in his total failure to construct a scheme for the evolution of gaits—regardless of its application to the study of movement through fast-moving cinematographic film. According to Croix, the initial form of movement in terrestrial vertebrates is slow walk (*prototipico*) in the lateral sequence (*RF-RH-LF-LH*). Its further development gave rise to gaits called *meserpetico*, *meterpetico*, and *paso pithecoide*. All these are based on the lateral sequence of limb movements and correspond to an increasing level of locomotion rate. Mainly independent of each other, the forms of locomotion in amphibians and reptiles are derived from this "central order": *parerpetico*—a slow gait in tortoises and tailed amphibians, *skirterpetico*—jump of batrachian amphibians, *calerpetico*—trot of reptiles, *trote bipodal* and *paso bipodal*—locomotion of reptiles and slow trot of mammals, *trote caminado*. In other words, Croix (1929, p. 8: *quadro filogenetico*) thinks that the lateral forms of locomotion preceded the two-paced and also the four-paced diagonal gaits based on the diagonal sequence in the functioning of limbs: *RF-LH-LF-RH*. In this context the extreme rareness of the lateral locomotion in nature met with in only some highly organized mammals, i.e., primates, or seen in high-speed movement (horse), does not bother the author. According to Croix the diagonal walk of mammals (*paso normal*) developed only from the trot and the amble (*sobrepaso* and *ambladura*) from the walk. The diagonal gallop could originate from both the trot and amble. The lateral gallop is secondary and the ricochet even a tertiary phenomenon.

On the whole, the merit of Croix's investigations, besides the idea of the evolution of gaits, lies in a clear understanding of the fact that the number of supporting limbs during some phase of the cycle[4] decreases with an increase in the rate of locomotion, and contrasts the symmetrical gaits (trot, gait, amble) with asymmetrical ones (gallop and ricochet).[5] The logic of Croix's evolution of gaits cannot be denied; only, judging from the author's studies, the sequential development of symmetrical gaits is exactly opposite to Croix's scheme.

The concept of gaits was raised to new heights by Howell (1944) who devoted a separate chapter to it in his book entitled *Speed in Animals*. In fact, Howell's book is the first theoretical elaboration of the problem of gaits as a whole. After Howell, much importance was given to the practical differentiation of the two types of locomotion—symmetrical and asymmetrical, viz., symmetrical (axial skeleton bends in a horizontal plane; the intervals between lowering of limbs to the ground are equal; the support plan in the cycle is, for the most part, repeatedly symmetrical, etc.) and asymmetrical (axial skeleton works on a vertical plane; the intervals between lowering of limbs to the ground are dissimilar; the support plan is asymmetrical, etc.). These ideas have a specific historical significance. According to Howell, asymmetrical locomotion appeared only in mammals.

In working on his classification of gaits, Howell modernized the diagrammatical method of gait representation suggested by Muybridge. Taking each gait in a sequence (from left to right), Howell divided the support plan into eight stages. But he depicts the support plan of stages in a different manner (Figure 1, F) using horizontal lines with points near the end to indicate supporting limbs. In this connection, the points lying on the top and on the bottom near the right end of the line correspond to the left and right forelimbs; points lying near the lower end correspond to the hind limbs (the upper one represents the left limb and the lower one, the right limb). Such a system

[4]Yet, according to the researches of Weber and Weber (1936), it was understood that an increase in speed in human beings brings about a reduction in the duration of the two fold support, and in running, a period of without-support occurs.

[5]The terms "symmetrical" and "asymmetrical" locomotion were introduced but not analyzed.

of recording provides a better graphical interpretation of the dynamics of the locomotory cycle when compared with the original records of Muybridge. At the same time, Howell brings into use the "support formula" representing the number of limbs touching the ground during each successive stage of the cycle; the formula 2-3-2-3-2-3-2-3 conveys the idea of "normal walk" as represented in Figure 1, F. The support formula has a purely secondary significance enabling one to reduce the "descriptive pictures" of gaits to the minimum.

Howell, while working on his classification of gaits, showed clearly the relationship between the forms of locomotion and speed. In this regard, a series of four-paced gaits (listed by Howell) are of special interest: crawl, slow walk, slow running walk, and fast running walk.Theoretically, all these forms may be accomplished in the diagonal as well as in the lateral sequence, but the last form is very rare, a fact which surprised Howell. He examined the two-paced gaits—trot and amble—separately, showing that each of these forms has only two speeds—slow (walking) and fast (running)—with stages of free flight in the cycle. Howell does not raise the question of a relationship between two-paced and four-paced gaits, either with regard to the history of their development, nor to their interchange in the "life" of a particular animal.

Gambaryan has worked out a classification of asymmetrical gaits in detail, including diagonal and lateral gallops (each in two series with a different number of paces; obviously, the four-paced forms are considered as basic and the three-paced as deviations), and the different canters presented in typical and atypical order, half-bound and bound.[6] The bipodal forms of locomotion, two-paced walking and running, and one-paced ricochet, are studied separately. He also refers to an intermediate form between the four-paced asymmetrical movement and ricochet, later defined as the "primitive ricochet jump" (Gambaryan, 1955).

It is difficult to re-evaluate Howell's contribution to the study of locomotion of animals. Due to certain drawbacks in his method of graphically representing gaits, he could not clarify many inconsistencies in his classification of symmetrical gaits, an analysis of which could have resulted in the establishment of a more perfect and practically comprehensive system of symmetrical locomotion. The shortcomings in Howell's system become very

[6]*Bound* is a special form of jumping locomotion in some mammals which is accomplished by a simultaneous extention of both the hind limbs followed by a rapid landing of both forefeet as, for example, in small dogs moving on soft and deep snow. In the *half-bound* type of gate, one forefoot touches the ground first, and only after a step ahead does the second foot come into contact with the ground. The *half-bound* form is common in many lower mammals : cats, weasels, squirrels, rabbits, and hares. We in the Soviet Union sometimes call them double and single ambles (Gambaryan, 1968).

apparent in their practical application, i.e., in the study of locomotion of lizards carried out by Snyder (1952 and 1962) and Urban (1965), a blind adoption of Howell's scheme led to an incorrect interpretation of some forms of locomotion.

In summary it is worth mentioning that every advance in the study of animal locomotion is hinged to a revolution in the methods of recording specific movements, and to the methods of diagrammatic representation. However, if the methods of recording are at present (at least theoretically) at a high level (photo and motion pictures, cyclography, moving x-ray photograph, the use of a mobile platform, etc.), then the only question which arises concerns the mode of applying these methods to a given animal. The second method, diagrammatic representation, suffers, as we have seen, from certain drawbacks which make understanding accumulated data difficult. For the most part, only two methods are used today—Marey's and Muybridge-Howell's; they are mostly used in isolation from each other. Since each method outlines different aspects of a single locomotory process, it would seem best to combine the two into one.

That is what the author has done here—combined the positive merits of the two methods of diagrammatic representation. This method exceeds the other two in its clarity, its absolute reflection of the basic limits of the locomotory cycle for each gait, and the ease with which different gaits can be compared (since it enables the researcher to outline separately the varying limits of each type of gait). It is equally convenient for practical purposes and for theoretical construction. In this combination method, Howell's records are supplemented by two "notation" scales (upwards and downwards), and the duration of support time for each limb is recorded by shading on a definite scale: the colorless (white) spaces in this context determine the transport time. The outer scales, uppermost and lowermost, show the working of the hind limbs; the inner scales show the working of the forelimbs. This method of combining the records of the support plan and the time of intervals are shown in Figure 1, G.

The record of one cycle as the elementary part of the locomotory process in principle, gives complete information about the whole process. However, in practice, it is necessary to take into consideration the fact that the basic nature of locomotion varies not only with the speed and form of movement, etc., but also with a number of incidental variations. For example, for one reason or another, the limbs of an animal may work in somewhat different ways; the reason can only be determined by recording several successive cycles.

The duration of the stage constituting a cycle is, as a rule, different. On a diagram, this can be shown by different lenghts in the horizontal line for the plan of support of stages. The variation in time of regularity can be easily explained by the effect of several factors which are discussed in Chapter II. In every animal, movement of any form varies, more or less, from the determined average of a given species's norm. However, in the construction of a general system of locomotion, it is easy to consider the conventional norm of gaits which can be denoted simply as "norm" when all the stages in the cycle are equal. This assumption permits one to express all the time interval of the relative sequence by a simple ratio of the number of equal stages, rather than the ratio of absolute numbers in seconds or a fraction thereof. The divergence of average and conventional norms should not disturb us. It will be further shown that each norm is only a function of certain values of speed and rhythm of locomotion and as such, there are no practical differences between norms. When speaking of an average norm, we mean the speed and rhythm which is preferred by animals. In the conventional norm, mention is made of such specific combinations of both factors which bring about the equilibrium of stages in a cycle (stride).

The analysis of gaits by Howell, as recorded by this new method, together with an interpretation of the photographs of a number of successive moments in the locomotory cycle of various animals carried out by Muybridge (1887) and other authors, led to the establishing of a new system of symmetrical locomotion for terrestrial vertebrates which explains many features of their movement (Sukhanov, 1963, 1964b, 1967a). Further studies on locomotion in lower tetrapods (amphibians and lizards) not only corroborate the universality of the system, but also provide it with many details (Sukhanov, 1964b, 1968b; see also the second portion of the present work).

It should be noted that the American scientist, Hildebrand (1963), came to a similar system by another method based on the study of movement in mammals caught on motion film. Such a coincidence illustrates the urgent need for establishing a general system of animal locomotion.[7] Hildebrand, like other zoologists working on mammals, stresses the study of asymmetrical locomotion while determining the elements that should be used for analyzing gaits. He views the system of symmetrical locomotion proposed by him as primarily the method of deciphering the material obtained from motion pictures.

* * *

A history of the study of animal gaits appeared simultaneously with a history of the development of diagrammatic methods for their representation. Marey's method stresses mainly the time ratio in the working of limbs, but the external features of gaits are not expressed clearly in his diagrams. This makes the comparison difficult. The method of Muybridge-Howell underscores the support plan of the locomotory cycle as a whole and of each

[7]The term "system" should be considered as the form of movement in its broader sense, rather than simply as "classification"; a system implies the understanding of the main factors determining the features of gaits.

of its stages individually which provides a clearer differentiation of gaits, but it does not take into account the time required for coordinating limb action. The author's new method combines the positive aspects of these previous methods. It includes a combination of the support plan of the stages of cycles by a parallel recording of the time of support and transport for each limb on "notation" scales arranged in a form that makes comparison easy and facilitates the subsequent computation of the principal features of the locomotory process. In the theoretical computation of a conventional norm for gaits, movement is used when all the stages in the cycle are equal.

CHAPTER II

SYMMETRICAL GAITS OF TERRESTRIAL VERTEBRATES AND THEIR RELATIONS TO ASYMMETRICAL FORMS OF MOVEMENT

1. GENERAL DEFINITIONS

Progressive movement in terrestrial vertebrates is composed of the actions of four, and rarely of two, limbs and a corresponding shift in the center of gravity in an animal. The two main periods of action for each limb are *propulsion* (support) and *restoration* (transport) which together form one full cycle (stride). In the cycle, each extremity makes one *double step*.[1] *Support time* refers to the duration of time that an extremity makes contact with the ground (limb retraction); the time taken from the limb's transport to the front (protraction) is known as *transport time*. The relationship between support

[1]The term step is used in two ways : 1) the name given to one of the forms of locomotion, and 2) the name given to the distance between the sequence of imprints on the substratum of one and the same foot (double step), or of two feet—front or back pair (simple step in symmetrical locomotion, if the distance is measured in the course of movement).

time and transport time is very specific to the action of each limb; this relationship has been taken as an index of *rhythm of limb action.* It is usual to compare the action of a limb to a pendulum: straight when it moves freely in the air, and reverse when the center of rotation is in the step (Raabe, 1870; Goubaux and Barrier, 1901; Bock, 1952). According to this analogy, each main period of limb action is subdivided into various phases. If a biomechanical analysis supports the existence of such a division, an attempt to analyze gaits (Croix, 1929a) without its help cannot be considered satisfactory.

The *locomotory cycle* is an elementary portion of the locomotory process during which each of the four limbs completes its work of a full cycle. Normal locomotion is possible only with the strict coordinated working of all four limbs. *Rhythm of locomotion* is the specific order of sequence at the time of similar moments in the working of each of the four limbs; for example, the moment of entry for limbs in contact with the substrate. This is the most important characteristic of the process of locomotion as a whole. What should be taken as an index of locomotion rhythm will be shown below.

Movement, when all four limbs of an animal work sequentially one after the other, is known as *four-paced,* unlike *two-paced* when diagonal or ipsilateral limbs work at one time. In fact, *pace* denotes the time interval between two subsequent strokes, for example, the hoofs of a horse on the ground.[2] As mentioned, the locomotory cycle in the four-paced movement consists of eight sequential stages, each differing in its *support plan,* i.e., the location of limbs in relation to the body (or trunk). The eight sequential support plans comprise the *support plan for the entire cycle.* The *support formula* therefore, shows the number of supporting limbs in each stage of the cycle. The support plan and the support formula indicate those external peculiarities of locomotion which, firstly, are visible to the observer; and which, secondly, form the basis for separating out different forms of movement, gaits (in other words, the external appearance of the gait).

Thus, for separating a gait, the moments of lifting the limbs from the substratum and their subsequent contact to it, are considered the most important functions of "gait activity." The results of experimental researches conducted on man (Bernstein, 1927, 1935, 1940) must always be viewed with this assumption in mind. For example, it is known that in the working of each limb there is a peculiar maximum and minimum development of vertical and longitudinal force which is approximately associated with just the start and the end of the support (footfall and liftoff)[3], and the middle time of trans-

[2]In the locomotion of man, pace characterizes the number of single (simple) step in a minute, and then the frequency—the number of steps in a second (Bernstein, 1935).
[3]In four-legged mammals, the front stroke is usually called the period during which the main propulsive force is established by the forefeet. Consequently, the hind stroke occupies that period of time when work is predominantly that of the back limbs. Both periods may partially overlap (during slow movement), or separate from each other at any interval (during movement at high speed).

port (transport minimum). It is not ruled out that the degree of this conformity may vary in different animals. Experiments have shown that the time of hind limb liftoff in lizards, for example, is not always synchronous with the beginning of femur protraction. However, comparative studies were not conducted on this line so we have to limit our analysis of gaits to the establishment of moments of liftoff and footfall.

The work of any pair of limbs in unison (diagonal in trot, one-sided in amble, fore or hind in bound and half-bound) leads to a reduction in the number of stages in the cycle. The locomotory cycle in all two-paced symmetrical movements consists of four stages; three-paced gallop, of six stages. However, the reduction in the number of stages does not alone determine the number of paces in locomotion: the reduction may result coincidentally at the time of footfall on the substratum by one limb or liftoff by another.

2. SYMMETRICAL AND ASYMMETRICAL TYPES OF LOCOMOTION

A comparison of *symmetrical* and *asymmetrical types of locomotion* is the most important part of the modern studies on gaits. Characterizing both types, Howell (1944) gives some features by which the two can be differentiated. Separately, he states that in symmetrical locomotion limbs may work in two known symmetrical sequences which differ from similar sequences of the asymmetrical type. No special attention is given by Howell to the difference in sequence of work by the limbs, perhaps because he takes into consideration that in trot and amble (included in the symmetrical type), two limbs are taken out in front at once, i.e., only when the four-paced form of locomotion is used, can the walk possess the symmetrical sequence. Similarly, while analyzing asymmetrical locomotion, Howell does not consider that there is sufficient justification for excluding from its special gaits "canter in atypical sequence"—the continuity of the latter in typical symmetrical sequence. As a result, Howell's important conclusion that two types of locomotion are based on entirely different models of nervous control (types of coordination) remains unexplained. On what these differences in coordination are based is not clear. Most of the characteristics described by Howell cannot be seen as cardinal, but rather the consequence of differences between the two main peculiarities of locomotion: in the sequence of work of limbs, and in the character of locomotory rhythm. These determine the type of coordination. It is known that in symmetrical types of locomotion, special significance is not given simply to one of the symmetrical sequences of the work of limbs, but only to the historical origin for the whole type. The difference in the nature of the work of the axial skeleton, only one of the peculiarities mentioned by Howell, is directly related to the history of the origin of both types of locomotion.

Sequence of Limb Action

In nature, all the six theoretically possible sequences in the working of limbs are realized in four-paced locomotion (Figure 2). For example, in the tables presented by Muybridge (1957), an elephant can be found (Pl. 112) using a *symmetrical-diagonal* sequence (Figure 2, A), a baboon (Pl. 142) using a *symmetrical-lateral* (Figure 2, B), horses (Pls. 70 and 72) moving on the support of both *asymmetrical-diagonal* sequences (Figure 2, C and D), a cat (Pl. 127) moving on the support of *straight asymmetrical-lateral* (Figure 2, E), and a dog (Table 119) moving on the support of *reverse asymmetrical-lateral* sequences (Figure 2, F).

Both symmetrical sequences produce a similar interchange of movement, i.e., only fore or only hind limbs. Both hind (or both front) limbs never work in the sequence one after the other, so analogical movement of any front or hind foot, is wedged between them. All four asymmetrical sequences are characterized, on the other hand, by the fact that the sequence of work, one after the other, of both the fore (or hind) limbs is followed by one and the same movement of both hind (or fore) limbs similarly in the sequence. The difference between diagonal and lateral asymmetrical sequences lies only in the relationship between the work of the fore and hind pairs of limbs: in the diagonal sequence, after the work of the second of the hind foot, the forelimb diagonal to it starts working, but in the lateral, it is the forelimb of the same side. It

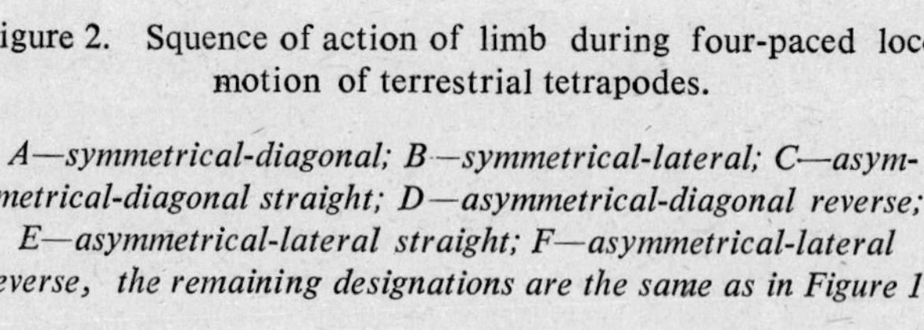

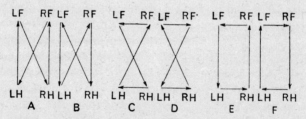

Figure 2. Squence of action of limb during four-paced locomotion of terrestrial tetrapodes.

A—symmetrical-diagonal; B—symmetrical-lateral; C—asymmetrical-diagonal straight; D—asymmetrical-diagonal reverse; E—asymmetrical-lateral straight; F—asymmetrical-lateral reverse, the remaining designations are the same as in Figure 1.

is clear that both diagonal asymmetrical sequences, like both lateral, are mutually reverse to each other and it is only convention which identifies one as straight and the other as reverse. Obviously, in nature, animals belonging to different groups prefer the diagonal or the lateral sequences and in equal degree, make use of straight or reverse variations of either. Literature on locomotion repeatedly mentions that horses, like many other mammals, may change the leading hind limb during the course of movement.[4]

The position regarding both symmetrical sequences is otherwise: the lateral is also reverse diagonal, i.e., if in the latter movement the forefoot is followed by a similar movement of the diagonal hind foot, then it is the reverse: the diagonal forefoot follows the hind foot and after the forefoot has moved, the hind foot of the same side moves. This difference is only external and would seem to be insignificant. As has been mentioned already, symmetrical locomotion on the basis of a diagonal sequence is inherent in all terrestrial vertebrates, but the lateral sequence is used rarely. It seems, as shown by Gray (1944), that the conditions for maintaining balance during movement on the basis of both symmetrical sequences, are diametrically opposed.

The balance of an animal during locomotion depends upon the position of the center of gravity relative to the limbs in contact with the substratum. The balance will be constant if the center of gravity is projected on the substratum inside the support triangle, formed by the limbs supporting the body at that moment or one side of it. Special significance is attached to conditions under which balance is maintained during slow motion, where there is no dynamic equilibrium. Gray diagrammatically analyzed slow motion in animals on the basis of all sequences (Figure 3)[5] initially from three situations concerning the center of gravity with regard to limbs: more anterior, middle, and more posterior. In the first moment (Figure 3, I) all four limbs have contact with the substratum when the right two are close in a manner such that they are in one point ($A+D$). In this instance, under any situation of the center of gravity, its projection falls within the support triangle BC ($A+D$) which is also shown by markings on the scale below (one scale for each situation of the center of gravity). The transport in front of the right forefoot does not change the form of the support triangle, but the center of gravity shifts in front so that the more anterior in situation in the second moment, may appear exactly over the side of triangle *BD*. Right up to the third moment, where the right forefoot is released on the ground, the "anterior" center of gravity lies inside the support triangle which is shown as white on the respective scale (balance is disturbed). However, if the center of gravity shifts further behind, equilibrium should be retained. Continuing the analysis, it is easy to observe that during the change of support triangles (from *BCD* to *ABD*), the more "posterior" center of gravity is similarly for some time (from the third moment to the fourth) in an unstable condition. However, the middle "center of gravity" throughout the duration of the entire locomotory cycle does not go beyond the limits of one or the other support triangle. In fact, an animal with such a condition for the center of gravity in any moment, may "freeze" with a raised paw without losing balance. Under the

[4]The guiding limb in asymmetrical locomotion refers to the one in the pair, fore or hind, which leaves the ground last.

[5]The diagram gives only an analysis of symmetrical sequences.

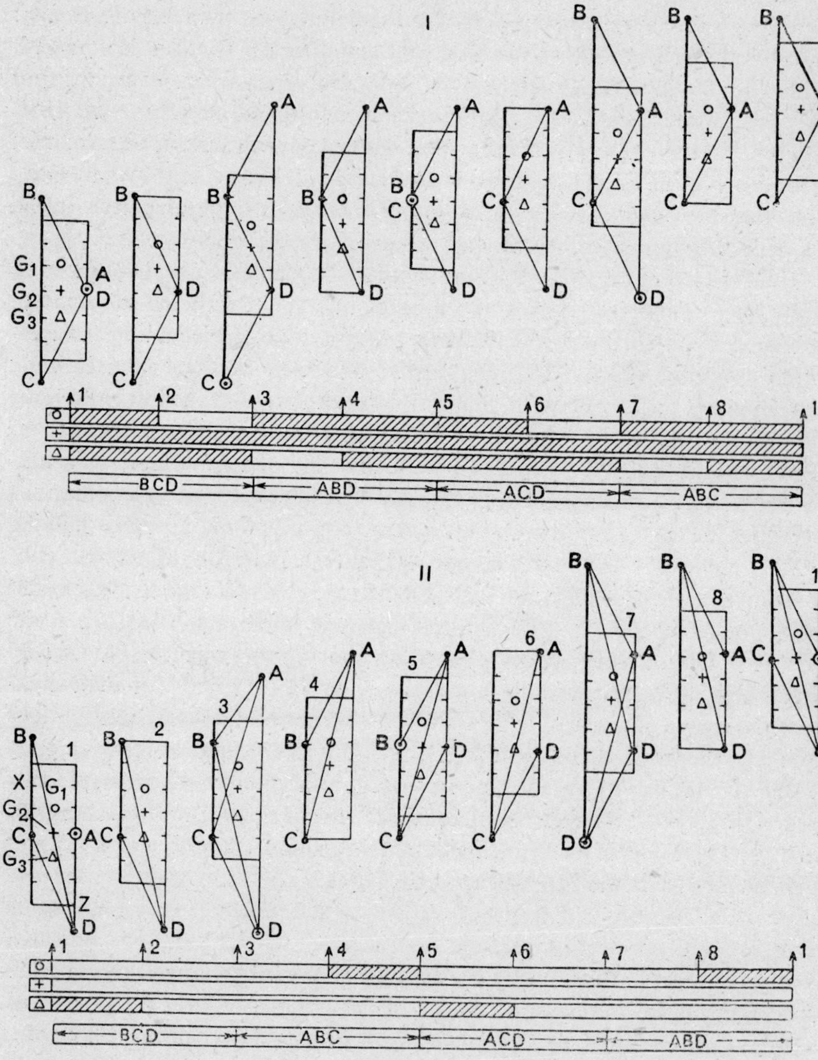

Figure 3. Conditions of equilibrium during slow four-paced locomotion for I—symmetrical-diagonal, and II—symmetrical-lateral with sequence of limb action. Data from Gray (1944).

Explanation in the text.

other conditions for the center of gravity in the cycle, periods of instability may appear for a short time, but their specific gravity is not much.

The conditions for maintaining equilibrium during locomotion with the lateral sequence of limb action is different (Figure 3, II). The form of support triangles is such that the center of gravity may fall in a stable condition of equilibrium only in exceptional cases under which the more anterior or more posterior situation with regard to limbs is favorable. In this way, the extreme rareness of symmetrical-lateral movement can be given a completely logical explanation. It is not by accident that this situation is seen only in primates with a high coordinate capacity where the instability of equilibrium is itself useful (with habitat, trees), or during fast movement in some other mammals (for example, horses) when dynamic equilibrium plays an important role, but reducing the period of stable equilibrium to a minimum is very important for locomotion. Gray similarly showed that balance during asymmetrical sequences is less stable than that under symmetrical-diagonal locomotion, but even here stability is more easily achieved than in symmetrical locomotion. However, Gray (1944: Figure 51, sequence 2) has mistakenly shown the differences in this regard between straight and reverse asymmetrical-diagonal sequences. In fact, all asymmetrical sequences establish the same conditions of equilibrium.

From the above-mentioned, the following conclusion is drawn: the first terrestrial vertebrates were undoubtedly slow animals with a high demand for maintaining equilibrium, having inherited horizontally placed stylopods from fish and should, therefore, have used the symmetrical-diagonal sequence of limb action on land, as providing maximum stability in all stages of the locomotory cycle. For them symmetrical-lateral locomotion was not possible as thought by Croix (1929a and 1936). They could not even move in a trot as Howell (1944) has explained for in its cycle, a big role is played by the relatively unstable stages with support only on two limbs of one diagonal stage of diagonal support, and amble with its stages of lateral support[6] is even more incompatible with the significant removal of the center of gravity from the line of support.

Locomotion in Fishes as a Basis for Development of Terrestrial Locomotion

Primary form of locomotion on land. In four of the primary diagonal-symmetrical locomotions, there are several other considerations. Coghill (1929) mentioned first the integration of movement of limbs in amphibian larvae (axolotl) with movement of body, and second, the origin of "local reflexes" in the limbs during the process of individualization. Even though

[6]In stages of lateral support, two limbs of the same side make contact with the substratum.

Coghill committed this mistake (see page 107), his main idea about the presence of an evolutional relationship between the mechanism of terrestrial movement and the swimming mechanism ought not to be doubted.

As a rule, progressive motion in fishes is connected with the movement from head to tail, of a wave-shaped bend of the body in a horizontal plane. In Figure 4, the displacement of place of the maximum lateral bend in the body of the fish, marked with dots or crosses, is well seen. Only one wave or two half-waves pass through the body of a fish (Shuleikin, 1934) irrespective of whether the fish is of serpentine or normal form. As is usual in oscillatory movement with the formation of transverse waves, where the points with maximum amplitude of oscillation are situated at a distance of one half-wave from each other, so also in the body of a fish, each point of the axial skeleton passes diametrically opposite phases with periods of half-wave. In other words, two consecutive points on a fish body, situated at a distance of a half-wave of the horizontal bend of the body, are always situated in different phases. If in one the maximum bend is toward the right, then the bend in the second is toward the left. In all terrestial tetrapods, the limb zones are situated within a certain distance, it would not be an exaggeration to think that this is the inheritance from their fish-like ancestors. Under the conditions of primary integration of body and limb movement (in the present case, the paired fins of crossopterygii), the beginning of the body bend toward the left should lead to the forward position of the right pectoral fin, and then afterwards, through the half-period of wave (time until the curve spreads from the front to the hind belt) should lead to a forward position of the left pelvic fin. The new bend starting from the right undergoes the same sequence of movement, beginning at the left pectoral fin and afterwards to the right pelvic fin.

This passing of a single wave-like curve on the body of a fish should induce a similar type of movement with paired fins in a typical symmetrical-diagonal

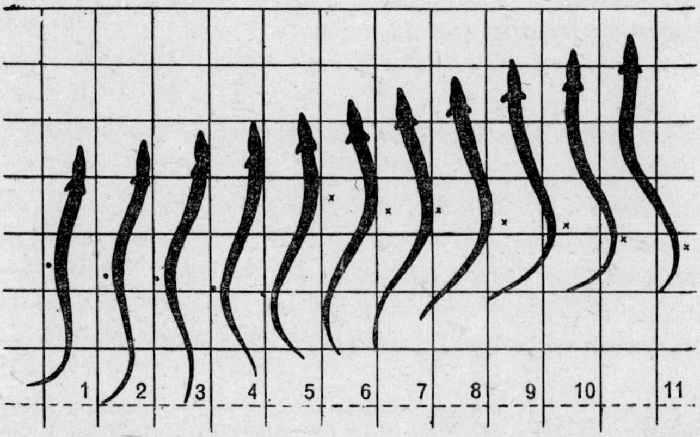

Figure 4. Progressive locomotion of eel-like fish (*Pholis gunnellus*), viewed from above. Data taken from motion pictures by Gray (1933).

sequence (Figure 2, A), this being known through equal intervals of time. This completely coincides with Coghill's results: "The primary starting component of motion seems to be a slow swimming movement, completed by the body and tail with the inclusion of limbs. The forelegs are integrated with the movement of the body until the anterior portion takes part in the movement, but when the movement of the body comes into the region of the hind legs, then they are also included in the integration. Therefore, the hind legs do not move in synchronism with the forelegs, but follow behind the forelimbs at an interval (required for this) so that the bend of the body can move through from the anterior region of the limbs to the posterior. Consequently, the coordination of legs during the walk should be understood not as the nerve coordination of limbs between them, but as the integration of limbs with the body" (1934, p. 72).

The above-mentioned work concludes that the four-paced symmetrical movement based on a diagonal sequence, i.e., locomotion by turn of transference of one limb after another in the following order: *RF-LH-LF-RH*, should be considered as the origin for all terrestrial vertebrates. It not only provides maximum stability during slow movement, but, as its basis is already established from the movement of fish, the transition from water to land must have happened without a radical breaking of the previous models for controlling muscular activity and building an absolutely new system of coordination of independently working limbs.

In this connection, it may be mentioned that there is a definite relationship between the symmetrical-lateral sequence and forward movement of fish with the tail, when the wave-like bend of the body spreads in a direction opposite from the tail to the head. On the basis of locomotion in fish, it is not possible to visualize the mechanism of locomotion with the trot and amble. The trot with its simultaneous forward movement of the diagonally-situated limbs, bespeaks disturbing the primary connection of the movement of limbs with the spread of the horizontal body bend from front to back. Here the interval in the half-period of wave between the movement of limbs of one diagonal, has been liquidated which is essential for the original form of four-paced locomotion. In the case of the amble, this interval is increased to a full period. In other words, movement by a trot and amble could be paralleled with the movement of fish only if the latter were performed by the method of stationary wave formation (stationary wave formation cannot provide forward movement), and the zone of limbs could have been situated in the wave knots (in the trot—by two contiguous, in the amble—through one). In this regard, literature displays a lively interest (see pp. 89-90) in connection with the nature of the horizontal bend of the body in amphibians and reptiles: whether stationary or concealed, the wave always spreads. Naturally, the solid fixation of limb support to the substratum in tetrapods, does not give a possibility for direct spread of the horizontal body bend from front to back with the corresponding lateral inclination of pectoral and pelvic zones. However, "delay" of the hind limb in the diagonal in rotation to the front one during four-paced locomotion, contradicts bending of the body by the method of stationary waves. It is natural to think that only the appearance of the trot as a form of locomotion could establish conditions for stationary wave formation; but this requires that the body of the animal be raised sufficiently above the substratum so as not to offer any inhibiting activity which is inevitable under simultaneous formation of anterior and posterior halves of the stationary wave. The non-simultaneous formation of different portions of the sigma-like body bends and, in turn, the limb movements connected with these in four-paced locomotion, should be seen as an echo of the highly characteristic fish wave-spreads from front to behind. This is stressed by the retention, even in exaggerated form, of such methods of locomotion as creeping by animals with a snake-like body, and swimming by many lower tetrapods.

The conditions for the appearance of asymmetrical sequences in the locomotion of tetrapods could only be formed through the decrease of dependence of these separate groups on the conditions of equilibrium. In mammals, this was achieved by the transfer of limbs to the parasagittal plane, the reasons for which are still not understood. In flying lizards and birds, changes in conditions of equilibrium are connected with a transfer to another kind of habitat. The flying, apparently evolved from parachuting, did not develop a genuine asymmetrical movement, i.e., limb movement unevenly spaced in time, but a unique form of locomotion with a simultaneous movement of the two front limbs. A similar limb movement developed sea turtles during their adaptation to water. "Asymmetrical" locomotion in anuran amphibians by a simultaneous push of the hind limbs, is evidently related to their change of habitat medium, and a radical change of conditions of equilibrium. At best, the jump in frogs appeared primarily as a result of a peculiar method of swimming.

Real or genuine asymmetrical locomotion is inevitably connected with the development of vertical motion in the axial skeleton. For only this development provides the conditions requisite to the work sequence for two limbs of one pair—fore and hind. If it could be stated with certainty that slow motion preceded fast in symmetrical locomotion, one could base further analysis of symmetrical gaits on this assumption; but here, such a consideration is purely vicarious. In any case, fast symmetrical movement with its respective locomotory apparatus preceded the appearance of asymmetrical locomotion as a whole.

In conclusion, it can be said that symmetrical and asymmetrical types of locomotion are based on different types of limb coordination which are reflected in the sequence of similar limb movements and are connected with peculiarities of movement in the axial skeleton. Symmetrical locomotion preceded the appearance of asymmetrical; its original form was a slow four-paced movement based on a symmetrical-diagonal sequence of limb action, commonly known as a very slow walk (see further). The trot as a two-paced form of locomotion could only appear after the development of the four-paced locomotion and represents the next stage in the development of terrestrial locomotion. The amble, a less stable form of two-paced locomotion, developed later (relative to the time of origin of symmetrical locomotion) as is indicated by its relative rareness in nature (appearing only in some mammals). It is important to mention that the development of the trot even required the rearrangement of the coordinating activity of the central nervous system which did not present any significant morphological changes as horizontal body movements were maintained. It is true, of course, that now it has some other functions, the primary one being an increase in length of walk. The amble is possible only in the absence of horizontal bends or, at least, in their minimal presence. The natural consequence of this seems to be a reduction in the number of animals capable of amble.

In the light of the afore-mentioned, it is necessary to interpret that the essence of the phenomenon of reciprocal inversion observed by physiologists lies in the fact that the stimulation of the flexure of any front limb is accompanied by the stimulation of flexures of the hind limb diagonal to it and the straightening of the second front and hind limb of the same side. Thereby the opposites of these limbs are relaxed. Bernstein sees in this "systematic process ...the rudiment of a basic coordination of movement by the walk: sequential moving of the feet (the so-called step reflex of stepping)" and reproduction of "...the usual crossed pattern of stepping by quadrupedal animals: the right front and the left hind forward, and the left front and right hind backward, and vice versa."[7] A little later Bernstein says that "the reciprocal scheme of association of the fore and hind limbs allows the walk and trot, but contradicts the amble and gallop" (1946, p. 248). In fact, the coordination mechanism of the trot should provide simultaneous progressive movement signals in the limb of one diagonal, the mechanism of the walk (four-paced movement with equal intervals), a signal stopping in the hind limb on one-half period wave, but the mechanism of the amble is a complete period. Physiologists themselves, speaking of reciprocal innervation, usually do not pay attention to the time differences in signals relayed to the limbs. An alternative appears. If reciprocal innervation is understood as stopping on the half-period (which seems more probable) and accordingly would appear to be the physiological basis of the walk, then it can be considered at any stage of inheritability from the fish, and simultaneously becomes incompatible to a proportionate degree with the trot and amble. If reciprocal innervation speaks of a simultaneous reception of signals in a limb in the diagonal,

[7]The interpretation of the "common crossed pattern of walking" given by Bernstein, has a double meaning as it decreases the difference between trot and walk.

then it corresponds only to the trot, appearing a relatively more delayed acquisition in vertebrates.

Rhythm of Locomotion

The second important difference between symmetrical and asymmetrical locomotion lies in the character of locomotory rhythm. Under uniform locomotion in any symmetrical sequence, the intervals between movements of limbs of a diagonal pair are equal to each other. In a similar way, the intervals are equal between limb movements of the ipsilateral pair, and these and others can be differentiated from each other. They are equal only when the primary form of movement is retained, i.e., each interval is equal to a half-period wave-like body bend. In any case, temporary intervals in the first half-cycle of symmetrical locomotion, are repeated in the second half-cycle, thus stipulating its internal rhythm. The movement of both hind limbs, similar to the movement of both forelimbs, follows the half-cycle exactly. Consequently by determining the relationship of the intervals ipsilateral limb movement and that of diagonal opposite limbs (since together both intervals constitute a half-cycle), it is possible to characterize the rhythm of the entire cycle and with it, the entire process of symmetrical locomotion. The given ratio can be expressed in absolute values; the data of intervals may be expressed in any form—in units of time or in number of stages (see pp. 18-19). In such cases, the rhythm of the trot is ∞ (Infinity) as the interval between the movement of diagonal limbs (important) is equal to zero. But, in the amble, the ratio is equal to zero and therefore, the rhythm of the amble should be expressed as zero. In four-paced movement with equal intervals (row of walk, see further), the index of locomotory rhythm is determined by the ratio of 1:1 (or in the number of stages, 2:2). In practice, it is convenient to express the rhythm of locomotion with the intervals between the diagonal limb movements to the duration of the half-cycle as a percentage. Then the rhythm of the trot becomes 0%, the amble 100%, and the walk 50%.

Asymmetrical locomotion presents another situation. Even Marey mentioned that "in some gaits (symmetrical) there is a rhythm in which strokes continue one after the other in a right order; in others, such as gallop (asymmetrical movement), rhythm is irregular, but it is repeated periodically" (1875, p. 186). Braune and Fischer (1899-1903), speaking of symmetrical movement in man, mention the periodicity of single walk (half-cycle) in the movement of the center of gravity in vertical and longitudinal directions. The same is also noted by Bernstein: "The main rhythm of walking is repetition of periods of double step...However, the points situated in the body on a middle line, are asymmetrical in relation to both the sides...and have a different rhythm of movement, but actually repeat their phases accurately after each single walk" (1935, p. 47). Consequently, if the rhythmic character of symmetrical locomotion may be determined as intracyclic, i.e., the internal rhythm is inherent for each cycle, then the rhythm of asymmetrical locomotion is intercyclic, i.e., internal rhythm is completely absent as all intervals between limb contact in one cycle are not equal, but successive cycles, a rhythm is observed as each successive cycle repeats the preceding. In this case, a single index for locomotory rhythm should not be given which comes to using several at once (Hildebrand, 1962; see also page 38 of the present work).

In summarizing this discussion of the two types of locomotion in terrestrial vertebrates, it may be concluded that the coordination difference between symmetrical and asymmetrical locomotion lies in the sequence limb movements and in their time-relationships of their movements.

3. SYMMETRICAL GAIT AS A FUNCTION OF SPEED AND RHYTHM OF LOCOMOTION

Bearing in mind the afore-mentioned situations, the author analyzed the photographs of Muybridge (1957) and several series of high-speed films of amphibians and reptiles. This analysis resulted in the conclusion that each separate gait in the system of symmetrical locomotion should be taken as the function of only two main factors: rhythm of locomotion (the index for which is the coordinating work of all four limbs), and speed, which takes part in the shape of the rhythm of work in the limbs (the index for which is the separate working of each limb).

The reduction in the number of limb supports in some moments of the cycle with increased speed of locomotion is wellknown (Croix, 1929a, 1936; Howell, 1944; Gray, 1953; Casamiquela, 1964; and others). However, the reason for this phenomenon is not satisfactorily explained. Naturally, increased speed results in a reduction of the duration of the locomotion cycle as well as the time of support and transport for each limb. But if support time is reduced absolutely and relatively, then the transport time is only reduced absolutely and only up to a particular limit. The relative duration also sharply increases. In other words, even a simple increase in limb action inevitably reflects a change in the relationship of support to transport, i.e., the rhythm of limb action. Perhaps, this is connected to elementary biomechanics: the problems of the transport period during limb work are more complicated than those of the support period (Schaeffer, 1941) although the important role in progressive locomotion is played by the latter. During the transport time, not only is a limb raised off the ground and put in front, but a complicated re-orientation of all its segments during preparation for the new support occurs. This provides a minimal limit to an absolute reduction in transport time. The support time changes in much larger limits and in other proportions.

Consequently, the particular duration of the locomotory cycle[8] corresponds to the particular significance of the rhythm of limb action: When the support time is greater than the relative transport time, then the slower the animal moves, and vice versa. This was first stated clearly by Hildebrand (1962 and 1963) and by the author of the present work (Sukhanov, 1963).

Thus, each concrete form of symmetrical locomotion may be represented as a dot on a coordinate system: speed (vertically) and rhythm of locomotion (horizontally), Figure 5,[9] the limits between gaits with lines, and the range of changes by the surface bounded by these lines. The limits between gaits are characterized by coincidence in the time of liftoff and contact of any limb: liftoff of a forelimb and contact of a hind limb of the same or the other side, liftoff of a hind limb and contact of any front one, contact of one hind limb and liftoff of the other at the moment of liftoff of any forelimb and a simultaneous contact by the other, etc. As mentioned above, this results in the reduction of the number of stages in a cycle. According to Howell, only the support plan within the limits of one gait and the support formula remain unchanged, i.e., when all stages of the cycle are represented equally.

The first conclusion from the diagram (Figure 5) is that the whole system of symmetrical locomotion can be viewed as continuous transitions connecting with the amble (line *AD*) and the trot (*BC*) at opposite poles. It is important to differentiate the main rhythms of locomotion: the rhythm of the amble (100%), the rhythm of the walk (50%) and the rhythm of the trot (0%); intermediate between these, the rhythm of the half-amble (75%), and the rhythm of the half-trot (25%). Gaits with the rhythms of the half-amble and half-trot should be considered separate categories and can be called the amble-like walk and trot-like walk, though they do not represent a continuous order on the vertical line similar to lines of the amble, walk and trot. The vertical scale, speed, is graded in conformity with the significance of rhythms of limb action on a norm of gaits represented by three different methods: (1) the ratio of the support time to transport time in absolute numbers, (2) the ratio of the number of stages, and (3) the ratio of the support time to the duration of the cycle in percents.

In spite of the principal similarity between the systems mentioned above (Figure 5) and the systems discovered by Hildebrand (1963), there are some significant differences. It is important that these differences be given detailed attention.

In Hildebrand's diagram (Figure 6), the abscissa represents the scale of speed given in percent of support time for each limb to the duration of the entire cycle (from 100 to 0%). The ordinate similarly represents the change

[8]Speed of locomotion is determind by the product of length of walk and size, and returning time required for its completion; otherwise, frequency of walks is the unit of time (Gregory, 1912).

[9]Dots in the diagram show the position of the norms of the gaits.

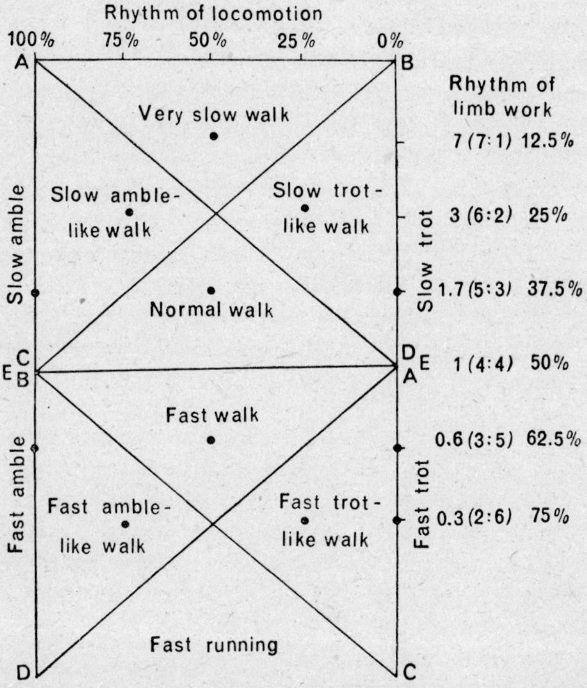

Figure 5. General system of symmetrical forms of locomotion.

On the horizontal scale—*values of the rhythm of locomotion.* On the vertical scale—*rhythms of limb action. Dots represent the positions in the system of norms of the main symmetrical gaits. On the line AA, each hind limb lands simultaneously with the liftoff of the ipsilateral forelimb, but on the line CC, with its diagonal forelimb. On the line BB, each forelimb touches the ground at the moment of liftoff of the diagonal hind limb, but on line DD, the ipsilateral hind limb. On the line EE, one hind limb lifts off at the moment of landing by the other, but each forelimb, at the moment of landing by the second forelimb. On the line AD, unison action of ipsilateral limbs, but on the line BC, of one's diagonal. The places of crossing shown by the lines of locomotion, correspond to each of the above-given rules at one time.*

in the proportion of the interval between the movements of ipsilateral limbs to the entire cycle (from 100 to 0%). Consequently, our system of symmetrical locomotion on the basis of the diagonal sequence (Figure 5), being "situated on the side," should occupy only the two upper squares on Hildebrand's diagram. The rhythm of the amble in our system corresponds to the line marked 0% on the horizontal scale in the diagram of Figure 6; the rhythm of the trot, lines marked 50%. Hildebrand's horizontal scale corresponds to our vertically-graded-in-percent-scale. The entire remaining area in Hildebrand's diagram (the two lower squares) presents a diagrammatical representation of symmetrical locomotion on the basis of lateral sequences.

This could not be seen by us in view of the total similarity during the diagonal sequence; rather, it appears to be a mirror reflection of the latter, if lines *AD* or *BC* in Figure 5 are taken as the axis of symmetry (or the 50%-line of the horizontal scale in Figure 6). Thus, lines 100% to 0% respectively on Hildebrand's horizontal scale reflect one and the same form of locomotion, the amble. Unfortunately, Hildebrand did not mention this, omitting the possibility of formulating an important situation: movement by the amble and by the trot as two-paced forms of locomotion may be taken theoretically as the transition from four-paced symmetrical-diagonal movement to a four-paced symmetrical-lateral. Therefore, the logical gradation of the scale of locomotory rhythm should be done as shown in Figure 5, but in the case of symmetrical-lateral movement, the graded values of rhythms should be marked as "minus."

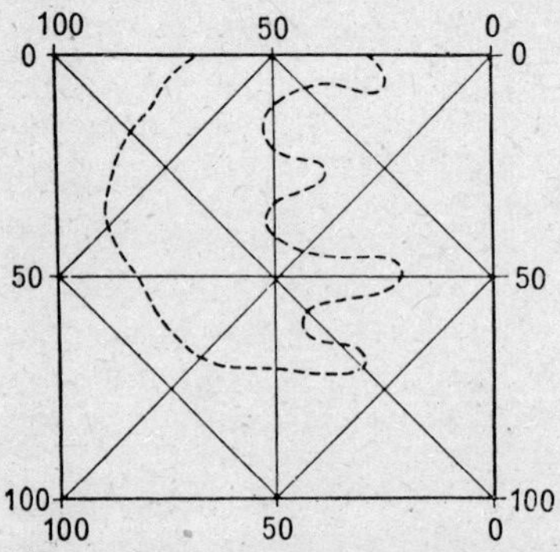

Figure 6. System of symmetrical locomotion by Hildebrand (1963).

On the horizontal scale (*expressed in percents*)—*the relation of support time of limbs to the duration of cycle* (*another expression of rhythm of limb action*).

On the vertical scale (*expressed in percents*)—*the relation of intervals between the motion of limbs of one side to the duration of cycle* (*another expression of rhythm of locomotion*).

Dotted line—*zone, including gait, common in nature.*

The remaining explanation is in the text.

In spite of the habit and group of gaits completed on the basis of symmetrical-diagonal sequences, Hildebrand (1963) names them as "gaits of lateral sequence", differentiating in them a group of "lateral couplets gaits", when similar movements of limbs on one side constitute one "couplet" (i.e., the relative analogous movements of diagonal limbs get closer in timings), and the groups "diagonal couplets gaits" in the reverse case.[10] Hildebrand considers this a basis for renaming the diagonal sequence as lateral, because the forelimb makes contact after the ipsilateral hind limb, unlike the "diagonal" sequence wherein it follows its diagonal hind limb. The name given to any phenomenon is immaterial so long as there is agreement on the meaning

[10]Other uses for the terms "diagonal" and "lateral" appear in literature. For example, Grogan (1951) sometimes call the amble the "lateral" gait, but the trot "diagonal". This is but one step away from an absured position in which the amble is closely connected with symmetrical-lateral forms of locomotion, but the trot with symmetrical-diagonal.

of the given term. However, not only is tradition against Hildebrand's nomenclature but also that important connection between movements of diagonally opposite limbs but not ipsilateral ones.

Hildebrand mentions that the area of each triangle in the diagram corresponds to locomotion with one particular formula of support. However, as the variations of some gaits are very high, attaining 25% on one axis and 50% on the other, he considers it important in general to refrain from using the customary gait names. In place of customary names, he suggests that each gait be given important basic parameters (for example, 35 to 50, i.e., 35% on the horizontal scale and 50% on the vertical should explain our quick trot) and gets out of the "name" situation through the system of coordination. For this he foresees on the axis of speeds (the abscissa) 10% intervals with these names: 90 to 80%—very slow walk; 80 to 70%—slow walk; 70 to 60%—moderate walk; 60 to 50%—fast walk; 50 to 40%—slow run; 40 to 30%—moderate run; 30 to 20%—fast run. The ordinate of each interval consists of 12.5%. Names here are more complicated: 0 to 12.5%—pace (amble); 12.5 to 25%—lateral sequence, lateral couplets gait; 25 to 37.5%—lateral sequence, single foot (walk); 37.5 to 50%—lateral sequence, diagonal couplets gait; 50 to 62.5%—trot; 62.5 to 75%—diagonal sequence, diagonal couplets gait; 75 to 87.5%—diagonal sequence, single foot; 87.5 to 100%—diagonal sequence, lateral couplets gait. Gaits common in nature do not occupy the whole area in the diagram (Figure 6). Therefore, Hildebrand does not give special names to the intervals of 100 to 90% and 20 to 0% on the axis of the abscissa. Similarly, the interval in nature, from 75 to 100% on the axis of the ordinate, is not used. By combining names on two axes, Hildebrand gives a complex of names. For example, in the case of leopards, he mentions fast, lateral sequence, lateral couplets walk; that in our terminology translates to slow amble-like walk with locomotion rhythm in limits of 50 to 75% and rhythm of limb action about 40 to 50%.

Is Hildebrand's innovation reasonable? Back in 1962 he still supported the more traditional names; for example, crawling walk, pacing walk, trotting walk, etc. The idea of expressing concrete forms of movement in a system of coordination is very important, but it must not form the basis for the denial of the earlier "big" gaits and their replacement with new squares of equal area (10 on 12.5%) on a diagram. The limits between gaits established by Hildebrand are completely arbitrary. The area marked with a dotted line in Figure 6 suffices to show the main drawback of his suggestion. On the lines corresponding to the amble (0% on the vertical), trot (50%) and walk in diagonal and lateral sequences (25 and 75%), we observe "tongues" taking part in the faster section of the diagram. It may be thought that there are some functional peculiarities, general for the whole tongue, which make use of these gaits at high speed, but not lying to the left or right from them in the diagram i.e., each tongue should be considered as but one gait. According to Hildebrand, the lower and upper halves of all portions of the tongues should be considered as independent gaits. The functional significance of limits between gaits may be illustrated by another method. In this way, line *AA* (Figure 5) limits the locomotion possibilities of lower tetrapods and mammals.[11]

The suggested system of symmetrical locomotion completely exhausts the whole collection of main, commonly-met-in-nature, symmetrical gaits. But in many cases, special variations of gaits are observed differing from the main plan and support formula. However, this resulted in no change in the coordination scheme, but in specialities of the same locomotory apparatus (see page 59). The division of main and additional variants of gaits does not coincide with the natural and artificial (Goubaux and Barrier, 1901; Grogan, 1951; Krasnikov, 1957) or regular and irregular gaits (Krasnikov, 1957) of horsebreeders.

Naturally, the methods of analysis for symmetrical gaits cannot be used for asymmetrical. Hildebrand (1962) mentions that for the complete characterization of asymmetrical forms of locomotion, it is important to know the following values: (1) the duration of the cycle; (2) the proportion of support time of a hind limb to the entire cycle; (3) the proportion of support time of a hind limb to that of the other hind limb; (4) to that of a forelimb; (5) the proportion of support time of a forelimb to that of the other forelimb; (6) the proportion of the interval between the footfalls of the hind limb to the entire cycle; (7) of the two forelimbs; (9) of a given hind and forelimbs; and (8) the sequence of limb action for both the front and the back limbs. The analysis of symmetrical gaits can then be carried out on these characteristics; it is significantly simplified as 6 and 7 are equal, [12] 3, 4, and 5 are similarly equal to each other and their observation is therefore useless. Consequently, the whole idea is—2 and 9 in symmetrical locomotion correspond to our rhythm of limb action and rhythm of locomotion; during analysis, 8 should sufficiently characterize each form of locomotion.

Hildebrand (1962, 1963) suggests that each asymmetrical form of locomotion in limits of one sequence and the study of its relative duration of support time for fore and hind limbs, be represented diagrammatically with dots in the system of coordination where, on the axis of the abscissa lie relative percents of support time of one or two hind limbs to the duration of the cycle, but on the axis of the ordinate—intervals between "midtimes"

[11]After the present work had gone to press, another article appeared by Hildebrand (1966) in which he further develops his system. Some of the objections given above, were considered by him. Hence, he divided the axis of the ordinate into intervals somewhat differently: their size remains the same (12.5%), but their borders were mixed below so that "tongues" appeared inside the intervals.

[12]We have already observed that in symmetrical locomotion, this interval is equal to a half-cycle.

(average time between the contacts of limbs of front or back pairs) in the work of front and back limbs, similarly brought to the duration of the cycle and expressed in percentages. Only a special study of mammalian locomotion, which is outside the main purpose of this work, would permit a practical study of the usefulness of this method suggested by Hildebrand for analyzing asymmetrical locomotion.

4. SYMMETRICAL GAITS

A systematic review of the main symmetrical gaits will be helpful to anyone studying animal locomotion in order to separate the natural gaits from those confusing ones considered as variations of gaits, and also those arising from morphological peculiarities of the animals. For this purpose, a short description of each gait together with a series of successive figures and diagrams is given. Through this delineation of symmetrical gaits, the main differences between asymmetrical forms of locomotion will also be seen.

Mention should be made here of a few of the works concerned with the modern standard of locomotion in different animals: some lizards (Snyder, 1949, 1952, 1962; Sukhanov, 1964b, 1968b; Urban, 1964, 1965); hedgehogs (Gupta, 1964); *Dipodomys* (Howell, 1932; Bartholomew and Caswell, 1951) and *Perognathus* (Bartholomew and Cary, 1954) from *Heteromyidae;* some jerboas (Fokin, 1963) Norway rats (Gambaryan, 1955); giraffes (Bourdelle, 1934; Dagg, 1960, 1962); okapi (Dagg, 1960); tapir (Gambaryan, 1964), leopard (Hildebrand, 1959, 1960, 1961); some primates (Ashton and Oxnard, 1964). These works present different types of problems. They vary in standards of accuracy and include extensive to negligible material on locomotory phenomena, which makes a comparison of their separate findings difficult. And although the external appearance of an animal will usually indicate its gait (Hildebrand, 1963) very little work has been done to confirm this.

Walk

A review of symmetrical gaits should be started with an observation of the historically original form of vertebrate locomotion on land, so known as a very slow gait in symmetrical-diagonal sequences, and the gait directly based on it, combines these terms into the generally understood walk. This is a four-paced gait with equal intervals between the movements of all four limbs. Supportive and propulsive efforts are continuous and of the same type, which gives a firmness to the walk and enough effectiveness in the entire duration of the cycle.

Very slow walk.[13] This walk is characterized by a rotation of tri- and

[13]Crawling walk (Muybridge, 1887; Hildebrand, 1962); *parerpetico*, in the lateral sequence *prototipico* + *meserpetico* (Croix, 1929a, 1936); crawl (Howell, 1944).

quadrupodel stages by the formula: 4-3-4-3-4-3-4-3, i.e., each hind limb leaves the ground earlier than the front one of the same side (Figure 7). This prevents the increase of step length during the locomotion of this gait. In the norm (Figure 5), locomotion rhythm is identified as 50%, but limb rhythm as 7 (7:1), i.e., the support time of each limb corresponds to the duration of seven stages of the cycle, but the transport time to only one. An increase of movement results in an absolute and relative decrease in the duration of guadrupodal stages for a relative but not absolute increase of tripodal stages. During the rhythm of limb action, equal to 3 (6:2), quadrupodal stages completely drop out. The cycle becomes: 3-3-3-3 (at the place of intersection of lines *AA* and *BB* in Figure 5). Movement of such kind is observed in a draft horse with a heavy load (Howell, 1944).

A change of the rhythm of locomotion in one or the other side, coincides with the change of relative duration of quadrupodal stages of the cycle. On the basis of their character, changes can be divided into primary *quadrupodal stages,* following after the landing of any hind limb (they are reduced during closeness of the rhythm of locomotion to the rhythm of the amble), and *secondary quadrupodal stages* connected with landing by the forelimbs (they are reduced during change of rhythm of locomotion toward the side of trot).

Figure 7. Very slow walk.

A—slow locomotion of land-walking tortoises and turtles (Testudo sp.), *quadrupodal stages released; Croix (1929a); B - gait diagram. Numbers over the diagram correspond to stages shown in A.*

In this way, primary quadrupodal stages in Figure 7, B, correspond to three and seven stages, secondary to first and fifth. *Tripodal stages,* following after primary quadrupodal stages, i.e., fourth and eighth similarly, may be distinguished as primary unlike the secondary (second and sixth). A reduction of primary quadrupodal stages coincides with the relative development of secondary, and vice versa.

During a definite combination of the rhythm of locomotion and the rhythm of limb action (on the line *AA* in Figure 5), primary quadrupodal stages completely drop out, and the cycle comes to six stages corresponding to the formula: 4-3-3-4-3-3. Similar to this, on the lines of *BB* (change of rhythm toward the side of trot) secondary quadrupodal stages drop out and the cycle is reduced to the formula: 3-4-3-3-4-3. This amends the afore-mentioned rule that an increase in speed results in a decrease in the number of support limbs in some moments of the cycle, but this only goes for the change of rhythm of locomotion toward the trot or amble. In the norm of a very slow walk, the duration of quadrupodal stages in changing gaits to slow amble-like, and slow trot-like walk, should double the duration of the tripodal stages. If one remembers the usual situation of limbs in the primary quadrupodal stages,[14] then it becomes clear that a uniform regular movement is only possible under a relatively slow duration of these stages. Consequently, the rapid development of quadrupodal stages during a change of locomotory rhythm toward the trot and amble puts a minimum on the speed of movement of the slow step in the rhythms of the half-trot and half-amble. This explains the location of the dotted line in Figure 6 within the area, corresponding to a very slow walk. A one-time increase in speed and the change of rhythm of limb action connected with it, prevents the formation of quadrupodal stages during the change of locomotory rhythm (Figure 5).

The very slow walk is rarely observed; it is seen in tortoise (Croix, 1929a; Sukhanov, 1968b), toad (Barclay, 1946), sometimes in lizards (Sukhanov, 1964b, 1968b), in newly-born cubs and kittens (Howell, 1944; Hildebrand, 1962), and in a child using all four limbs (Muybridge, 1887).

Normal walk[15]. This walk is characterized by a rotation of bi- and tripodal stages by the formula: 2-3-2-3-2-3-2-3 where secondary quadrupodal

[14]In the primary quadrupodal stages the limbs on one side are closed at a maximum; on the other, set apart. In the secondary quadrupodal stages, the limbs on one side are stretched in front at a maximum; in the second, behind.

[15]Walk—*pas* (Marey, 1873, 1901; Goubaux and Barrier, 1901); including the irregular amble, high walk and irregular walk of Lenoble du Teil; walk (Muybridge, 1887; Smith, 1912; Slijper, 1946; Grogan, 1951; Wynmalen, 1954); *paso normal=paso diagonal+osobrepaso=paso lateral,* in lateral sequence *paso pithecoide* (Croix, 1929a, 1936);=*der Schritt* (Durst, 1936); light walk (Tsichmann,* 1930); fast walk (Howell, 1944); walk (Krasnikov, 1957); four-paced walk (Hildebrand, 1962).

**Editor's note:* As Tsichmann does not appear in the bibliography while Tsilman does, this might be a typographical error in the original.

stages of a very slow walk are replaced by the stages of diagonal support, but the primary by lateral support (Figure 8). In the norm (Figure 5), the rhythm of locomotion, as in all of walks, consists of 50%, but the rhythm of limb action 1.7 (5:3), i.e., on three stages which occupy transport of limbs, five stages occur when it contacts the ground. Unlike the very slow walk, each hind limb does not land earlier than the liftoff of the ipsilateral forelimb. Consequently, greatly increasing the walk and crossing into a movement with an overlapping footstep is possible. Horse-breeders have long differentiated three different types of walk: in one, the step of the hind limb does not go into the step of the same side; in the second, it covers it; in the third,

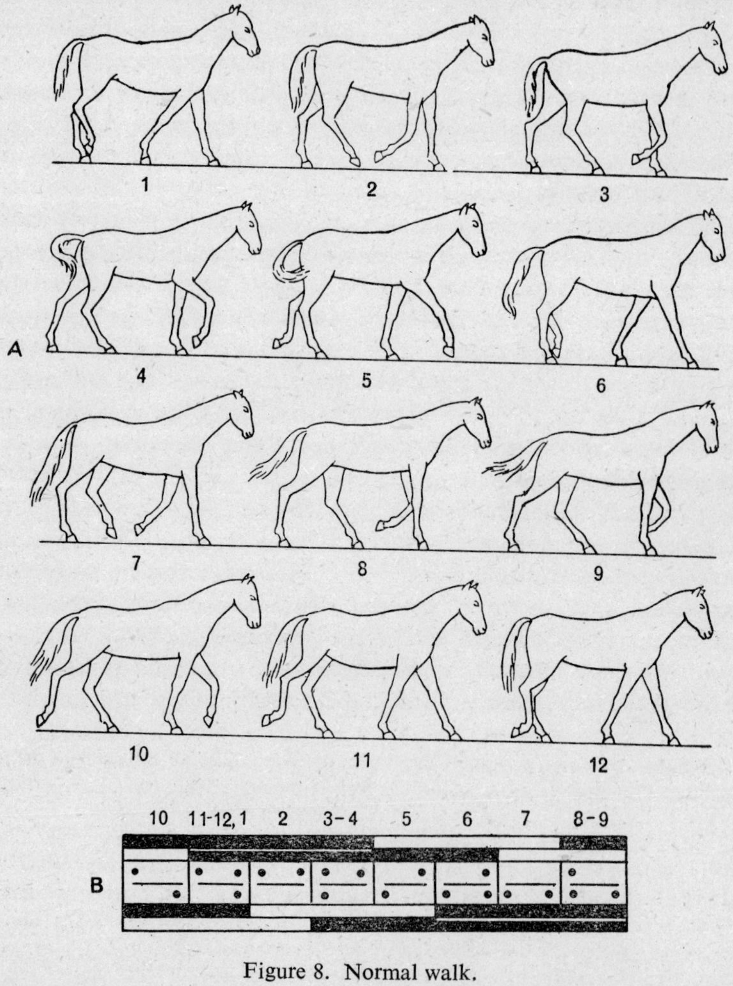

Figure 8. Normal walk.

A—usual locomotion of horse; photo-tables by Muybridge (1957); B—gaits diagram. Numbers indicate position in the diagram of stages shown in A.

it overlaps and is situated anterior to it in the direction of movement. This differentiates their names: short, normal, and stretched (Raabe, 1870); incompletely covered, and overlapping (Goubaux and Barrier, 1901); slow, moderate, and fast (Howell, 1944); short (retarded or calm), normal and long (speedy or fast) (Krasnikov, 1957). This division reflects the speedy gradation of locomotion in horses and may serve as a distinctive index for the horse's individual characteristics (Smith, 1912; Grogan, 1951), but this does not coincide with the limits of the real gait. If in very slow and slow trot-like walks, the step may be only incompletely covered, then in normal walk, incomplete covering may result from a heavy load (Muybridge, 1957; Pl. 1), artificial reduction of walk with exterior peculiarities of the animal, and so on.

An increase in the speed of a normal walk coincides with an absolute and relative decrease in the duration of tripodal stages with the relative enlargement of bipodal stages. During a maximum increase in gait, the rhythm of limb action is equal to one (4:4), i.e., on the line *EE* (Figure 5) tripodal stages drop out and the cycle goes by the formula: 2-2-2-2 (rotation of stages of lateral and diagonal support). Retardation otherwise leads to a reduction of bipodal stages right up to their joining the point of intersection for lines *AA* and *BB*. A change of rhythm of locomotion toward a trot draws after it the relative development of the diagonal support during the reduction of the lateral. On the other hand with a change of rhythm toward the amble, lateral support increases, but the relative duration of diagonal support decreases. During the combination of the rhythms of locomotion and limb action corresponding to lines *AA* and *BB* (Figure 5), stages of lateral support (2-3-3-2-3-3) or diagonal support (3-2-3-3-2-3) decrease in the cycle. As seen from the diagram, the variations in the rhythm of locomotion of a normal walk, especially during increased speed, are much enlarged. This resulted, in the past, in discussions about which of the different normal walking patterns in horses, was the norm: the more stable, with increased duration of diagonal stages (Raabe, 1870) or the more speedy where lateral stages prevail (Lecoq, 1843).[16] Only the appearance of objective methods for registering movement (Marey, 1873), stopped the argument and showed that the width of the diapason of changes in normal walk in horses (Goubaux and Barrier, 1901).

The normal walk is the main gait for the majority of mammals during slow movement. For example, Muybridge (1957) shows a series of Plates on the movement of the normal walk for the horse (Pls. 1 to 7, 9 to 24, 27 to 29), for the ass (Pls. 89 to 90), for the bull (Pls. 93 to 95), for the pig (Pls. 97 to 98), for the goat (Pls. 100 to 101), for the elephant (Pl. 112), for the dog (Pl. 114), for the cat (Pl. 124), for the lion (Pls. 129 to 130), for the tiger (Pl. 136), for the water pig (Pl. 141). Plates of the normal walk were not

[16]In Figure 1, C is registered as the normal walk where the lateral stages twice exceed the diagonal.

available for amphibians and reptiles (Sukhanov, 1968b).

Fast walk.[17] This walk is characterized by a rotation of bipodal stages, alternately of diagonal and lateral, with a unipodal stage according to the formula: 2-1-2-1-2-1-2-1 (Figure 9: Figure 10, A: 8 to 12, B). Here the tripodal stages of slower walks are replaced by unipodal walks where the primary tripodal types have been replaced by one front limb support (primary unipodal stages), but the secondaries are on one hind limb support (secondary unipodal stages). In the norm (Figure 5), the rhythm of locomotion consists of 50% and the rhythm of limb action 0.6 (3:5). Retardation leads to reduction of unipodal stages right up to their dropout at line *EE*; speed, on the other hand, decreases the relative duration of bipodal stages, but unipodal stages develop. Theoretically, at the point of intersection of lines *CC* and *DD*, bipodal stages should be reduced to zero. As in the normal walk, the change of locomotion rhythm toward the trot leads to a relative increase in stages of diagonal support in place of lateral. This is reversed during the change toward the amble. On the lines of *DD*, stages of lateral support dropout (2-1-1-2-1-1). On the lines of *CC*, the same is true with the stages of diagonal support (1-2-1-1-2-1). Theoretically, the limits of variation of the fast walk are not much less than in the normal walk, but in practice this is not so. Not only is it rarely met in nature, but it is changed entirely within restricted limits (dotted line in Figure 6). The fast walk is the main gait during speedy locomotion for several large and heavy-weight mammals: some horses (Figure 10), eland-antelope (Muybridge, 1957; Pl. 160), and elephants (Figure 9). Slijper (1946) names this as an important method of locomotion for camels, giraffes, elephants, hippopotamuses, and big bears.[18] The fast walk is also seen in horses, dogs, aurochs, bisons, and gnu-antelopes, but Slijper considers that these result from domestication. At least in horses and dogs, it is, very doubtful that the fast walk is a natural gait.

Howell (1944) postulates that the reason the fast walk is rarely seen lies in its being comparatively more exhausting than a trot or amble of equal speed. It is difficult at high speed to operate all the four limbs working one after the other and not at one time (coordination difficulties); it is impossible to completely use the body musculature; and it is important to keep the hind limbs at a wide distance so as to avoid "overreach" the hind and forelimbs of the same side meeting in air. However, there are other reasons. Already

[17]Amble (Muybridge, 1887; Smith, 1912; Slijper, 1946; fast running walk (Howell, 1944); rack (Grogan, 1951).

[18]According to Slijper, an increase of speed causes the fast walk to change from a diagonal to a lateral sequence. However, this is doubtful. Clarification and also confirmation are required by Slijper about the change during this to the amble. By all means the problem of terminology is in doubt, as in identifying the "amble" accurately by Muybridge (Slijper, 1946; Pl. 13), Slijper speaks still about the slow amble with tripodal stages, i.e., possibly the slow running walk of Howell (see further).

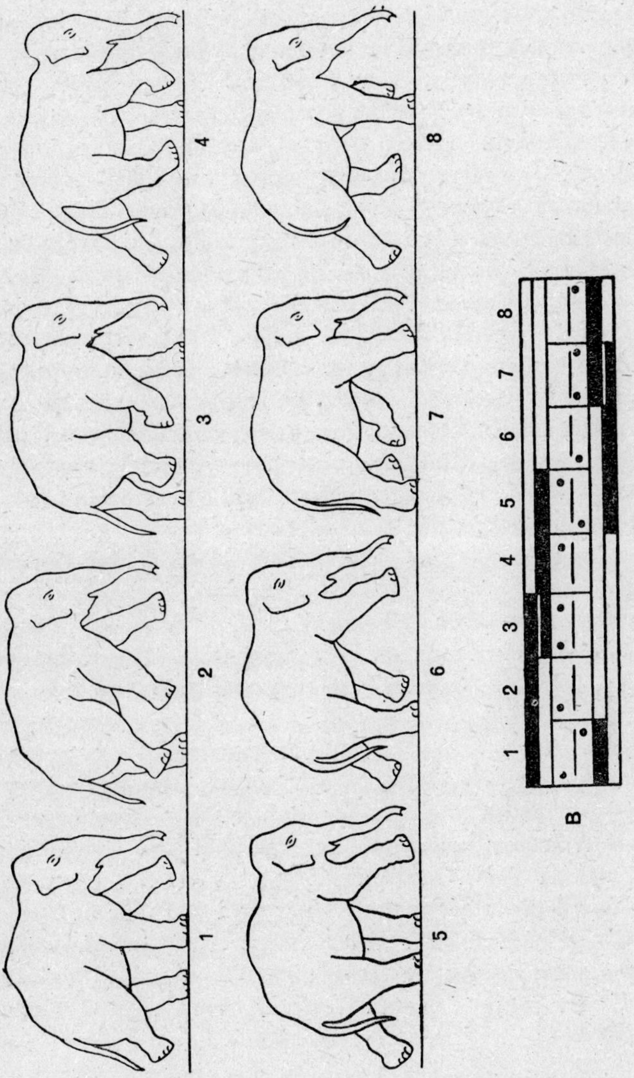

Figure 9. Fast walk.

A—fast locomotion of elephant, by Gambaryan (1967); B—gait diagram. Numbers indicate position in the diagram of stages shown in A.

in the normal walk, the ability to increase the length of maximum step, which is established by the swing of limbs, is completely used. Thus, increased speed may occur mainly at the cost of quickened limb movements, which brings about extreme exhaustion and are not compensated for by an observable increase of speed. Quickness of movement itself is similarly restricted by the necessity of observing a particular minimum of absolute transport time for each limb. Work on lizards has shown (see Part II) that this minimum is often achieved long before reaching the speed corresponding to the fast walk: in the Komodo monitor (a lizard), it is already seen in the norm of slow trot-like walk (Figure 5). Over-exhaustion of the transport period in man especially leads to a reduction in the walk (Popova, 1935). Man's expenditure of energy during very fast movement is more than his expenditure of energy during a slow run, though the latter happens during high absolute speed (Kotikova, 1939). Thus, it is natural that animals capable of fast locomotion, try during an increase of speed "not to withhold" on the fast walk and at once come to a faster form of locomotion wherein the confusion between length of step and number of limb movements is decided by the introduction in the cycle of a stage of free flight. Only in cases of animals "not under power" because of heavy weights, etc., do we regularly observe movement by the fast walk. The appearance in a cycle of a stage of free flight (theoretically, there exist three methods) leads to that; the particular factor increasing the length of step seems to be, not the swinging of limbs, but the force of hind stroke and a corresponding duration of periods without support. In lizards the simple walk may develop in 3-4 time A significant reserve in the development of speed as a result of increased step, not only compensates the increased expenditure of energy, but also "unloads" the transport period by reducing the frequency of movements.

One of the methods of transition from running to locomotion with free flight which leads to very fast running (Figure 10, D) with the formula—0-1-0-1-0-1-0-1—is practically closed for animals. It is difficult to think that any one of them may be pushed, e.g., one hind limb or one forelimb with strength enough for a subsequent flight in the air. However, the appearance of free flight is not possible solely by a sharp increase of speed and strength of the push. Even a simple change in rhythm of locomotion toward the trot (during intersection through line *DD*) or amble (through *CC*) leads to this. If the change of rhythm is greater, then transition is achieved with a lesser speed.

Trot-like Walk

The trot-like walk is characterized by a closeness in time of corresponding movements of the diagonal pair of limbs, due to which the rhythm of locomotion in the norm is equal to 25%. The two different types of trot-like walk,

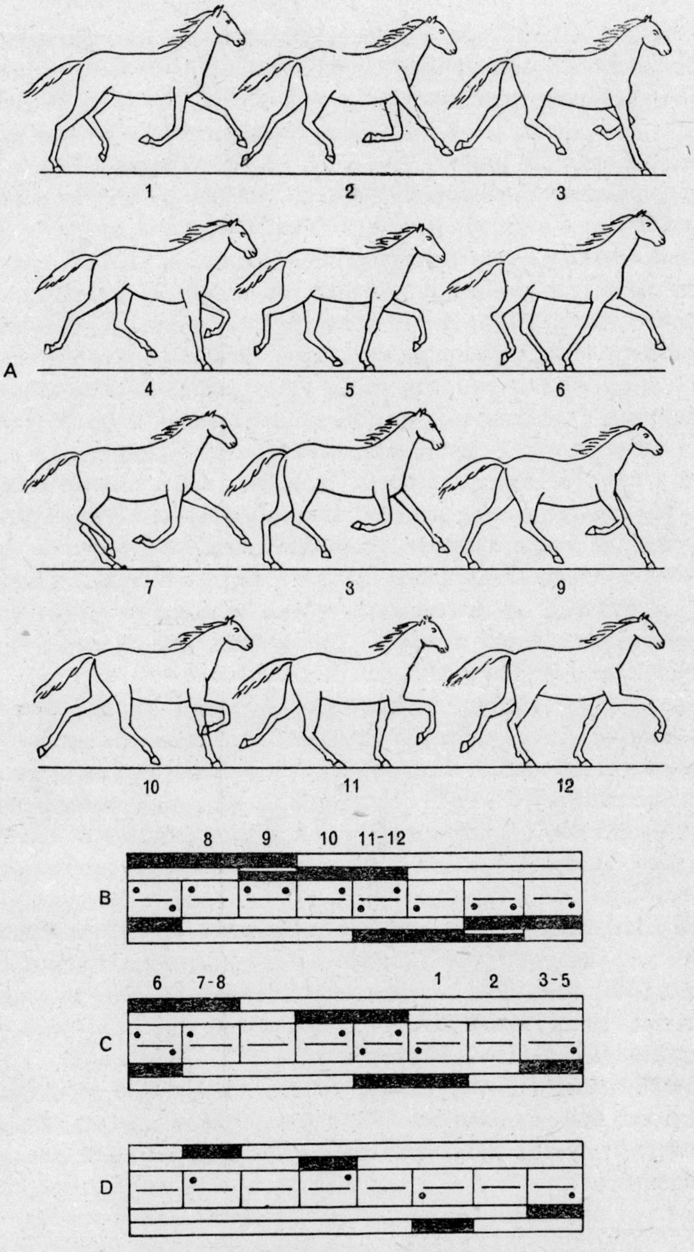

Figure 10. Fast walk, fast trot-like, and "very fast" gaits.

A—horse during slowing to change motion from fast trot-like walk (1-8) to fast walk (8-12), Photo-tables by Muybridge (1957); B—gait diagram fast walk; C—gait diagram fast trot-like walk; D—theoretical gait diagram of "very fast" walk. Numbers indicate position in the diagrams of stages shown in A.

slow and fast, do not form a single continuum, similar to that of the walk (Figure 5), thus a direct transition from one to the other without the mediation of other gaits is impossible.

Slow trot-like walk.[19] This walk is characterized by a rotation of bi-, tri- and quadrupodal stages: 2-3-4-3-2-3-4-3, i.e., compared to a very slow walk, the primary quadrupodal stages are retained, but the secondaries are replaced by stages of diagonal support (Figure 11, A and B). As in the very slow walk, braking by the forelimb takes place earlier than the release from the ground of the ipsilateral hind limb. Movement is possible only with incompletely covered footsteps in mammals or "step in step" in some lizards with long and widely separated hind limbs. Unlike the very slow walk, the braking of a hind limb continues to the diagonal footfall of its anterior; this leads also to the appearance in the cycle of two stages of diagonal support.

In the norm, the rhythm of limb action in a slow trot-like walk is characterized as 3 (6:2). Increase in speed coincides with a relative decrease of quadrupodal stages up to a complete dropout on line *AA* (Figure 5), during development of diagonal support. Retardation leads to the reverse. A change of rhythm in locomotion towards the trot requires a decrease in duration of tripodal stages right up to their dropout with transition to the trot (line *BC*). During this, bi- and quadrupodal stages develop. The closeness of rhythm of locomotion to rhythm of walk, on the other hand, leads to a relative development of tripodal stages at the cost of decreasing bi- and quadrupodal stages. During the simultaneous change of rhythm toward the walk and a speeding up of movement, the bipodal stages stabilize, leading to a transition into the normal walk (through line *AA*). If the change of rhythm takes place slowly, then a more or less constant and relative duration of quadrupodal stages is established. This, in its turn, may lead to a transition to a very slow walk (through line *BB*).

The slow trot-like walk seems to be the main form of rapid movement in tailed amphibians (Figure 30), walking toads (Figure 31) (Schaeffer, 1941; Barclay, 1946; Sukhanov, 1964b, 1968b), tortoises and slow moving lizards (Sukhanov, 1964b, 1968b). Similarly, the retarding walk of horse movements (Figure 11) (Howell, 1944; Muybridge, 1957, Pls. 30 and 32).

As already mentioned, Howell put his slow gait in the straight row between very slow and normal walks. Really, this is a faster gait than the first, but the very slow walk comes into it only during the simultaneous change of locomotory rhythm and a speeding up of movement toward the trot. In the second part of this work, it will be shown that in the case of lower tetrapods, an increase of speed is always related to a change in locomotory rhythm.

[19] Irregular trot—*traquenard* (Goubaux and Barrier, 1901); in the lateral sequence: *metherpetico* (Croix, 1929a, 1936); quick walk, or *entrepas* (Durst, 1936); slow walk (Howell, 1944); ? [sic] running walk (Grogan, 1951); trotting walk (Hildebrand, 1962).

In this way, the slow trot-like walk really replaces the very slow. In mammals, the slow trot-like walk is less characteristic, but it is often observed in decrepit animals. A change of speed takes place mainly within the limits of the normal walk or also in the trot. However, it is not ruled out that the separation of this gait as independent, differing from the categorized walk, may help one to recognize it in other forms, and the conditions of its use in mammals may, thus, be written with greater clarity.

Fast trot-like walk.[20] This walk is characterized by the appearance of two free flight stages in the cycle in place of primary quadrupodal stages of the very slow and slow trot-like walk (Figure 10, A: 1-8; B). In its turn, tripodal stages are replaced in the fast walk by unipodal stages, i.e., the cycle corresponds to the formula: 2-1-0-1-2-1-0-1. The rhythm of limb action in the norm is considered as ~0.3 (2:6). Increase of movement leads to a reduction of diagonal stages under the development of without-support; retardation, on the other hand, leads to a reduction of free flight up to zero on line *DD* (Figure 5). The closeness of the locomotory rhythm to the rhythm of the trot corresponds to an increase in the relative duration of bipodal stages and stages of free flight; closeness to the rhythm of the walk, on the other hand, corresponds to a relative increase in unipodal stages.

The status of the fast trot-like walk in literature is questionable. At best, it can be identified as a deviant of the natural gait of quick trot, resulting from "separation" of diagonal limbs at the time of movement and hence, is included in trot. Howell generally does not mention it. Horse-breeders consider its appearance in horses as irregular, but mention that it causes an extreme increase in the speed of movement (Goubaux and Barrier, 1901) and an increase of fatigue. In fact, it is logical to consider the fast trot-like walk as a natural gait, a peculiar change from running to fast trot. Its demarcation from running is fixed on the basis of a support formula change. Its demarcation from the trot, if not considered by the condition of the latter's strict observance of synchronism, and this, as a rule, is not met with in nature, is more conditional and possibly connected with physiological requirements (see below). The fas trot-like walk is often fixed in horses—walking by a trot—rather than the present synchronistic trot (Muybridge, 1957; Pls. 43-49). Even then, mention is often made that "asynchrony" in the work of the diagonal limbs in horses leads to an excessive load on the front limb which bears the entire weight of the animal after free flight, and on the back limb which should provide a stroke of great strength. Thus, compared to trot, the fast trot-like walk is more tiring for the animal (Goubaux and Barrier, 1901), but this is compensated for by an increase in speed. As the horse often runs to this gait, it is quite obvious that considering the fast

[20]Discontinued trot (Marey, 1875); discontinued trot="walk" (Krasnikov, 1957); types of trot (Muybridge, 1887); flying trot Goubaux and Barrier, 1901; Smith, 1912); irregular trot, foreleg in advance (Wynmalen, 1954).

trot-like walk as merely irregular is not permissible.

It is important to mention one more peculiarity of the fast trot-like walk compared to the slow: If the latter is completed between the wide limits of variation in rhythm of locomotion, then the rhythm of locomotion is, as a rule, closer to the rhythm of the trot than to the walk.

Trot

In the trot row (line *BC*, Figure 5) generally acccepted for differentiating gradations of speed, there occur slow trots,[21] characterized by the formula: 2-4-2-4 (Figure 11, B), and fast trots[22] (Figure 12). Taking the trot as a gait, it is important to define a few of its limits. Theoretically, the trot has complete synchronism of the action of the diagonal limbs and, consequently, the smallest deviation will cause a change to the trot-like walk in diagonal and lateral sequences. During the slow trot, a tendency toward the lateral sequence (i.e., on the line *BC* right, Figure 5),[23] as a rule, is not observed. However, Muybridge (1887) has mentioned that during the trot there is no hard rule about which leg of a diagonal pair is first raised and set down, though this is usually done by the front one (just as in the fast trot-like walk, Figure 10, C). Among his plates, it may be possible to search for photographs of horses alternating the "leading" limb during the course of motion (Muybridge, 1957; Pl. 39), moving in a lateral sequence (Muybridge, 1957; Pl. 33) or a diagonal sequence. An analysis of the fast movement of lizards (see Part II) similarly shows that the rhythm of locomotion and the trot varies in the limits of $\pm 10\%$; in addition, the variation is irregular: one half-cycle may go with a positive rhythm, and the second, with a negative. It seems that these variations do not change the conditions of equilibrium and are immaterial to the animal. Therefore, it is reasonable, at least for this group, to include the limit of variation, $\pm 10\%$, as the limits of the trot. If the variation is close to any one region, e.g., to the diagonal sequence, it preferably explains the trot-like walk. In the case of lizards, variation lies, as a rule, in the zone toward the left from $+10\%$ limits. It is interesting to note that when the movement is faster, very often a tendency to the lateral sequence can be observed.

According to Howell (1944), trot is used by the majority of ungulate animals, cats, and dogs. This is a more tiring method of fast movement; however,

[21]Low and short trot (Marey, 1873, 1901); low trot (Goubaux and Barrier, 1901); slow trot (Smith, 1912); *trote caminado* (Croix, 1929a); shortened trot—*der kurze trab* (Durst, 1936); walking trot (Howell, 1944); soundless trot (Krasnikov, 1957).

[22]High and long trot (Marey, 1875); high trot (Goubaux and Barrier, 1901); trot (Muybridge, 1887; Grogan, 1951; Wynmalen, 1954); ordinary trot (Smith, 1912); *trote*, in reptiles, *calperpetico* (Croix, 1923a, 1936); ordinary trot—*Normaler oder Mitteltrab* (Durst, 1936); running trot (Howell, 1944); speedy trot, and trot (Krasnikov, 1957).

[23]Irregular trot, hind leg in advance (Wynmalen, 1954).

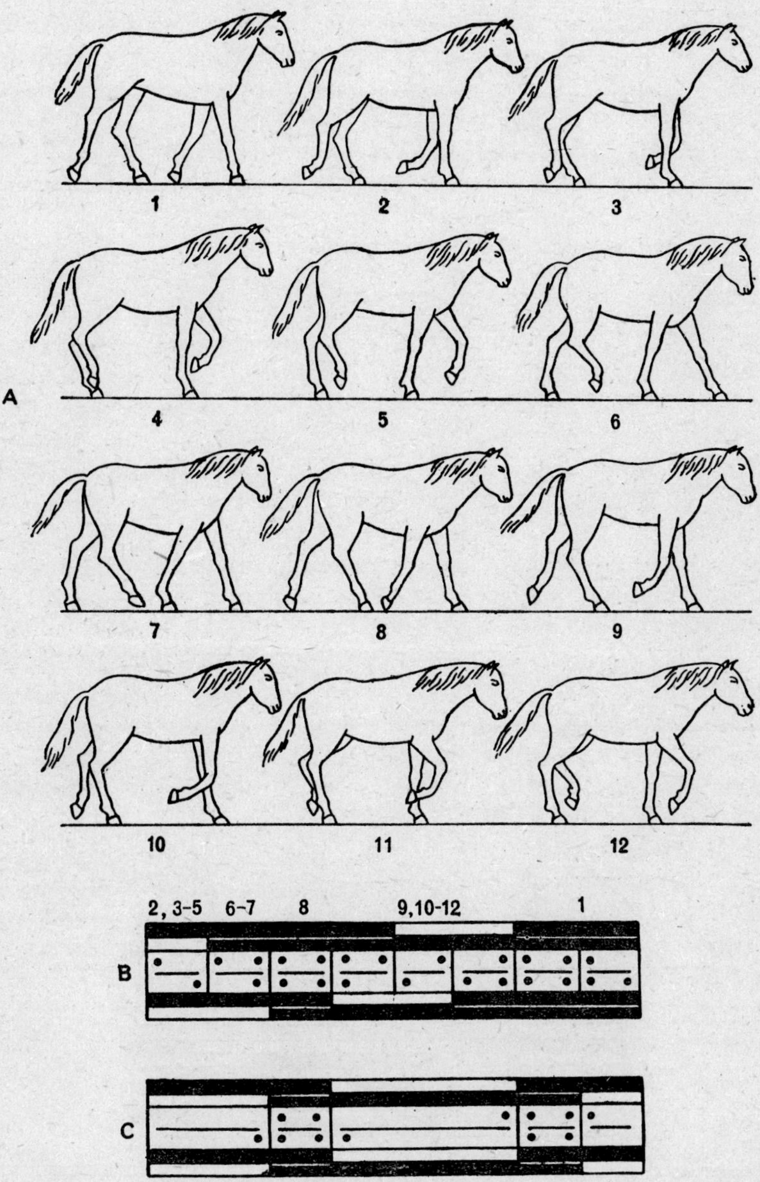

Figure 11. Slow trot-like walk and slow trot.

A—conversion of walk of horse to slow trot-like walk; photo-tables by Muybridge (1957); B—gait diagram of slow trot-like walk. Numbers indicate position of stages shown in A; C—gait diagram of slow trot.

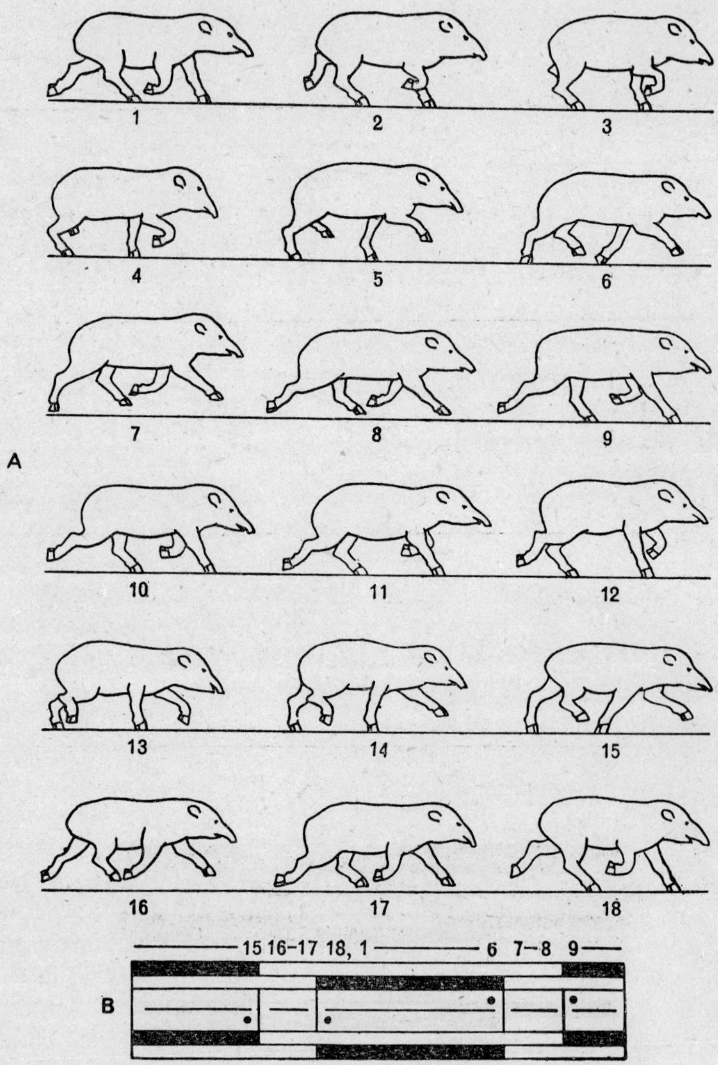

Figure 12. Fast trot.

A—tapir during locomotion by fast trot, by Gambaryan (1964); B—Gait diagram of walk. Numbers indicate position of stages shown in A.

the musculature of the back is not fully used under this type of locomotion. Because of the possibility of locating one-sided limbs, the trot is more characteristic of long-bodied forms with relatively short and widely-placed hind limbs; however, even the leopard (Hildebrand, 1961) tends toward a fast trot or a fast trot-like walk under normal speed (20.4 kilometers per hour). In addition to the sequence of movement in horses in literature, there are sequences of movement of trot in several other animals: deer and gazelle (Muybridge, 1957; Pls. 154 and 158), tapir (Gambaryan, 1964; see also Figure 12 in the present work), but often, as mentioned earlier, an asynchrony in movement of diagonal limbs is observed, to some extent, or the trot appears as a form of special external variations which will be seen below.

The selection of a norm for the slow and fast trots should be based on principles other than those for the four-paced gaits, since there is no equality in the four stages of the cycle. When analyzing very slow walks, we mentioned that the normal slow movement is only possible under a small sequence of primary quadrupodal stages. This is more closely related to the trot where, under low speed of movement, these stages are longer. However, an analysis of the material shows that, in fact, the quadrupodal periods in a trot are very short. In horses, the trot is generally recognized as a gait with two stages of free flight. With reference to this, the norm of a slow trot is logically considered to have a faster standard than the norm of a slow trot-like walk and more so than the norm of a very slow walk. In Figure 5, the norm of a slow trot has been shown in a diagram where the rhythm of limb action is identified as 1.7 (5:3). In this case, the stages of diagonal support are twice as long as the quadrupodal stages (Figure 11, C).

An increase in the speed of locomotion coincides with the reduction of the quadrupodal stages to zero (at the point of intersection of lines *BC* and *EE*, Figure 5), and the cycles are represented by the formula: 2-2. Further increase of speed involves an appearance of a free flight stage and changes to a fast trot with increasing durations of without-support periods. Reservedly, the norm of fast trot is considerd to be when the stages of diagonal support are twice the duration of the stages of free flight. In practice, we have seen sizable variations in this, but the periods of support always increase the periods of free flight. particularly when the horse's center of gravity is trajectorily considered (Goubaux and Barrier, 1901), and the animal loses support, not as a result of a jump upwards, but as a result of bending the limbs. The maximum observed duration of free flight in horse (Lenoble du Teil, 1877) consists of only a two-third period of operation, i.e., does not reach the point corresponding to the rhythm of limb action 0.3 (2:6) (Figure 5), where the flight is equal to support (conditionally—norm very fast trot).

Amble-like Walk

The amble-like (rack-like) walk is characterized by a closeness in synchrony of the similar movement of the limb pair of one side, thereby eliminating the danger of their intersection. This is often adopted by long-legged, light animals similar to the leopard, giraffe, and gazelle (Hildebrand, 1962). The amble-like walk is more stable than the amble; the transverse inclination of the center of gravity is significantly less, but there is an increase in the rhythm of limb action, so it is necessary to differentiate slow and fast amble-like walk.

Slow amble-like walk.[24] This walk is characterized by a rotation of tripodal stages alternately with bipodal stages (stages of lateral support) and quadrupodal (secondary) by the formula: 4-3-2-3-4-3-2-3 (Figure 13). In the norm, the rhythm of locomotion is identified as 75%; the rhythm of limb action as 3 (6:2). Increase in speed is associated with an increase in duration of bipodal and a decrease of quadrupodal stages right up to their drop-out on line *BB* (Figure 5) where the cycle comes to six stages (3-2-3-3-2-3). Further speed should theoretically involve a change to the normal walk in the rhythm of half-amble; during retardation, the reverse occurs. The stages of lateral support fall on line *AA* (4-3-3-4-3-3); above this line the slow amble-like walk changes to the very slow walk. A change in the rhythm of locomotion toward the amble results in a relative growth of bi- and quadrupodal stages with a decrease of tripodal stages. The reverse happens during a change toward the walk.

Elephants (Figure 13), camels (Muybridge, 1957; Pl. 104), bisons (Pls. 164 and 165), gnu-antelopes (Pl. 161), asses (Pls. 89 to 91), lions (Pl. 135), leopards (Hildebrand, 1961), giraffes (Bourdelle, 1934; Gambaryan, 1967), and some horses (Goubaux and Barrier, 1901) move with a slow amble-like walk.

Fast amble-like walk.[25] This walk is characterized by a rotation of unipodal stages alternately with stages of lateral support and free flight by the formula: 0-1-2-1-0-1-2-1 (Figure 14). In the norm, the rhythm of locomotion, like that of the slow amble-like walk, corresponds to 75%, but the rhythm of limb action is ~0.3 (2:6). Slow movement results in the reduction of free flight stages to zero (in line *CC*, Figure 5), during an increase in the stages of lateral support. A direct change between the fast and slow amble-like walks is impossible. However in the literature, the term "irregular amble" is often used to suggest a normal walk with the rhythm of the half-amble. As in the case of the fast trot-like walk, the status of the fast amble-like walk in literature is subject to doubt, for during high speed, the change in the rhythm

[24]Irregular amble (Goubaux and Barrier, 1901); *marche rompu* (Bourdelle, 1934); pacing walk (Hildebrand, 1962).
[25]Different types of amble (Muybridge, 1887).

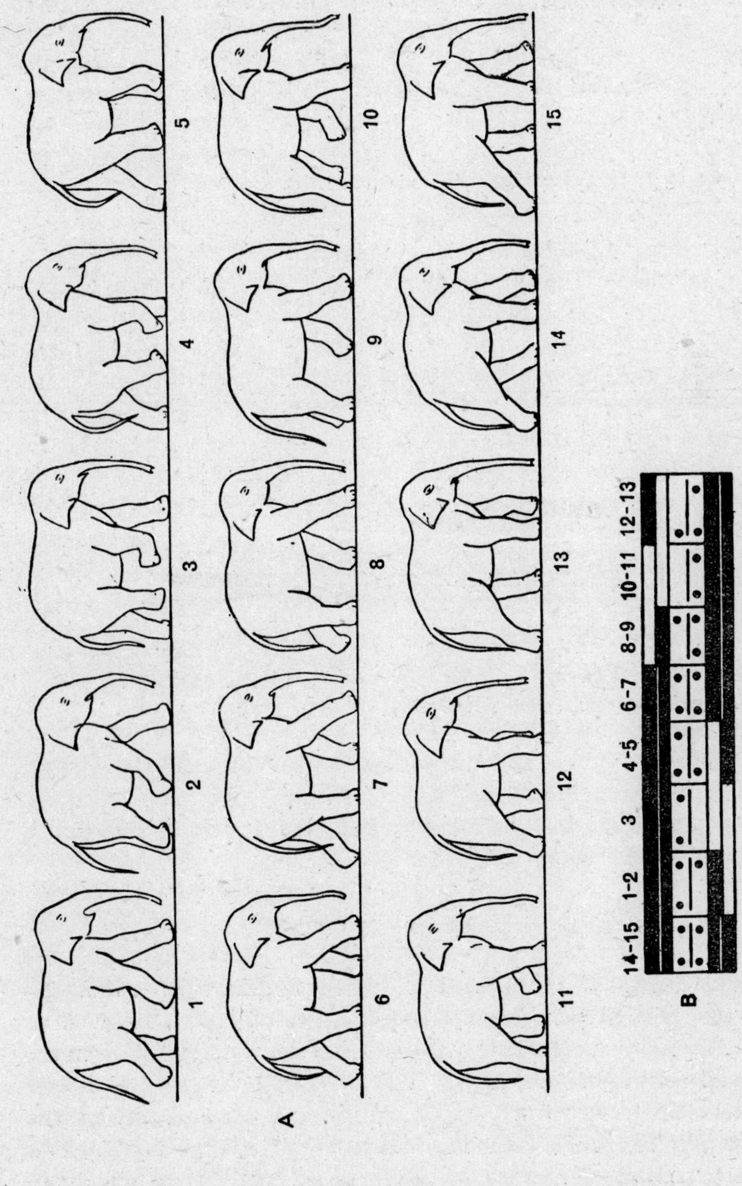

Figure. 13. Slow amble-like walk.

A—slow locomotion of elephant; photo-tables by Muybridge (1957); B—gait diagram. Numbers indicate position of stages shown in A.

of locomotion from that of the amble to that of the trot-like walk is slight and it is almost impossible to aurally differentiate the footfall of limb pairs. The range of variation "in horizontal" of the slow variant is greater. Gambaryan (1967) mentions that for the giraffe the movement is almost equal to

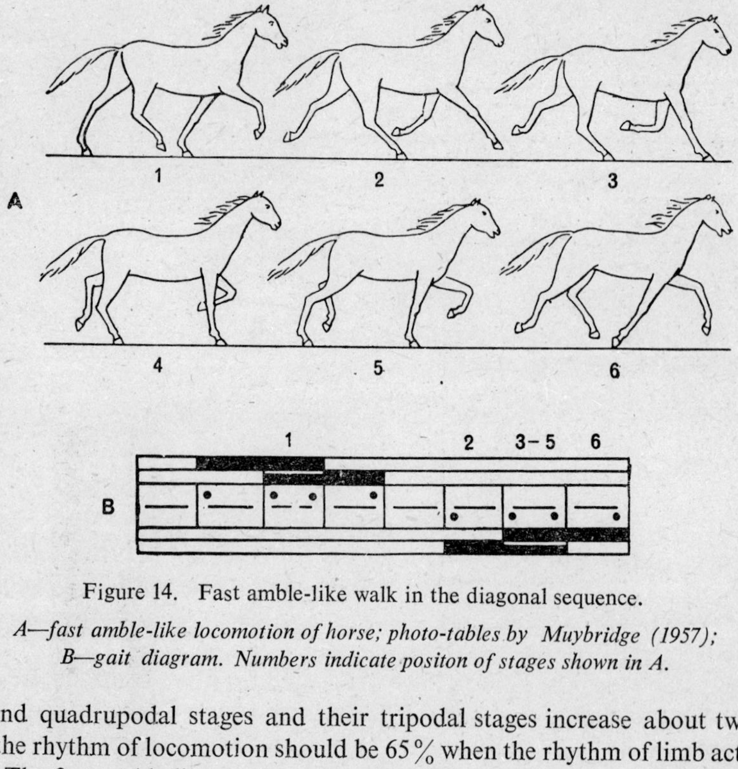

Figure 14. Fast amble-like walk in the diagonal sequence.

A—fast amble-like locomotion of horse; photo-tables by Muybridge (1957); B—gait diagram. Numbers indicate positon of stages shown in A.

bi- and quadrupodal stages and their tripodal stages increase about twice, i.e., the rhythm of locomotion should be 65% when the rhythm of limb action is 3. The fast amble-like walk occurs often in horses (Figure 14) and camels (Muybridge, 1957; Pl. 106).

Amble

The amble or rack, as a two-paced gait like the trot, has many advantages over the walk: first, the simplicity of coordination of limb movement as ipsilateral limbs move synchronously to the touch down and liftoff from the ground (rhythm of locomotion, 100%). This completely removes the danger of intersection but results in a significant transverse displacement of the center of gravity. The amble is the most unstable gait of all, being based on the diagonal sequence, but may for this reason give a higher speed of locomotion (with considerable fatigue) on a flat surface than the trot. However, during an amble the limbs are protracted close to the ground and quite often

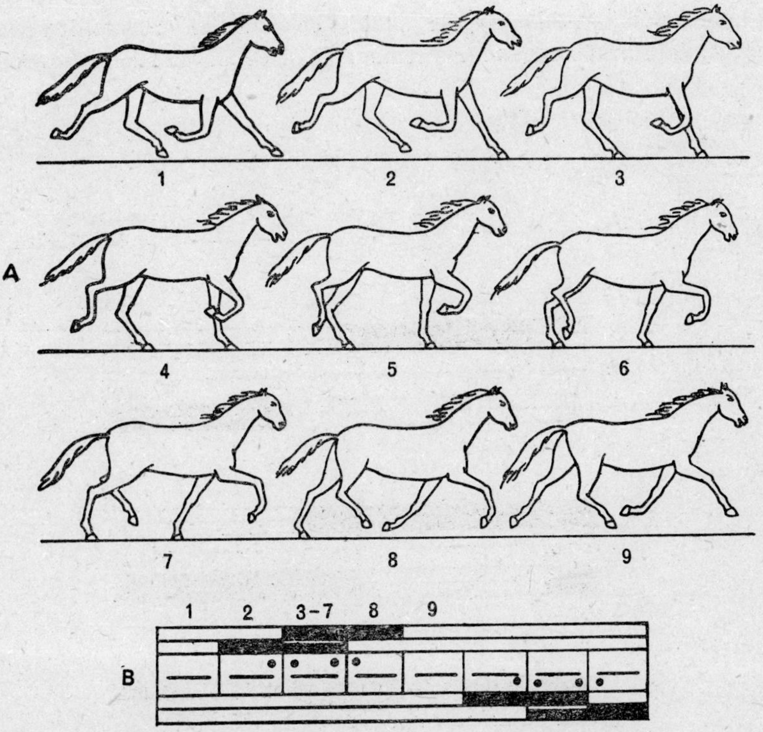

Figure 15. Fast amble-like walk in the lateral sequence.
A—fast amble-like locomotion of horse; photo-tables by Muybridge 1957); B—gait diagram. Numbers indicate position of stages shown in A.

causes stumbling. An increase in speed is attained mainly through the quickness of limb movement and is not due to a significant increase in step length (Krasnikov, 1957). As a rule, animals using an amble can change gaits only with great difficulty. The peculiarities of the amble are due to contradictions in animals with widely-placed limbs, and is often used by the elongated forms with shorter bodies and high placement, displacement somewhat in front of the center of gravity. This is regularly adopted by camels, giraffes, elks, bears, and some horses (Krasnikov, 1957). Exceptionally, the amble may be seen in bulls and dogs (Goubaux and Barrier, 1901).

As in the trot, there is some uncertainty in the amble over which limb from a pair precedes slightly in touchdown and liftoff (Muybridge, 1887). Usually, the hind precedes the forelimb as in trot. In this way, the amble often "strikes" an "amble-like" walk in the diagonal sequence which is more stable than the amble itself. Occasionally the forelimb precedes (amble-like walk in the lateral sequence). One of the plates of Muybridge (1957; Pl. 52) presents such a deviation. In the first half-cycle (Figure 14 of the present work), the right hind foot touches down at the start, but in the second (Figure 15), the left forefoot. In this way, the amble, like trot, may be seen theoretically as a changing form between movement in the diagonal and lateral sequences.

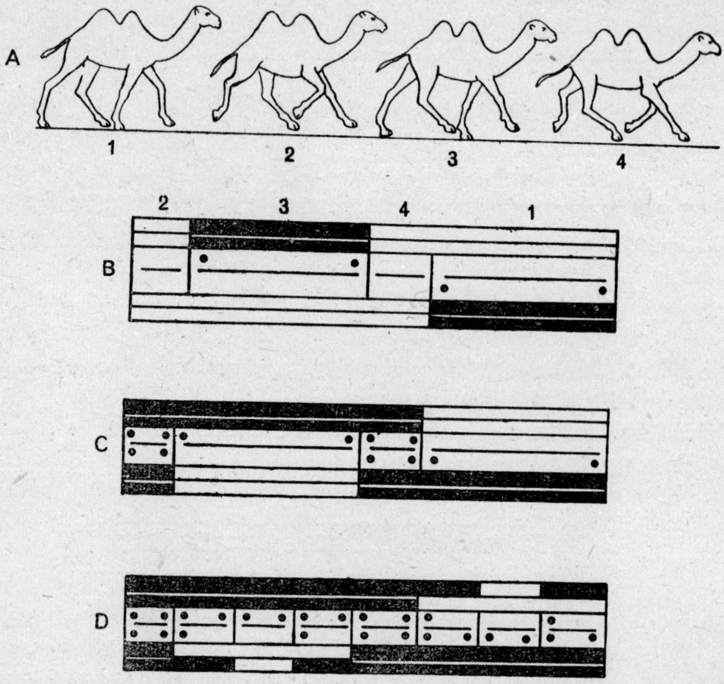

Figure 16. Fast and slow amble; slow amble with predominance of hind limbs. *A—fast locomotion by amble of camel; Croix (1929a): B—gait diagram of fast amble. Numbers indicate position of stages in A; C—diagram of slow amble; D—gait diagram of slow amble with predominance of hind limbs.*

Slow amble.[26] This form is characterized by the alternation of quadru- and bipodal stages in the formula: 4-2-4-2. In the norm, the rhythm of limb action is determined as 3 (6:2). Retardation is followed by an increase in the duration of quadrupodal stages during a decrease in stages of lateral support. Increase in speed, on the other hand, results in the reduction of quadrupodal stages to zero (at the point of intersection of lines *AD* and *EE*, Figure 5).

Fast amble.[27] The fast amble (Figure 16, A, B) is characterized by a

[26]Low amble (Goubaux and Barrier, 1901); *ambladura*=walking amble (Croix, 1929, 1936; amble *marche ordinaire* (Bourdelle, 1934); amble—*der Pahs* (Durst, 1936); walking pace (Howell, 1944).

[27]High amble (Goubaux and Barrier, 1901); rack or pace (Muybridge, 1887); pacing or racking (Smith, 1912); *ambladura*-amble (Croix, 1929, 1936); amble *saute ou volant* (Bourdelle, 1934); running pace (Howell, 1944); rack (Slijper, 1946); amble (Krasnikov, 1957).

rotation of stages of free flight and lateral support by the formula: 0-2-0-2. Like the trot, the conditional norm has a rhythm of limb action equal to 0.6 (3:5). An increase in speed involves a relative increase in the duration of the without-support period and a reduction of lateral support. Retardation leads to the opposite.

External Variants of Symmetrical Gaits

In addition to the important symmetrical gaits described above, there are several recognizable external variations. It has been known for a long time that during a horse's trot, the front pair of limbs not only lifted earlier from the ground (occurring similarly in the trot-like walk with a lateral sequence and the amble-like walk with a diagonal sequence) but touch down later under the following conditions. Stillman (1882) describes some situations in which both the forelimbs of the horse, but not the hind limbs are simultaneously in the air. However, Howell (1944) referring to Stillman, commits the mistake of unreservedly connecting the above phenomenon with the average speed of walking and keeping the gait named by him as the slow-running walk in the row of walk between the fast walk and fast running walk. Howell analyzed the trot and mentioned that the longer hind legs of horses sometimes perform a longer swing than the front ones "in spite of the latter's desire." This leads to a much earlier break by the front pair of limbs and an upward thrust of the front portion of the body. The forelimb, at the cost of an additional appearance in the air, makes a step longer than its own swing. Therefore a possibility appears, not considering the difference in the length of both limbs in a pair, to satisfy the basic rule of symmetrical locomotion, i.e., compulsory equality of steps by front and back limbs. Howell should have considered these phenomena together as they are caused by the same factors, but lack of clarity in his method of diagrammatically presenting gait conceals the difference in duration of support time for the front and back limbs in "slow running walk."

Figure 17 diagrammatically presents Howell's slow running walk in the method suggested by us. One glance reveals the inequality in support time. One more speciality deserves attention: Figure 17, **B** differs from the normal walk presented in Figure 8, **B**, only by the replacement of secondary tripodal stages by unipodal ones in which both types of support are completed by one of the hind limbs. The rhythm of action of the hind limbs completely corresponds to such a normal walk, but in the case of the front limb, it is artificially lowered and externally coincides with the rhythm of the fast walk. Therefore, it is correct to identify this gait as a normal walk with a predominance of hind limbs.

Phenomena of different types rest on the basis of anterior variations of gaits: difference in limb length, difference in the angles of swing, etc.—

all of which lead to one: The swing of one pair of limbs (anterior or posterior) begins to increase the swing of the others. From this an interesting investigation is generated. As previously said, animals increase their step with speed.

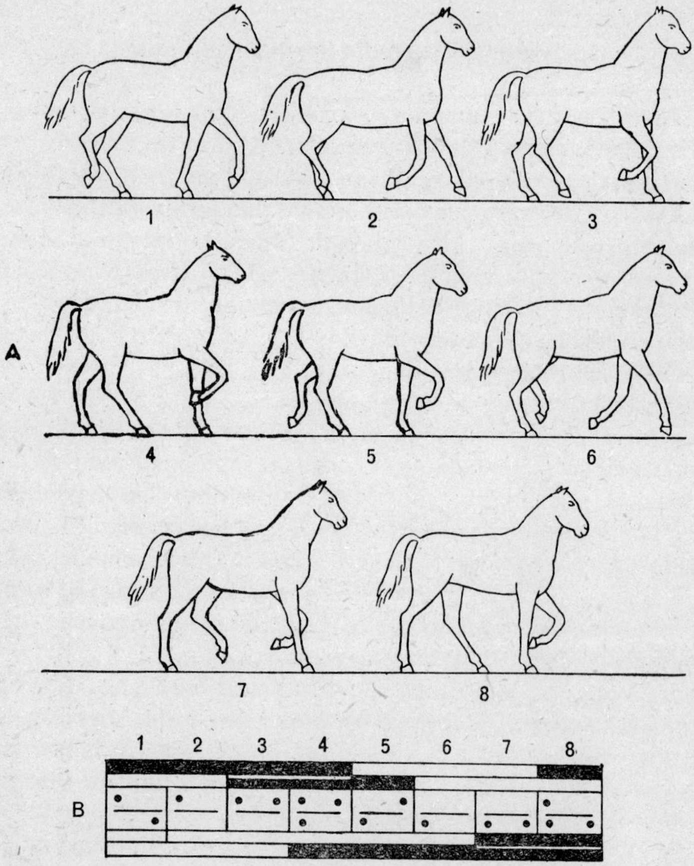

Figure 17. Normal walk with predominance of limbs.

A—horse using this gait, by Howell (1944); B—gait diagram. Numbers indicate position of stages shown in A.

In so doing, the swing of the hind limbs, usually longer than the forelimbs, begins to increase the maximum swing of the forelimb only under a particular speed of motion. In other words, external variations should be more distinct and more observable during fast movement Work with lizards shows that really the degree of predominance of the hind limbs is as high as the speed of motion At the same time "externality" is also observed in very

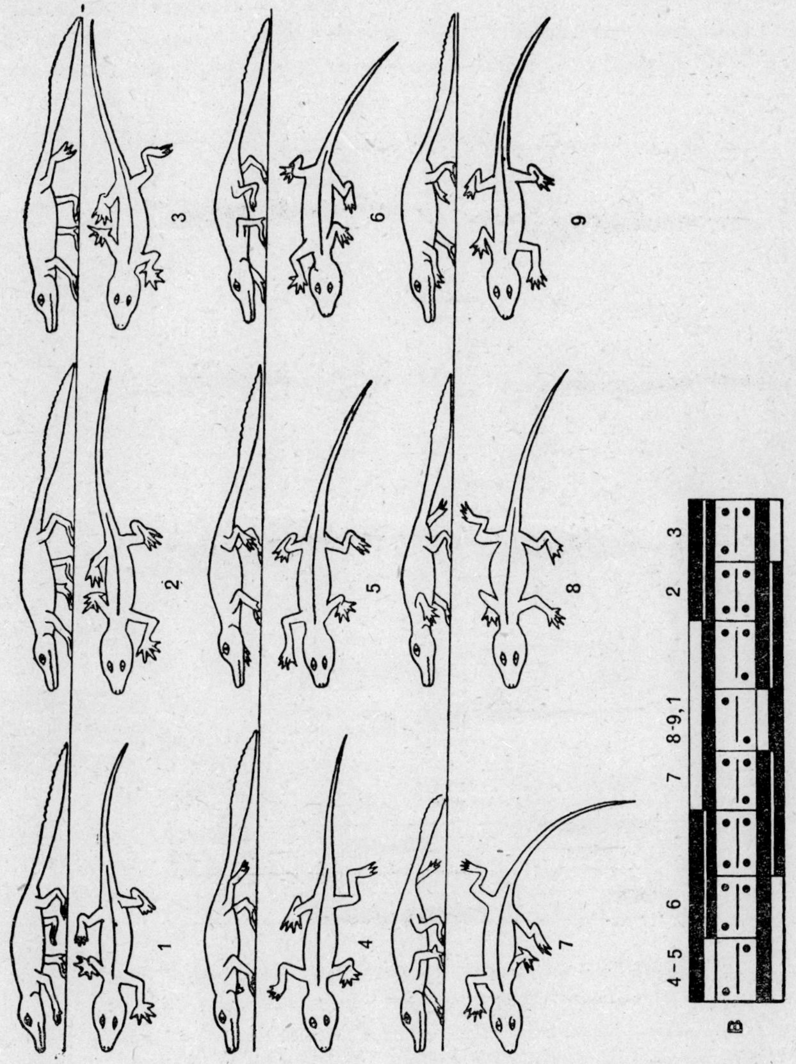

Figure 18. Slow trot with predominance of forelimbs.
A—alligator using this gait, by Schaeffer (1941); B—gait diagram. Numbers indicate position of stages shown in A.

low speeds when the limbs do not work within the limit of their own swing. Consequently, it is necessary to determine the factors which lead to the "advantage" in the retention of this inequality in the swing of the fore- and hind limbs (see Part II of the present work).

The predominance of these limbs usually leads to the appearance in the cycle of additional stages which conceal the real basis of this gait so that it is not difficult to accept it as an independent one, as was done with the slow

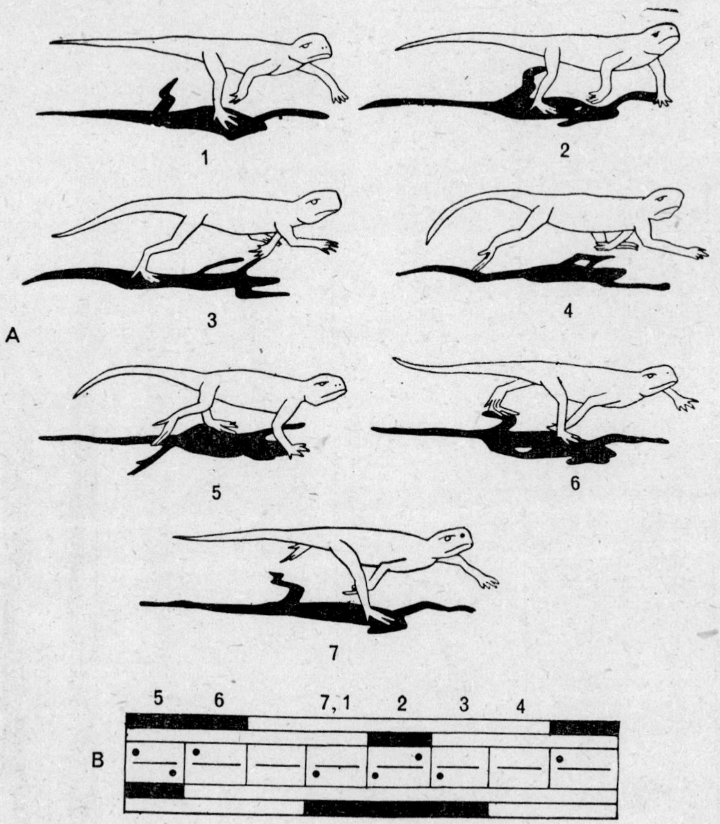

Figure 19. Fast trot with predominance of hind limbs.
A—fast run of lizards (Phrynocephalus); *B—gait diagram. Numbers indicate position of stages shown in A.*

running walk. It is not easy to observe external variations during motion by the trot or amble, as the smallest inequality in the duration of support time for front and back limbs leads to the appearance in the cycle of tripodal stages in the slow trot and amble, and unipodal stages in the fast. At present, the following external variations of two-paced gait are fixed; slow trot with

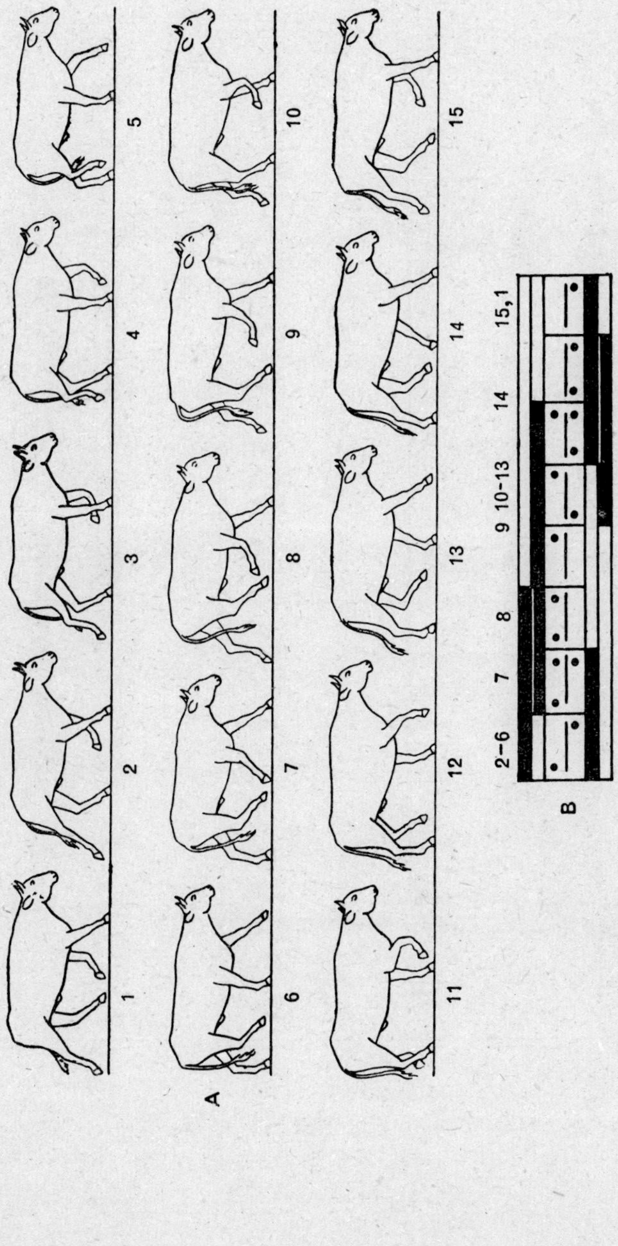

Figure 20. Normal wa k with predominance of forelimbs.
A—bull using this gait; photo-tables by Muybridge (1957); B—gait diagram. Numbers indicate position of stages shown in A.

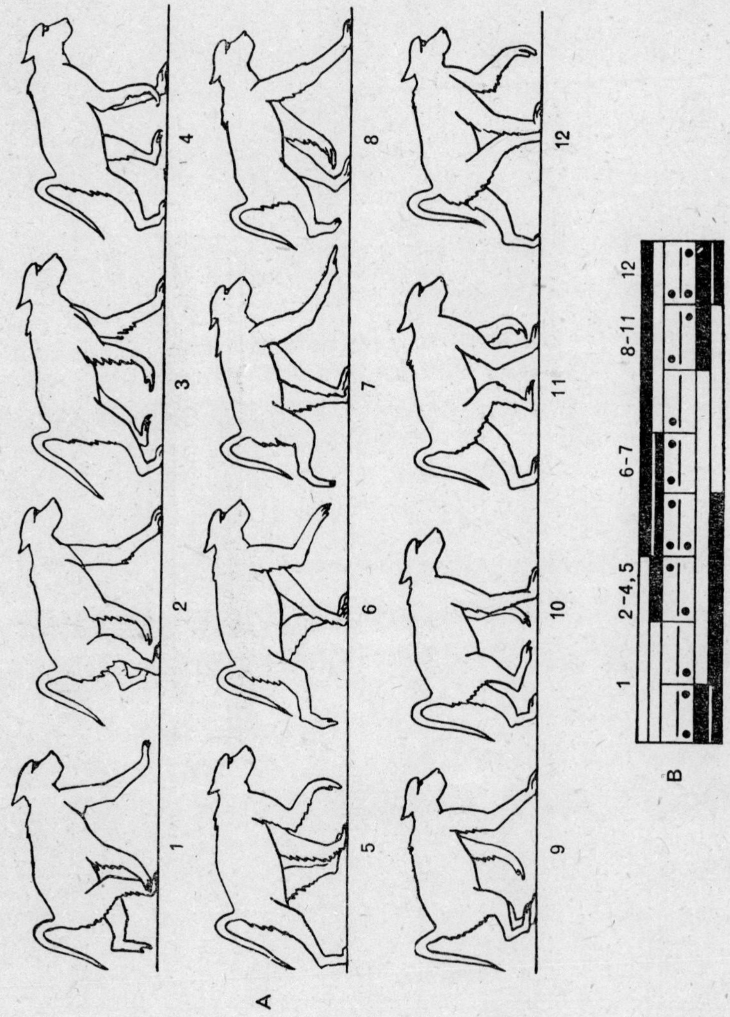

Figure 21. Normal walk wish predominance of hind limbs in the lateral sequence. *A—a baboon using this gait, photo-tables by Muybridge (1957); B—gait diagram. Numbers indicate position of stages shown in A.*

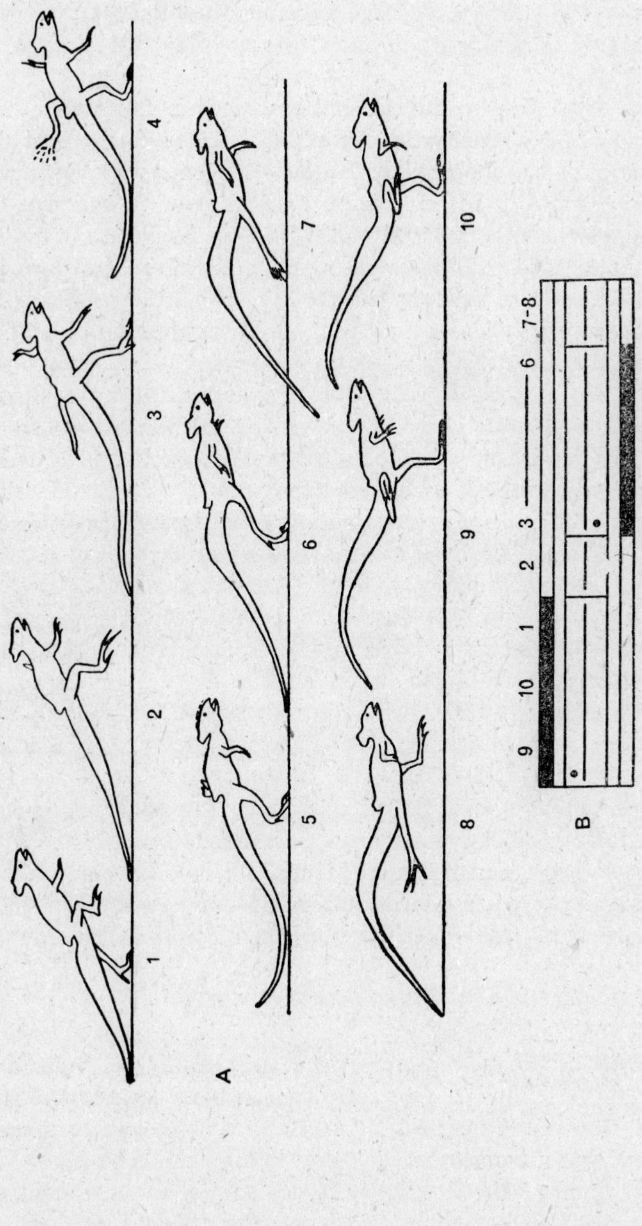

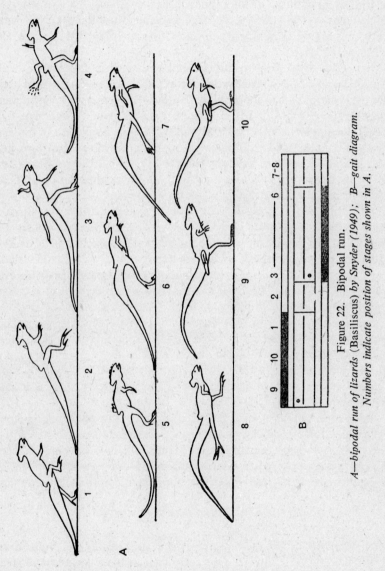

Figure 22. Bipodal run.
A—bipodal run of lizards (Basiliscus) *by Snyder (1949); B—gait diagram. Numbers indicate position of stages shown in A.*

predominance of forelimbs in crocodiles and lizards (Figure 18) (Sukhanov, 1964b, 1968b); slow trot with predominance of hind limbs in lizards (Figure 62 and 63) (Sukhanov, 1964b, 1968b; see Part II of the present work); fast trot with predominance of hind limbs in lizards (Figure 19) (Snyder, 1952, 1962; Sukhanov, 1963, 1964b, 1968b); and horses (Howell, 1944); slow amble with predominance of hind limbs in camel (Figure 16, D) (Muybridge, 1957, Pl. 106 partially).

It is difficult to observe the external variations in four-paced walks. Only variations of the normal walk, one of which has been described above, differ by a change in the support plan. Besides the normal walk with a predominance of hind limbs in horses (Figure 17) and goats (Muybridge, 1957, Pl. 102), there exists another normal walk with a predominance of forelimbs in bulls (Figure 20) and a normal walk with a predominance of hind limbs in the lateral sequence in baboons (Figure 21). In all the remaining four-paced gaits, the support plan remains fixed but the relative duration of some stages changes. It is too early to imagine on Figure 10, C, what changes would take place in the fast trot-like walk with the appearance of a predominance of hind limbs; the equality of unipodal stages would be disturbed—the primary reduced and the secondary increased. However, similar in quality in these stages does not always speak of the predominance of, say, the hind limbs. Other peculiarities of limb action may similarly leave impressions on the cycle. For example, in the toad, the front foot in the slow trot-like walk always leaves the ground earlier than its diagonal hind foot, but sets down earlier (Figure 31) or simultaneously with it (Figure 33, D). In the latter case, secondary trepodal stages are absent in the cycle. In lizards, sometimes both the limbs lose contact with the substratum at once, but the hind one passes ahead of the front one during landing. During this, primary tripodal stages drop out of the cycle. However, a predominance of one and the same limb is also observed in toad and lizard.

External variations of symmetrical gaits play an important role in nature. So, through the fast trot with a predominance of the hind limbs (Figure 19) lies the way to the two-legged run of lizards (Figure 22) where the diagonal stages of support are changed to unipodal as the front feet stop touching the ground. This problem will be discused in detail in the second part of the present work.

5. MAIN ASYMMETRICAL GAITS

The analysis of the main asymmetrical gaits should be prefaced with a few remarks. Variations in asymmetrical forms of locomotion greatly surpass those seen in symmetrical locomotion. It is enough to remember the existence of four asymmetrical sequences in limb action versus two symmetrical ones. Besides this, asymmetry is not subject to such strict rules, for under symmetrical locomotion much more variation is observed than would be imagined. At the same time, if symmetrical gaits are determined by the coordinated action of limbs, then such asymmetrical gaits as the ricochet jump or gallop are, to a great extent, connected with the biomechanical peculiarities of locomotion in animals; (in this case they are close to the external variation of symmetrical gaits). Individual forms of gallop especially differ, not only in this or that combination of support of limbs in the duration of a cycle, but also in the degree of participation in the motion of the muscles, strength of forelimbs, and so forth. For example, the gallop of rabbits (Gambaryan, 1968) is different from the gallop of cats. It is not enough to know one diagram of the cycle in order to differentiate the primitive ricochet jump of rat (Figure 25) from the fast gallop of the leopard (Figure 27). Here the character of the rhythm of limb action itself is changed (Gambaryan, 1967); if in symmetrical locomotion, transfer of limbs in front takes place at once after their liftoff, in gallop this transfer is withheld.

The slowest motion in mammals takes place in four paces, as a rule. It can be symmetrical, as often observed, or asymmetrical. The very slow walk in an asymmetrical-diagonal sequence has been fixed by Gambaryan in hamsters (Figure 23). As in a very slow symmetrical walk, the quadrupodal stages alternate with the tripodal and every following foot is not disengaged from the ground before the preceding one is released.

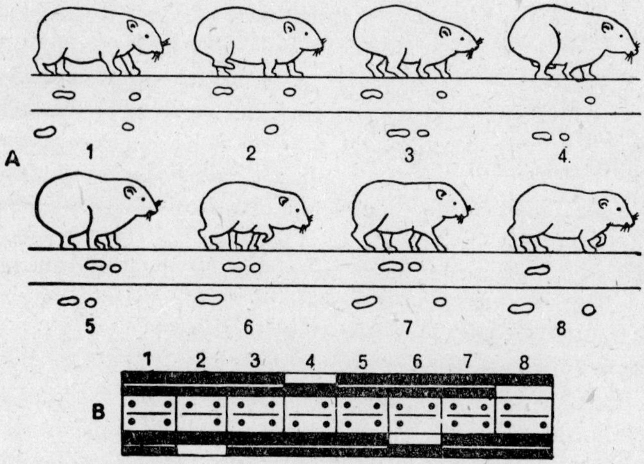

Figure 23. Very slow asymmetrical walk.

A—slow locomotion of hamster from unpublished data of Gambaryan; B—gait diagram. Numbers indicate position of stages shown in A.

In some rodents (*Dipodomys*), it is true that slow motion may occasionally be completed with the help of jumps formed by the paired work of fore and hind limbs: After a single stroke by the latter and a short period of flight, the animal lands simultaneously on the two front feet (Howell, 1932). This becomes the rule during moderate speed of motion in Heteromyidae and other small rodents (Bartholomew and Cary, 1954). Such a walk is labelled as spring (Hatt, 1932), bound (Howell, 1944) or simply slow (four-legged) jump. In the case of a squirrel jumping on ice, the impression is given of both limbs working in pair, being accommodated almost on one level. In rabbits during high speed, but under the same gait, synchronization in the work of the forelimbs is disturbed (half-bound). According to Hatt (1932), the quadrupodal jump precedes ricochet or bipodal jump in jerboas (Figure 24, A) and Heteromyidae; the jump takes place by a sudden single action of the hind limbs followed by free flight and landing again on both hind paws. In this, the forelimbs do not take part in locomotion. A change from quadrupodal jumps to bipodal seems to result from an increase in the elevation of the hind limbs.

Howell (1944) suggests that the development of jumping in small mammals is connected with their habitat, e.g., in plains with low obstacles which were easily stepped over by larger animals (the ancestors of kangaroos were small animals). Others (Fokin, 1963; Gambaryan, personal communication), while considering the entire, gentle character of the trajectory of free flight in jerboas, think that jumping as an adaptation of speedy locomotion on the open plains, is based on the primitive character of limb action (Gambaryan). Still others are inclined to deny the locomotory nature of ricochet (Bartholomew and Cary, 1954), in general connecting it with the search for food and the necessity of freeing the front limbs. This problem becomes complicated by the presence of "a more advanced type of ricochet jump" in jerboas (Fokin, 1963) where the hind limbs do not work in synchronism but in sequence (Figure 24, B).[28] Landing takes place in the beginning on one of the hind limbs which is joined by the second one afterwards (with walk in front—"walk of momentum"—according to Fokin). In the same sequence, limbs lift off. During the course of locomotion, the "leading" limb may change. This type of ricochet has its origin, perhaps, in the primitive ricochet jump of many rodents. Unlike the ricochet of the two-paced, this primitive ricochet jump (Figure 25) seems to be a typical asymmetrical four-paced gait established on the basis of asymmetrical-lateral sequences. It is completed in the following manner. After free flight, because of the stroke by the hind limbs, the animal subsequently lands on one front foot. Then stepping forward in contact with the substratum, the second front foot also touches. They lift-off in the same sequence, but prior to the liftoff of the second forelimb, the ipsilateral hind limb, whose forward movement started immediately after

[28]In some large jerboas, a similar bipodal run (Figure 24, C) is observed with alternate support on the right and left limb (Fokin, 1963). Undoubtedly, this is a symmetrical locomotion; it takes place in slow pace with not much speed.

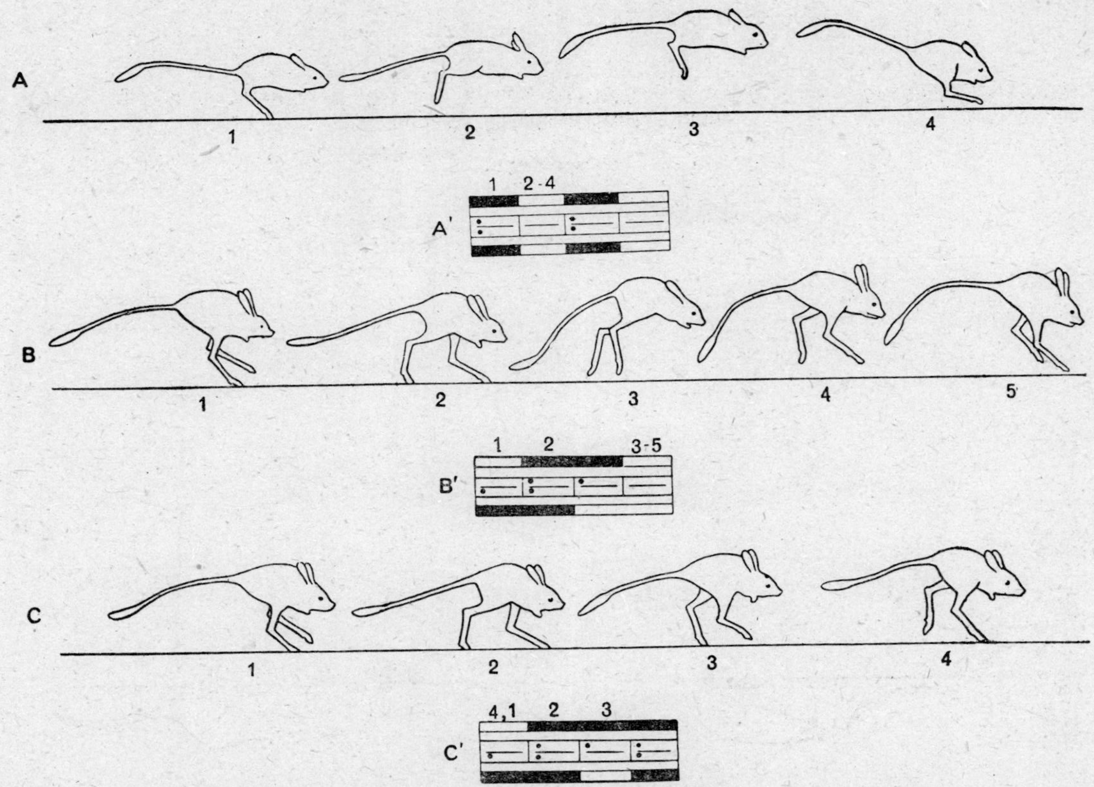

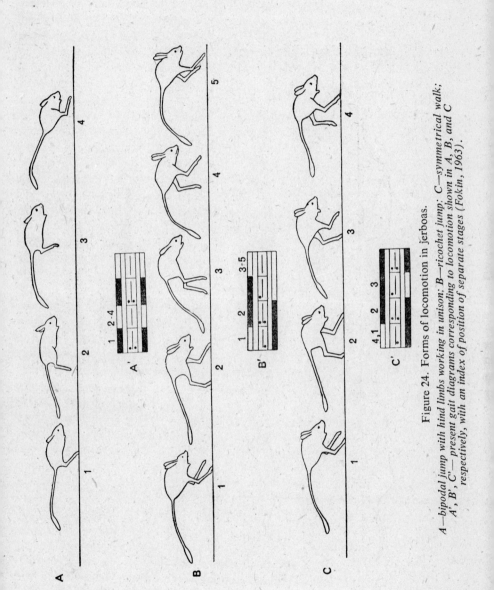

Figure 24. Forms of locomotion in jerboas.

A—bipodal jump with hind limbs working in unison; B—ricochet jump; C—symmetrical walk; A′, B′, C′— present gait diagrams corresponding to locomotion shown in A, B, and C respectively, with an index of position of separate stages (Fokin, 1963).

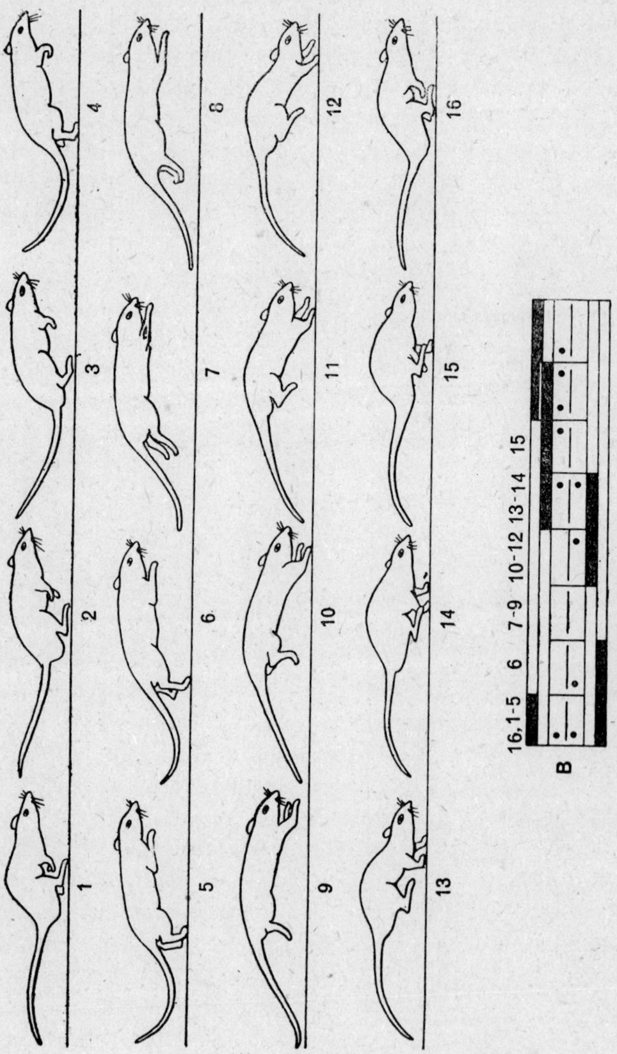

Figure 25. Primitive ricochet jump.

A—Norway rat using primitive ricochet jump in asymmetrical lateral-straight sequence by Gambaryan (1955); B - gait diagram. Numbers indicate position of stages shown in A.

its liftoff, touches the substratum. As a rule, the raising of the hind limb after the forelimb is so high that the impression of the latter is considered to be posterior to the hind impression. For a short period, support is formed only on the two limbs of the same side. Thus, the formula for the primitive ricochet jump in rats is (Figure 25); 2-1-0-1-2-1-2-1. The first bipodal stage corresponds to the hind stroke; the second equals the front; the third represents the stage of lateral support. A change of speed brings about specific corrections in the support plan of the cycle. For example, in the sand eel, Gambaryan observed that the hind limb may land not only up to the liftoff of the second forelimb, but also the first, i.e., during slower motion the third unipodal stage is replaced by the tripodal. The same may happen also in the fourth unipodal stage if the second hind limb is released up to the disconnection of the second forelimb.

Front limbs in the primitive ricochet jump play mainly an amortizing role and do not provide a significant forward thrust which can bring the animal into a condition of no support. Therefore, this gait is often identified as the "lateral gallop with weak forelimbs" (Hatt, 1932) unlike the normal gallop wherein the front stroke is usually followed by free flight. However, the differences between the two forms of motion are, in the first instance, connected with the change of character in the rhythm of limb action. Consequently, it is wrong to list the primitive ricochet as a gallop. The speed of the primitive ricochet jump is connected with an increase in the duration of free flight after the hind stroke. This is well observed on the path of impressions where the distance increases between the impression of the second hind limb and the first forelimb; the track has a characteristic appearance—the impression of all four limbs are collected together in a natural group separated by a considerable distance from the next group on the path of locomotion. At the same time, the raising of the hind limbs after the front ones is increased. Now they may be observed touching the substratum even earlier than the front limbs, i.e., the latter are completely excluded from the process of locomotion. The primitive ricochet jump then changes to a real ricochet which was also observed in the sand eel by Gambaryan (1968).

The fastest gait of mammals is the gallop. It takes place under the condition of maximal effective propulsive activity of the entire locomotory musculature of limbs and body. When this condition exists, the frequency of limb motions is relatively not large. There are many different forms of gallop. These forms are determined by the speed of motion with the use of this or that asymmetrical sequences,[29] change in number of paces, the degree to which the strong curving back takes part in propulsion, the power of the

[29]Diagonal sequences are preferred by horses, rhinoceroses, goats, large cattle, camel, sheep, and cats; lateral sequences are preferred by antelopes and giraffes (Howell, 1944).

stroke in the fore and hind limbs, the inequality in support time for limbs of one pair, and so forth. As a rule, with an increase in speed many of these differences smooth out.

The four-paced gallop works out on the following general plan (Figures 26 and 27). After the restoration period, one of the hind limbs enters into contact with the ground, with a step in front also done by the second hind leg. As a result of this posterior stroke condition and together with the activity of both the hind limbs, though the activity may not be synchronized, the animal may be completely free from the ground and, for an interval of time, move freely in the air with the hind limbs extended back, and the forelimbs stretched in front (stage of extended flight). In other cases, when the stroke is not strong enough, up to liftoff of the second hind limb, but more often at the time of contact of both limbs with the ground, one of the front limbs sets down, either one-sided with the second back one in the lateral gallop, or diagonal from it in the gallop based on asymmetrical-diagonal sequences. Together, but again with unsynchronized activity of the forelimbs, the frontal stroke is produced, placing the animal in the condition of free flight, but with the limbs already crossed (stage of crossed flight), as the forelimbs have left the substratum and are in a state of extreme retraction while the hind ones are preparing for the new operation of protraction. In several cases, the anterior stroke is not enough for the transfer of the animal to a state of without-support, and the corresponding hind limbs remain in contact with the ground until the liftoff of either the front or back limbs.

The main difference between the gallop and the primitive ricochet is an interruption of the accurate sequence of support-transfer and the inclusion of a cycle of limb action to an additional period of passive transfer. This leads to the appearance in the locomotory cycle of the fast gallop (Figure 27) of two stages of free flight (extended and crossed) together with one. When this happens, the stage of free flight in the ricochet should not be associated with that the similar stages in the gallop, though it is completed after the hind stroke. In the beginning, the limbs are extended, but at the end, the hind limbs are already directed in front. Real crossing has already taken place during the period of frontal support. The character of impressions on the track is also changed. Increase in speed now leads not only to an increase of distance between natural groups of impressions, but also the group itself is stretched at the cost of increased distance between the impressions of the second forelimb and the first hind limb (as also in the case of the primitive ricochet, impressions of the hind limbs are arranged on the course of motion anteriorly to that of the forelimbs).

The slow (heavy) gallop of the tapir (Gambaryan, 1964) is shown in Figure 26. In the cycle there is only one stage of free flight connected with the front stroke. The entire cycle corresponds to the formula: 2-3-2-3-2-1-0-1. The support time of the left limbs is relatively longer than the right, which explains the appearance of two tripodal stages in the cycle. In the giraffe (Bourdelle, 1934), a more uniform type of slow gallop is observed. The support time for limbs of one pair is similar, which leads to the following formula: 2-1-2-1-2-1-0-1. The same holds true for horses (Hildebrand, 1960), but here the gallop is completed on the basis of asymmetrical-diagonal sequences and

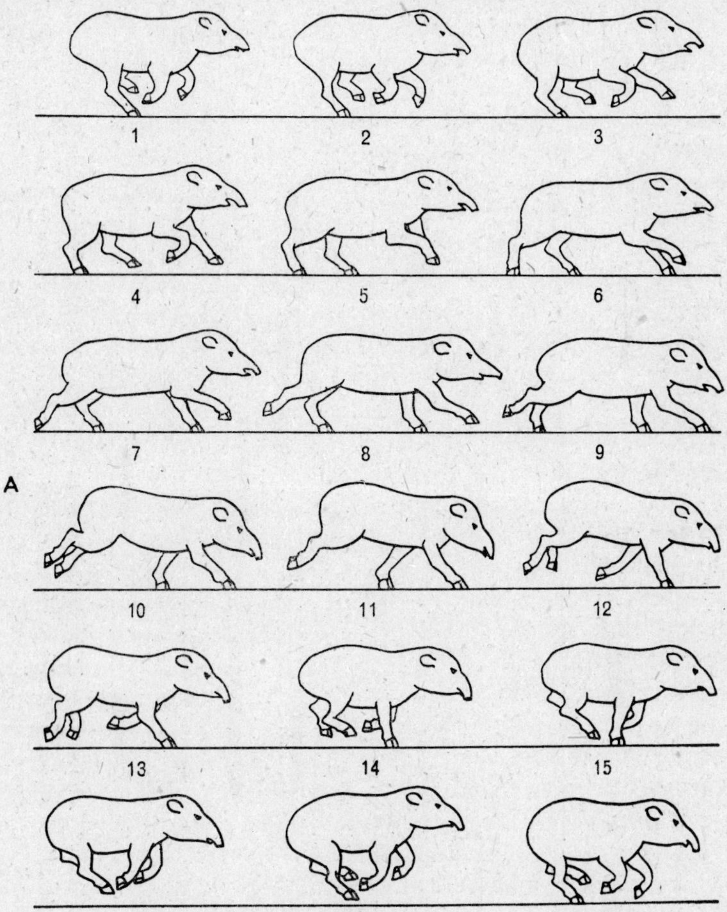

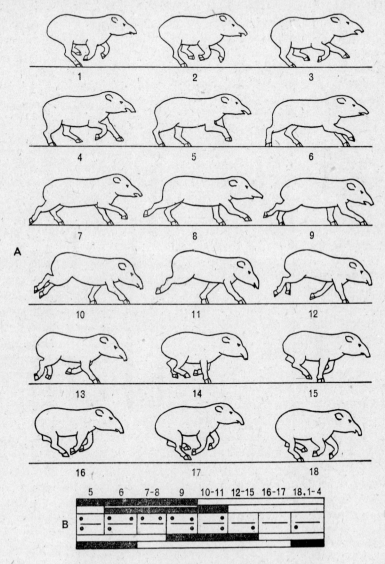

Figure 26. Slow gallop in the lateral reverse sequence.
A—slow (heavy) gallop of tapir by Gambaryan (1964); B—gait diagram. Numbers indicate position of stages shown in A.

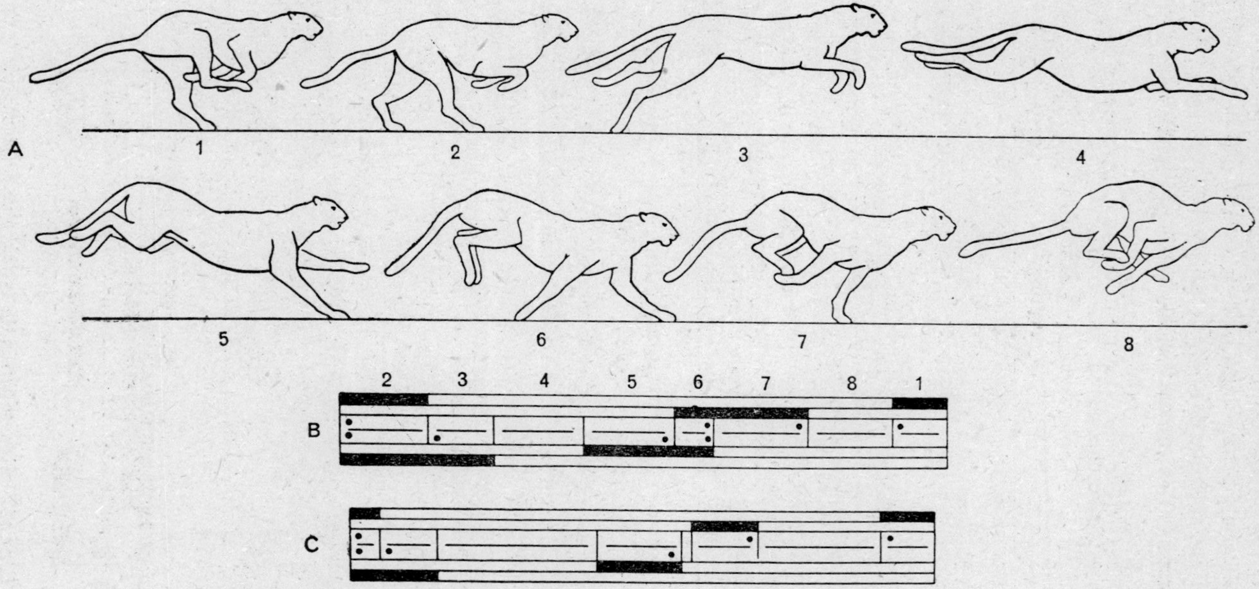

Figure 27. Fast gallop in the lateral-straight sequence. After Hildebrand (1961).
A—gallop of cheetah at a speed of 50 km per hour; B—gait diagram of gallop shown in A, with index of position of corresponding stages; C—gait diagram of a very fast gallop of cheetah at a speed of 90 km per hour.

the stage of lateral support (second bipodal) is replaced by a stage of diagonal support. Tapirs, like horses and other heavy-weight animals (Howell, 1944), have a stage of free flight only after the front stroke (crossed flight). Lighter-bodied antelopes, deer, and other animals have only one stage of free flight, but this is connected with the hind stroke (2-1-0-1-2-1-2-3).

The fast (full) gallop observed in tapirs (Gambaryan, 1964), as well as horses, is shown for the cheetah in Figure 27 (Hildebrand, 1961). Like the slow gallop in tapirs, it is completed on the basis of asymmetrical-lateral (straight) sequences, which facilitates comparison; the diagram for the cheetah gives the real time of support and transport of limbs. The cycle of the average fast gallop (51 km per hour) for the cheetah (Figure 27, A and B) continues approximately for 0.3 seconds. The support time for the hind limbs is equal to, or only slightly more than, that of the front. The support formula is: 2-1-0-1-2-1-0-1. The duration of both stages of free flight is nearly similar, but the stage of hind support, i.e., one time contact of both hind limbs is more than twice as long as the stage of front support. Increasing the speed up to 90 km per hour (Figure 27, C) introduces some changes in the cycle which are not characteristic for other animals. There is a sudden increase in the duration of extended flight in relation to the crossed flight during the absolute rise of both (crossed and extended). The stage of bipodal support drops out, and in its place comes an extraordinarily short without-support moment, (third in the count of the cycle 2-1-0-1-0-1-0-1). The stage of hind limb support is reduced nearly three times. The duration of the cycle remains almost at the same level, but the distance required for one cycle is doubled.

It is important to mention that there are two forms of locomotion in mammals—known as the fast and slow canter—traditionally belonging to asymmetrical locomotion. Often the canter is known as any form of a slow gallop, though on the strength of its first usage by Muybridge (1887) the term should have been fixed only for those gaits which seem to be externally asymmetrical and take place on the framework of a symmetrical-diagonal sequence. But since it was not, confusion exists [for example, the term gallop is used for motion in the symmetrical sequence (Kas'Yanenko, 1947)] which is not reduced by Howell's suggestion (1944) that the two types of canter be differentiated as typical and atypical gallops.

An accurate analysis of both forms of the canter shows that it belongs to symmetrical locomotion. Correctly, this is an asymmetrical and a uniform type of symmetrical locomotion.

Slow canter (Figure 28), the cycle for which is governed by the formula: 2-3-2-1-2-1-2-3, finds similarity at once with two symmetrical walks: the rotation of tripodal stages transversely with stages of lateral or diagonal support reminds one of the normal walk (Figure 8), but the rotation of unipodal with the same bipodal in the second half-cycle of the canter is the fast walk (Figure 9, B). If the relative increase of the intervals in the working of the limbs during

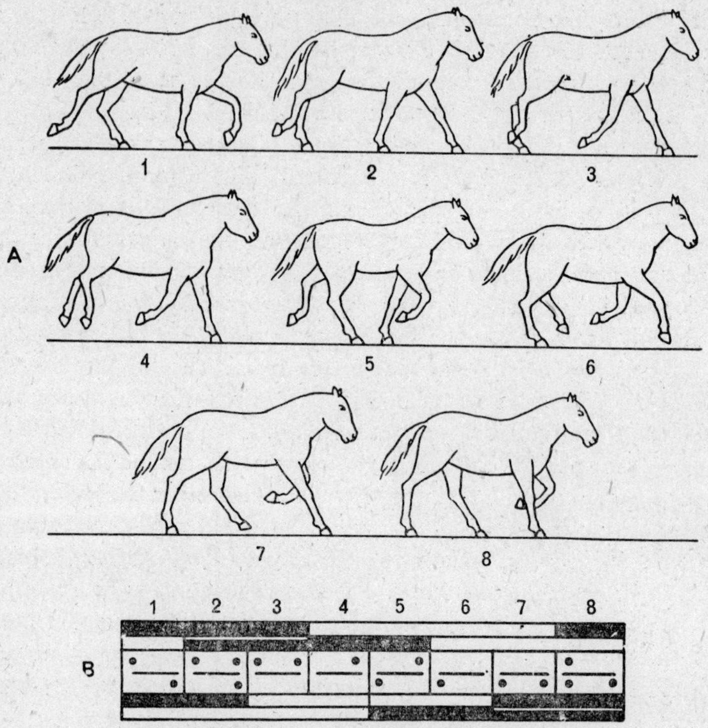

Figure 28. Slow canter.
A—slow canter of horse by Howell (1944); B—gait diagram. Numbers indicate position of stages shown in A.

a slow canter is considered as the norm, presenting the track of several sequence figures, taking as a unit the interval between the movement of the right forelimb and the left hind limb (Figure 28, B), then the following picture is obtained: 1-2-3-2-1, and so forth, in the same order. Thus, the movement of the limbs in one diagonal gets closer in time, but is increased in the second; intervals between the movement of ipsilateral limbs are equal and correspond as such to the normal and fast walks.

Fast canter (Figure 29) is externally more identical to galop, since its formula contains one stage of free flight: 2-3-2-1-0-1-2-3. This stage follows the "forward" push (true, only one front limb participates in this and the hind limb of the same side "helps" it) and take place with "almost crossed" limbs. This picture becomes clear when we see many numerals reflecting the relative magnitude of intervals in the limb work: 1-1.5-4-1.5-1, and so on. At a relatively nonchanging interval between the limbs of one diagonal (*FR-HL*), which decreases still more in slow canter, there is a sharp increase in the interval between the limb movements of the second diagonal (*FL-HR*) due to a decrease in anologous time intervals in the limb work of the same side, i.e. the propulsive action of all the four limbs are shortened in time. This provides a powerful asymmetric push, putting the animal in the state of free flight. Moreover, the sequence of limb movement, typical of symmetric locomotion, is retained. Even a further change of intervals in the work of limbs, moving in the same direction of reducing their propulsive action, cannot lead to a change of sequence to asymmetry, i.e. cannot lead to a transition to a real galop. The graphs of slow and fast canter show how increase of the asymmetry in motion takes place. If the slow canter (Figure 28, B) is understood as a disturbance in the uniformity of locomotion leading to a succession of normal and fast walk within a single cycle, then in fast canter (Figure 29, B) inequality in the support time of limbs of different diagonals is added to this non-uniformity.

The relationship of asymmetrical forms of locomotion in their evolutional development is still not at all clear. There exist two tendencies: to consider gallop as the original form of locomotion in mammals, from which developed the primitive ricochet jump and in its turn the present ricochet (Hatt, 1932), or to consider gallop as the "crown of discovery" changing the ricochet forms of locomotion, in relation to changing conditions of existence. The last point of view is discussed in detail by Gambaryan (1967 and 1968). Commenting upon the primary scansorial type of life in mammals, he explains the change of limbs in the parasagittal plane and in connection with this, the change in the symmetrical model of nerve control to asymmetrical, as a search for food in litter and in the upper layers of the soil. Gambaryan says that the retention of a general eurybiotic form of living in the ancestors of mammals should have led to burrowing or semi-burrowing. Ricocheting forms of asymmetrical locomotion retained as a primitive form the rhythm of limb action characteristic in reptiles and preceded the more complex form of locomotion, gallop. The change in the character of the rhythm is directly related to the habitat, the moving branch of a tree or clusters of rocks, where maintenance of balance requires special accuracy in jump, an accuracy not possible with the primitive ricochet, since in the latter the magnitude of skidding in the hind limbs varies with the speed of motion. As a result, in slower speeds and less length of jump, the animal lands on the forelimbs; but with faster speeds, it lands on the hind limbs. The gallop, because of the change in character of the rhythm of limb action, provides landing always on the forefeet, independent of the magnitude of jump. It is not difficult to imagine the advantages to those animals in which the transport of the hind limbs in front is stopped until landing on the forelimbs, in living conditions wherein the substratum demands a constant change in the length of jump.

The picture constructed by Gambaryan is convincing though several doubts still remain. The primitive burrowing mode of life should perhaps

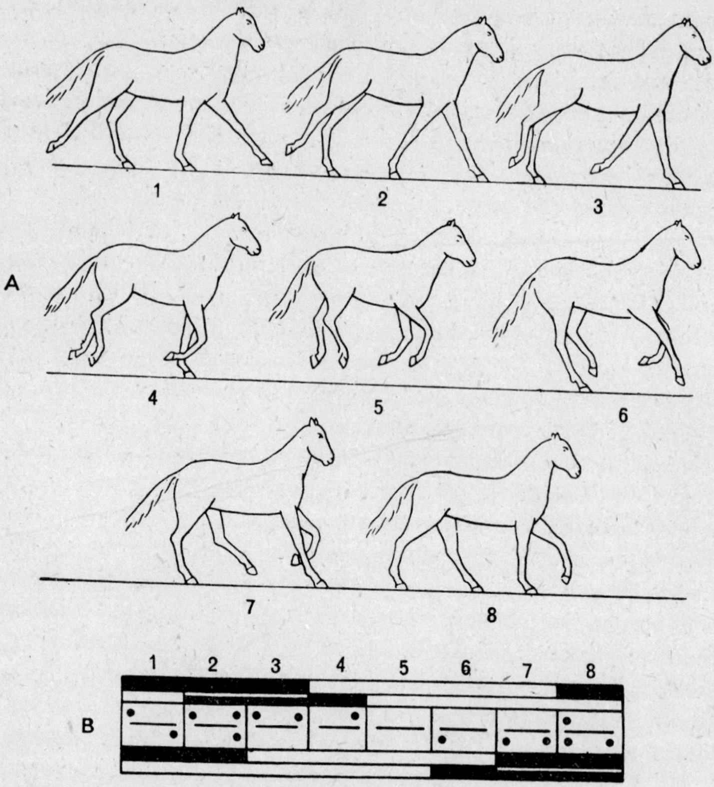

Figure 29. Fast canter.
A—fast center of horse by Howell (1944); B—gait diagram. Numbers indicate position of stages shown in A.

be brought to the level of reptiles, as in higher mammal-like reptiles the limbs have already changed to the parasagittal plane. The origin of the ricochet, particularly in its synchronized form, is not motivated by anything, the presence of which Gambaryan explains by the impossibility of a primary scansorial mode of life, as under this the length of step is smaller than under four-paced symmetrical locomotion. Perhaps the answer to this question is through further studies of ricochet forms of asymmetrical locomotion and the establishing of a connection between two- and four-paced walks with these different forms.

* * *

The cycle of limb action consists of two periods, propulsive and restorative. Their duration is determined as support time and transport time. The relation of the latter to the former is taken as an index of the rhythm of limb action. The working of all limbs characterizes the rhythm of locomotion; the index provides the relationship of intervals between the movement of diagonal limbs to the duration of half-cycle in percent. Four-paced and two-paced locomotion differ. The first cycle consists as a rule of eight stages; the second of four stages. The externality of each gait reflects the plan and formula of support.

The two types of locomotion, symmetrical and asymmetrical, differ by the sequence of limb action and the character of the rhythm of locomotion—intracyclic (with periodicity in the half-cycle) or intercyclic (with periodicity in one cycle), respectively. Constant slow locomotion is possible only on the basis of symmetrical diagonal sequences, historically connected with the wave-like bends of the body in the locomotion of fish-like ancestors of terrestrial vertebrates. The primitive form of locomotion on dry land was probably a very slow walk, four-paced gait in a diagonal sequence with a locomotion rhythm of 50%. Two-paced gaits (trot and abmle) are secondary in origin. The physiological basis of the walk consists of asymmetrical innervation, possibly inherited from fish. The coordinative mechanism of the trot and amble is incompatible with such a walk as this requires the registration of motor signals in the limb of one diagonal respectively with a zero interval, or an interval equal to the time of one way passage through the body (for the walk, a half-period of wave). Asymmetrical locomotion requires the complete reconstruction of coordination models.

Symmetrical gaits should be seen as a function of only two factors: First, speed of motion (through the rhythm of limb action, the index of which is expressed in absolute numbers and decreases with an increase in speed) and second, rhythm of locomotion. Consequently, the entire system of symmetrical locomotion should be considered as a chain of continuous gaits, connecting the amble and trot, resting on opposite poles from each other with walk in the diagonal sequence in the middle (in the system of symmetrical-lateral locomotion, the walk as in all other four-paced gaits is completed in the lateral sequence). Each concrete form of locomotion (norm of gait) may be represented by dots in the system of coordination (Figure 5). It is convenient to differentiate the five main rhythms of locomotion: the rhythms of amble (100%), half-amble (75%), walk (50%), half-trot (25%) and trot (0%). Consequently, there are five main gaits (or types of gaits) with several speed grades in each. A systematic review of the main symmetrical gaits and their speed variations include: amble, slow and fast; amble-like walk, slow and fast; walk, very slow, slow, normal, and fast; trot-like walk, slow and fast; trot, slow and fast. A special category includes external variations of gaits which differ from the main ones by morphological peculiarities in the locomotory apparatus. The main asymmetrical gaits include very slow asymmetrical walk, slow four-legged jump, primitive ricochet jump, ricochet, and slow and fast gallops. Canters, usually considered as a different type of gallop, should be considered as non-uniform and asymmetrical forms of symmetrical locomotion.

PART II

THE LOCOMOTION OF LOWER TETRAPODS AND ITS STATUS IN THE GENERAL SYSTEM OF LOCOMOTION OF TERRESTRIAL VERTEBRATES

This particular portion of the present work pursues several objectives. It documents several situations mentioned in Part I on the basis of concrete material and accurately identifies, those forms of locomotion available to lower tetrapods and under what conditions changes in motion take place. In addition, new research is reported in which the differences in the locomotion of specific groups of lizards such as scincogeckonomorphs and iguanomorphs are delineated, and a solution is offered to the problem of establishing a basis of morphological differences in their locomotory apparatuses (Sukhanov, 1961)[1]. *This particular section is introduced by an important but short preface summarizing all that is presently known about the locomotion of lower tetrapods.*

[1]Differences in locomotion are readily observed but to explain morphological differences directly by these would have been somewhat premature.

Chapter III

A GENERAL OUTLINE OF LOCOMOTION IN LOWER TETRAPODS

Studies on the locomotion of lower tetrapods are, for the most part, inaccurate. Specific works are extremely few and do not give a comparative picture of locomotion in different groups of amphibians and reptiles. The majority of works are of "incidental character," mentioning the particular specialities of motion for this or that form. However, a few works stand out in the semi-popular reviews of locomotory adaptations in lower tetrapods; these include *The Natural History of North American Amphibians and Reptiles* by J. A. Oliver (1955) and *The World of Amphibians and Reptiles* by R. Mertens (1960b). Information about the forms of locomotion is very scanty. To give a historical review of such literature is not only difficult, but rather pointless, because of the extraordinarily uncoordinated information about locomotion in the groups which interest us. It seems more desirable to summarize the available data whose investigations correspond to the present inquiry in literature, based on such groups of tetrapods as tailed and batrachian amphibians, tortoises, lizards, snakes and crocodiles, even though not all of them have been studied to the same extent. Particular attention has been given to amphibians and to a lesser degree, lizards. Far less material has been published concerning locomotion in tortoises and crocodiles.

1. CAUDATE AND ANURAN AMPHIBIANS

Locomotory Adaptations in Amphibians

Three main methods of locomotion on dry land are observed in amphibians. These are usually, the four-legged gait in tailed (Figure 30) and several batrachian amphibians (Figure 31), jumping in Anura (Figure 32), and locomotion by wave-like body movements in the caecilians, Apoda. The locomotion of tailed amphibians is generally accepted as the primitive type for all terrestrial vertebrates (Gray, 1944). There exist also several more secondary locomotory adaptations: climbing, ricochet jumping on water, and parachuting. Furthermore, all amphibians swim well.

Climbing actually does not differ from terrestrial locomotion. It is the same walk and jump, sometimes with additions by special morphological adaptations: grasping feet in *Phyllomedusa, Hyla venulosa, H. spegazzini,* and adhesive discs in *Hyla* (Boker, 1935). Ricochet jumps on the surface of water are wellknown in *Rana cyanophlyctis* (Annandale, 1919), *R. macrodon* (Dunn, 1928), *R. occipitalis* (Chabanaud, 1949), *R. erythrea, R. taipehensis* (J. Romer, 1951). *Acris crepitans* (Blair, 1950), and *Hyla cinerea* (Hudson, 1952; Janson, 1953). Parachuting is observed among amphibians only in web-footed frogs of the genus *Rhacophorus*[2]. However, as an initial adaptation to parachuting, one observes the ability of some amphibians to correctly orientate their bodies during a fall from a great height to avoid injury on landing. *Hyla venulosa* (Cott, 1926) always falls with the abdomen toward the ground and feet stretched toward the sides; the fall itself is slow, the vertical inclination sometimes reaches to 30°. One case has been noted about the fall of *Hyla venulosa* from a 42 m height when it landed 6 m off the vertical plane. Another species of the same genus, *H. arborea,* make a disorderly turn during falls in a vertical manner, and landed badly. However, while *Rhacophorus* has a special wide web in the feet which slows its falls, *Hyla venulosa* and *H. arborea* do not have any special structures of that type. Hence, one must assume that correct body orientation during falls is subject to the special development of the central nervous system (Oliver, 1951; J. Smith, 1952; Savile, 1962).

All amphibians except Anura swim with the help of lateral curves of the body and tail in the usual method of fish. It is true, however, that *Ensatina eschscholtzii,* a short-tailed form with well-developed limbs which usually

[2]Speaking of similar adaptations, it is advisable to keep the terminology given by Oliver (1951): parachuting descent with decreased speed and a vertical inclination of not more than 45°; gliding inclination is more than 45°.

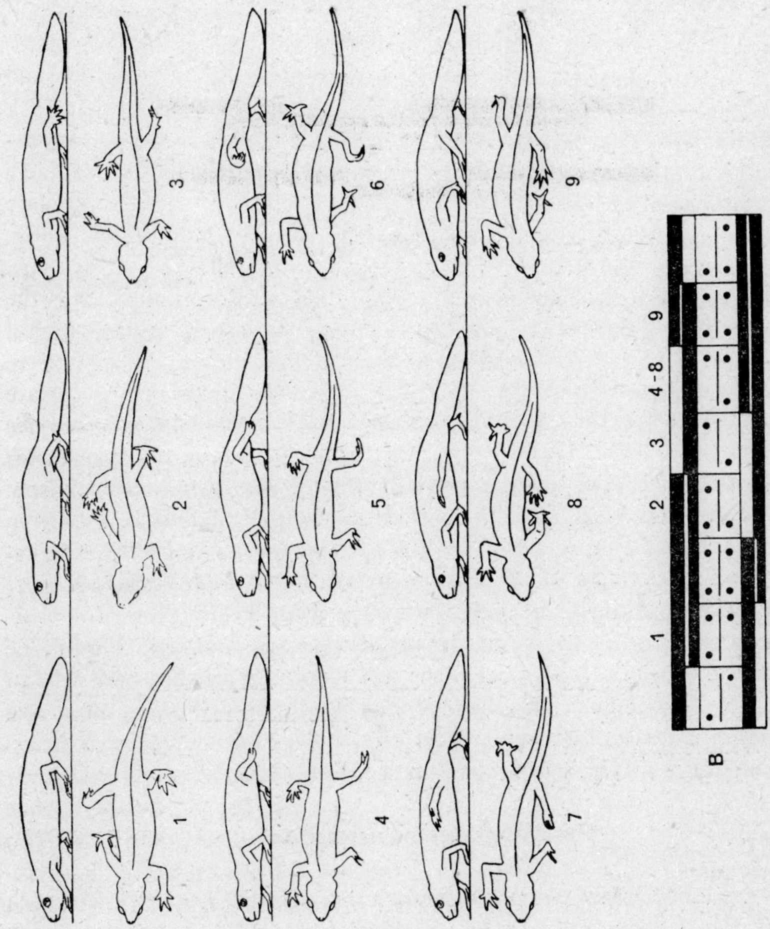

Figure 30. Slow trot-like walk of a newt *(Cynops)* on hard dry substratum. *A—consecutive phases of locomotion by motion pictures (Schaeffer, 1941); B—gait diagram with index to film shown in A, indicating which stage is being approached.*

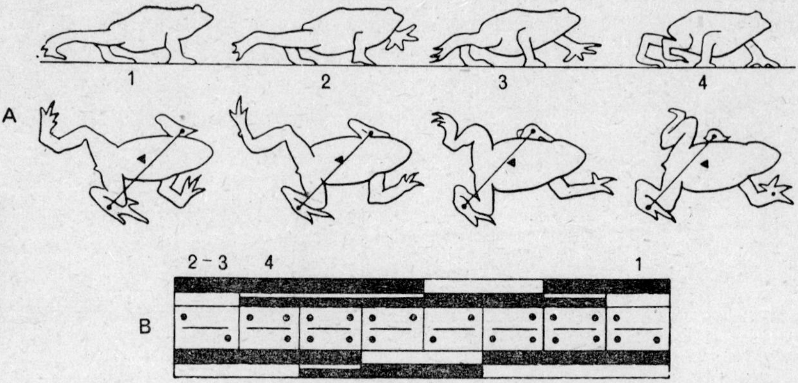

Figure 31. Locomotion of toad (*Bufo*) by slow trot-like walk.
A—four consecutive stages of locomotion, viewed first from the side and secondly from above. Black triangle*—position of center of gravity in relation to line of support on the diagonal limbs (Barclay, 1946); B—gait diagram showing the place in the locomotory cycle of the stages shown in A.*

avoids water, swims by a series of uncoordinated and unnatural curves (Gnaedinger and Reed, 1948). Frogs swim by pushing both the hind limbs simultaneously which move closer to a horizontal plane than during a jump, but the feet are kept back by the ventral surface in the caudal plane. Initially, both limbs are pulled forward with the knees flexed and a maximum straightening (dorsal extension) of the foot segments. Later, both limbs suddenly flex and push posteriorly. In such a way, the frog usually moves forward until the protraction of the limbs. However, transport is completed quickly, and immediately following a stroke, the feet revolve somewhat and reduce the area of water resistance. The bend of the body during swimming, naturally does not play any role (Tatarinov, 1953). The forelimbs either remain motionless or may move simultaneously, or even at different times (Holmes, 1906).

The Extremities in Locomotion

On dry land, newts and salamanders move with the help of limbs, the proximal portions of which work in a horizontal plane. Such a limb position requires an additional expenditure of energy in supporting the body above the substrate; in connection with this, the animal usually rests with the abdomen flat against the ground. However, during motion, the body and frequently the tail are clearly raised; this condition[3] obtains in some thin-bodied and long-legged forms, but is clearly unrelated to our gait representations for

[3]See, for an example, the photograph of *Typhlomolge rathbuni* (Orr, 1961).

creeping locomotion. The latter, as mentioned by Tatarinov (1953), is overemphasized in many references and books—so much so that several absurd situations are depicted: the abdomen is considered as dragging on the substrate; the distal portions of limbs are considered as standing inclined in front and outside; the role of the forelimbs is reduced to partial support of the body during motion, they pull it at the cost of bending the "funny bone" joints in the feet; and finally, the hind limbs, important organs of motion, touch the body in front when the knee bends. In fact, the body is incompletely raised only in elongated bodies with reduced limbs, like the *Batrochoseps attenuatus* (Oliver, 1955). During locomotion, the hands and feet of tailed amphibians are oriented at all the time along the direction of motion (Schaeffer, 1941), but the fore and hind limbs seem to be equally propulsive organs working on the principle of levers (Gray, 1944). The experiments of Evans (1946) show that one of the forelimbs with no motion of the back ones may move the body forward, dragging the posterior half of the body on the substrate; this means of bringing the posterior portion of the body forward and lowering it, minimizes friction and locomotion is completed in an entirely normal manner. In their turn, the hind limbs may move the body forward while the forelimbs remain motionless; but in actuality, this is very difficult especially if the anterior portion of the body is reclining on the substratum. The retraction of humerus and femur plays an important role in propulsion.

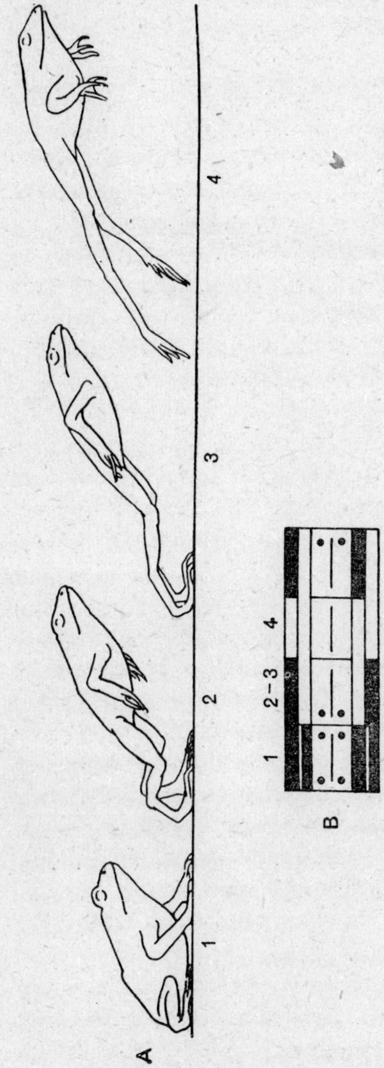

Figure 32. Jump of frog.
A—four stages in the beginning of a jump in Rana catesbeiana; *photographs by Gans (1961); B—gaits diagram with index of corresponding stages in A.*

Foot movement in amphibians during the locomotory cycle of gaits is described many times. Published materials present information about the motion of the hind limbs for a newt and salamander (Schaeffer, 1941), the forelimbs of a newt (Barclay, 1946), the forelimbs of a toad and newt which work almost identically (Evans, 1946), and for both pairs of limbs in tailed and anuran forms (Tatarinov, 1953).

In *Taricha granulosa* (Evans, 1946), the fingers are disconnected from the earth in the following order: IV-I-III-II, i.e., the longest, last. In transporting the foot forward, the humerus and femur move in an almost horizontal plane (the distal end is slightly higher than the proximal): they protract and supinate (an anti-clockwise rotation if observed from the right) and are slightly raised. Thereby, the shoulder is moved forward on an average by 20 to 40° (Tatarinov, 1953), in newts by 45° (Evans, 1946) and femur by 60 to 80° (Tatarinov, 1953)[4]. Elbows and knees bent at the beginning of the restoration period, are more or less straightened at the beginning of propulsion. Here the forearm stands in relation to the shoulder at an angle of 110 to 130° (Tatarinov, 1953). The shank, like the forearm, supinates before establishing contact with the ground (the forearm revolves in the plane perpendicularly to the bend of the elbow). The swing of the revolving motions of the forearm attains 60 to 90° and that of the shank is only 20 to 30°. At the same time, the arc of the shoulder swing is about 70° (Tatarinov, 1953) or 83° (Evans, 1946) in the newt, 90° in the toad (Evans, 1946) and less than the swing of the hips (110 to 130°)[5].

Hands and feet are oriented parallel to the direction of motion at the beginning of the propulsive period. When propulsion starts, in addition to retraction and a slight releasing of the shank, flexion in the elbows (to 80-90°) occurs in the feet. Immediately, the flexors of the hands and feet press them flat to the substrate to prevent sliding. The proximal and distal sections of the limbs make the feet adhere to the surface so that they cannot change their position in relation to the substrate. At the end of the propulsive period, both the limbs straighten at the elbow and knee. It is important to mention that while the propulsive period naturally plays an important role in progressive locomotion, the function of limbs in the restoration period is far more complex (Schaeffer, 1941).

The movement of the hind limbs in toads during walking (not jumping) differs considerably from that in newts: the femur does not go as far forward, and since the curvature of the knee at the end of protraction does not take place, the center of the foot pressure always lies posterior to the acetabulum (Barclay, 1946); consequently, there is no knee bend at all in the beginning of the propulsive period (Watson, 1926; Schaeffer,

[4]Figures given are very approximate and highly subjective. If for mammals the determination of angles does not present great difficulty, parallel methods of computation should be improved for amphibians and reptiles.

[5]Sometimes the figures given for the humerus in newts do not exceed 75° (Roos, 1964).

1941; Gray, 1944; Tatarinov, 1953; Roos, 1964).

In the jump of anurans the forward thrust is achieved by extending both hind limbs simultaneously (Figure 32). The forelimbs evidently only give direction to the jump though they are retracted simultaneously with the hind limbs. Naturally, they lose contact with the ground earlier than the hind legs. In the beginning of free flight both forefeet start moving at once toward the front. The hind feet are similarly somewhat protracted but not synchronously, resembling "a ballet step in the air" by a frog (Davidson, 1963). At the end of free flight, they are drawn back, at least for the jump in the water. Landing takes place on the forelimbs which are principally responsible for the shock absorption of the jump. The period of this stroke (or thrust) is very short, not more than 0.1 seconds (Hirsh, 1931). In the stroke, retraction of the femur takes place first (up to 50-60° towards the body axis), then an extension of the knee (first period of stroke); only then does the extension occur in the shank of the foot and in the metatarsal joints (second period of stroke) and finally, the retraction of the femur (up to 10° toward the body axis). The connection of the plantar surface of the foot with the substrate is achieved by the transfer of the entire limb to the sagittal plane (up to 60° toward the support plane), which is larger than during walk and particularly swimming (Tatarinov, 1953). The duration of the first period of the stroke is almost twice that of the second. The force developed in the first period is 6.5 times more than the force in the second period (Hirsh, 1931).

Both periods of the stroke may also be observed in the action of the hind limbs of tailed amphibians, but the second stage is weakly expressed since the feet work mainly as elastic cushions providing a stable contact with the substrate (Schaeffer, 1941; Barclay, 1946; Evans, 1946). Accepting, as compared to reptiles, the lesser role of the bending movements of feet and hands in tailed amphibians to produce propulsion, Tatarinov (1953) suggests that we should not overestimate their passive nature. Similarly, he also defends the more active role of the forearm and shank in progressive movement to counterbalance the assumptions about their function as immovable axes, which transfer stress from the shoulder to the substrate (Schaeffer, 1941; Gray, 1944; Barclay, 1946).

The Body During Locomotion

Lateral body movements play an important role in the locomotion of tailed amphibians, attaining maximum significance at the moment when all four feet are in contact with the substrate. On the other hand, during support by only two diagonal limbs, the bends nearly disappear and the body is almost straight (Roos, 1964). Body bends increase the step length of an animal by helping the rotation of limbs and increasing the general amplitude of the forward-backward motion of each limb. As a result, according to the opinion of several authors, additional propulsive power is carried through the limbs (Gray, 1944; Tatarinov, 1953; Oliver, 1955). On the other hand, some authors (Roos, 1964) contradict this, showing that the bending of the body in tailed amphibians is not similar to that of fish as mentioned by Gray (1953). It must be said that the viewpoint defended by Gray is wellknown, although it has been noted many times that the wave-like bend of the body is not observed in a walking newt. Gesse wrote that the body bend has the "form of a stationary wave whose nodal points pass through the pectoral and pelvic zones; the shifts and drifts of the nodal points are disturbed by the simultaneous bending of the head and particularly the tail, in the side opposite to the body bend" (1913, p. 192). Slijper (1941) also mentions that because of the firmness of the zone the wave appears to be stationary. Roos (1964) conducted special experiments using high-speed film and thereby measuring the amplitude of variation for different points on the body of a newt. It was readily apparent from these studies that the passing of the wave on the body of newt was difficult to observe. Points on the skull, the sixth spinal vertebra, the sacrum and the tenth caudal vertebra are not generally subject to variation, being the nodes of stationary waves. The maximum bend of the body lies constantly in the region of the ninth to the eleventh vertebrae and of the tail, in the region of the fourth and fifth caudal vertebrae. Thus, according to Roos, propulsion seems to result not from body bends but rather, the movement of the zones and limbs. Undulation of the body increases only the step. In *Triturus vulgaris*, the revolution of the zones attains 55° (pectoral zone) and 35° (pelvic zone). Because of this, the general amplitude of motion of the mechanical axis (line passing through the foot pressure center and the proximal pectoral or pelvic, joint of the limb) attains 130° in the forelimb and 110° in the hind limb (Evans, 1964).

These observations demand some reservations. Roos' results have been obtained on scansorial newts, i.e., the newt's body and tail touch the ground (moist substratum) as differing from that of a walking newt (dry substratum). Evans (1946) observed that in *Ambystoma opacum* and *Notopthalmus* there are two forms of locomotion: the first, slow with the help of limbs with a normally raised body and tail, only the tip of the tail drags along the soil; the second, during very fast motion, where the limbs play only a passive role being either pressed against the body or together, with the body bend carried forward in the usual sequence. The animal as it were, swims on the substrate. Usually, in gill-less salamanders with long bodies, sinusoidal bends are generally less observed. For example, locomotion in *Batrachoseps* is compared to the movement of two men carrying a pole on their shoulders. But even in this salamander, a sudden increase in speed shows lateral bends in the body (Peabody, 1959). An increase of bends during speed is also observed in the common newt by Barclay (1961). Faber (1956) relates an increase in the amplitude of the bends in newts to conditions which make locomotion difficult. An increase of external resistance (increase of friction with the substratum or movement in a marshy medium), as well as its decrease (movement on the surface of mercury) also leads to the same result. One would have thought that this would increase the length of step. But an examination of the impression tracks of *Ambystoma* and the newt (Evans, 1946) shows that in the present case this is not possible: the impressions of limbs in general are not differentiated but the wide impression of the twisting body and tail is well seen. It is difficult to compare Evans' movements in newts with Roos' crawling: one speaks about an increase in speed, the other, only about the quality of the substrate. But nevertheless, it is clear that body bending by the method of stationary waves, may not lead in this case to progressive locomotion of the animal. A photograph of the impression tracks made by *Batrachoseps attenuatus* (Peabody, 1959, Pl. 5, E) shows clearly that bending of tail helps in the faster propulsive movement. Moreover, on entering water, caudal amphibians swim nicely, wholly at the cost of lateral body bends (Gray, 1953; Oliver, 1955), i.e., in the present case the waves passing from the front to the back is absolutely clear. Thus, it seems that it is not necessary to relate the capacity to bend their body by two methods, the normal fish-like method with wave-like bends passing from front to back, and the method of stationary waves where the motion of the tail plays only a balancing role (see further, p. 151), as an inherent property in salamanders and the other lower tetrapods.

Forms of Locomotion

It is generally known that the limb movement of walking salamanders are in the diagonal symmetrical sequence: *HR-FR-HL-FL* (Gray, 1939a, 1944, 1953). During very slow movement, not less than three feet are always on the ground, so that at any moment the animal may stop without losing balance as its center of gravity always lies inside the support triangle (Gray, 1944; Barclay, 1946). With an increase in speed, movements develop progressively. When the body is supported only on two diagonal limbs, balance becomes less stable (dynamic equilibrium), but the length of the step and the speed increase. Simultaneously, the expenditure of energy may even decrease to some extent at the cost of lowering the frequency of limb movements (Barclay, 1946).

Questions about the forms of terrestrial locomotion, gaits of salamanders, are sometimes encountered in literature. Usually, the authors mention simply the gait, where the movements of all four limbs, as a rule, follow one after the other with definite intervals. Illustrations, given by several authors (Schaeffer, 1941; Barclay, 1946; Evans, 1946; Gray, 1953; Peabody, 1959), reflect only movement by the slow trot-like walk. However, Gray mentions that during an increase of speed "the time interval between the members of each diagonal pair is decreased so that the movement of both members is stopped almost simultaneously" (Gray, 1939a, p. 48). This is also repeated by others (Tatarinov, 1953; Faber, 1956) but in a more categorical manner: during fast movement, both the diagonal feet move at once. Howell (1944) unabashedly writes that when earlier tetrapods came out of water they should have moved like present-day salamanders, i.e., in slow trot, the limbs of one diagonal pair are lifted simultaneously, placed in front, and immediately stopped on the ground. However, our observations show that complete synchronization of diagonal limbs during terrestrial is not attained even during maximum speed.

Automatization in locomotion on dry land, such as occurs in all other lower tetrapods, is mentined by many authors as occurring in amphibians. In this connection, attention is drawn to Faber's explanation (1956) of changing the sequence of limb action. He showed that in water the diagonal limbs of a walking (not swimming) newt may work simultaneously even during slow movement, but in the same conditions on dry land, the hind limb of the diagonal is always somewhat behind the forelimb. The stereotype process of locomotion is disturbed. The forelimbs become capable of arbitrary movement, although the hind limbs still continue to be in coordination with each other and with the movement of the body. According to Faber, of the three known factors (animal weight, specific gravity of the liquid in which the newt moves, and the liquid's viscosity), only a change in the specific gravity determines the nature of locomotion. A newt may change from a diagonal sequence to a lateral one, if it is held by its tail during movement on a wet glass or during an attempt to climb up a wet vertical wall. From all this, Faber concludes that the degree of automatization is usually exaggerated. All these facts simply confirm our viewpoint stated earlier namely, that the determining factor in the selection of movement seems to be the condition of maintaining balance. On dry land, balance is easily attained during movement in the symmetrical diagonal sequence, but in water, strict coordination loses its importance.

The Mechanics of Movement

A real biomechanical analysis of limb action in amphibians is a work for the future. However, Nauck (1924) tried to give an outline of the action of force in the hind feet of amphibians during rest and movement. A somewhat deeper analysis was conducted by Schaeffer (1941). A powerful impetus to the development of research in this line was given by the classical work of Gray (1944) on the mechanics of the skeleton in tetrapods. Gray considers the animal in the state of rest or movement as a horizontal beam raised by the four stretched and mobile limbs.[6] The limbs work simultaneously as supports and propulsive levers. In the first case, internal (acting on the internal joints) muscles function. As a result of the combined activity of the body and these internal muscles, mainly vertical and small horizontal forces are developed. As propulsive levers, external muscles connect the limbs to the body. The limbs in this instance develop mainly horizontal force. The function of support and propulsion depends upon the high degree of coordination of the muscles acting near each joint (Gray, 1961).

With the help of a specially constructed mobile platform, Barclay (1946) observed longitudinal, transverse, and vertical force in the foot action of toads (*Bufo bufo* and *B. calamita*) and the newt (*Triturus vulgaris*) and showed that the system of distribution of forces in limbs, as well as their changes in the locomotory cycle, is not only more effective (of all the possible modifications) as suggested by Gray, but also highly similar in most diverse animals: cats (Manter, 1938), dogs, goats, and sheep (Barclay, 1953), and man (Elftman, 1940). Records of vertical forces show that they increase when the leg changes from a complete protraction to a vertical position, and afterwards decrease to zero: in each limb of a standing animal the amplitude of the change in vertical force may vary from half of the animal's total weight to zero (Gray, 1961). When the toad is moving, the period of complete static stability (moment of support on three limbs) in relation to vertical forces is replaced by a short period of static instability (moment of support on two diagonal limbs), but in view of receiving a particular momentum of motion, directed upward and forward in the preceding period, the animal is in a condition of dynamic equilibrium until the start of the next period of static stability. The longitudinal horizontal forces consist of two components: one is due to the action of the leg as a support (horizontal strut effect) and the other is related to its function in the capacity of lever (horizontal lever effect). Both components are opposite in their sign. Factual horizontal strength registered on the platform (Figure 33) is equal to the difference of both components. On the whole, according to Barclay (1946 and 1953), the retractive moment acts on the limb, if it is in the condition of protraction and protractile, under the retraction of the feet along the vertical plane passing through the proximal joints.

Barclay's last comment seems doubtful. Tatarinov (1953) mentions that though protractors should act even before the end of the propulsive period, stopping the feet at the moment of their liftoff (Bernstein, 1947), even the immediately appearance of a protractile moment during the change along the vertical plane would have stopped only the forward movement of the animal. This doubt is stressed by the movement of the hind feet of a toad, the mechanical axis of which, even during maximum protraction, lies caudally

[6]In popular form, similar representatives were developed by Gregory (1937).

to the vertical plane, i.e., if one were to follow Barclay, there cannot be any forward directed horizontal force at the cost of foot retraction.

The mistake possibly lies in the faulty method of identifying the magnitude of the horizontal strut effect, calculated from the position of limbs in space and the weight for a given limb, which in turn is calculated from the position of the center of gravity of the body in relation to all four limbs. The results of these calculations in dogs, goats and sheep (Barclay, 1953) show that the horizontal (longitudinal) component of weight, acting on the limb situated behind the vertical plane is so large that the lesser value of actual horizontal force in the foot can only be explained by the braking action of protractor muscles at this moment. The faults in Barclay's calculation seem to lie in the assumption of the constancy of loads shared by the limb during the locomotory cycle. Factual calculations usable in the state of rest are mechanically transferred to the moving animal. The final solution to this question can only be gotten through experimental studies on the change of loads. However, even now, it is necessary to look at the other possible interpretations of Barclay's data (see p. 150).

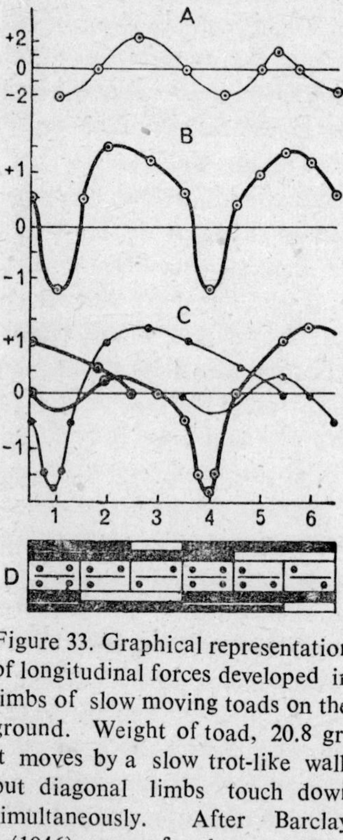

Figure 33. Graphical representation of longitudinal forces developed in limbs of slow moving toads on the ground. Weight of toad, 20.8 gr; it moves by a slow trot-like walk but diagonal limbs touch down simultaneously. After Barclay (1946), except for changes in D. *A—speed changes in center of gravity during a single cycle; B—chaninges total longitudinal strength; C—changes of longitudinal forces in right limb (thin line) and left limb (thick line); D—abscissa of graph, consecutive stages of cycle coorresponding to the given divisions of axis; ordinate rate of movement (in arbitrary units) or forces (in grams).*

Jumping in Anura

The most frequent question in literature with regard to locomotion in amphibians, relates to the magnitude of jumping in anurans and its relationship to the size of the body and hind limbs The absolute length of the jump in frogs is frequently very large. For *Rana dalmatina*, Mertens (1960b) mentions that the length is almost two meters with its height of about one meter. The length for three consecutive jumps in *R. catesbeiana* (Rose, 1954; Oliver, 1955) measured 4.9 m (an average of 1.6 m per jump), but in the South African *R. oxyrhynchus* with a body legth of about 5.5 cm (Rose, 1950), these jumps measure up to 9.8 m, i.e., on an average of 3.3 m per jump.

The magnitude of a jump depends on the size of the animal, the nature of the substrate, etc. Jumping capacity is noted from the ratio of the length of the jump to the length of the body or limbs (Wermel, 1934; Rand, 1952). Among the forms studied by Rand (1952) (*Bufo woodhousei, Acris gryllus, Hyla crucifer, Rana catesbeiana, R. clamitans* and *R. pipiens*), the coefficient of jumping is highest in *Acris*, i.e., length of jump may be 36.2 times body length. Perhaps, this figure is the highest obtained for all frogs. In *R. catesbeiana*, jumping on the grass is rated comparatively low (8.9), but on soft soil, it is smaller yet (Stokeley and Berberian, 1953). The figure is lowest in toad (7.8). Oliver (1955), however, quotes several other figures which are even lower, the lowest being for the small (about 3 cm) frog *Eleutherodactylus ricordi* (which varied from 6 to 12 cm) with coefficients ranging from 2 to 4. The figures for our (Russian) frogs are as follows: the maximum measured jump for *Rana ridibunda* (Wermel, 1934), 73 cm; *R. esculenta*, 78 cm; *R. temporaria*, 67 cm; *R. terrestris* and *R. camerani*, about 90 cm, i.e., coefficients in them vary from about 7 to 8. Tatarinov (1953) gives a table of jumping coefficients for 14 forms of our fauna and notes that the smallest jumps occur in toad (2 to 3.3), fire-bellied toad (3 to 4.9) and spade-foot toad (3.4 to 5.7); for the majority of these frogs, the coefficients range from 4.7 to 8. The best jumper of our fauna is the common frog (up to 9.4).

Evolution of Locomotion in Anura

The origin of a particular mode of terrestrial locomotion, like jumping, is interpreted differently by different authors. The question becomes complicated because of the uncertain origin of frogs and the absence of intermediate fossil forms which would connect the typical frogs (Anura) with possible ancestors in the Permian and Triassic periods. Analysis of a few morphological characters does not give an adequate answer. Each viewpoint is based mainly on a logical construction of this or that, often contradictory rating of the individual characters and the degree of specialization in some forms.

Three principal theories on the origin of anuran jumping are discussed by Gans and Parsons (1966). Inger (1962) considered jumping as a special adaptation for terrestrial movement; he considered an aquatic origin unlikely, since it requires a contraction of the body and a denial of the highly effective undulatory method of swimming. The development of the terrestrial type is usually associated with elongation of limbs (Wermel, 1931), and the development of motion in the articulation of the pelvis and sacrum (Gesse, 1913; Whiting, 1961), and even the appearance of an additional segment in the hind limbs (Terent'ev, 1961). Actually, the advantages of such methods of locomotion on land for overcoming possible dangers are many. Jumping provides quick movement in a direction which cannot be predicted earlier;

the broken line of impressions makes it difficult for a predator to find a frog except by smell as the sudden alternation between motion and immobility makes visual shadowing of the victim difficult (Gans, 1961). However, this terrestrial hypothesis cannot give a satisfactory explanation to the gradual development of jumping.

The hypothesis for aquatic origin of a synchronized stroke by the hind limbs presents a contradictory viewpoint (Boker, 1935; Tatarinov, 1953; Griffiths, 1963; Nevo, 1964). The basic position of their hypothesis is that in aquatic animals with shortened bodies and elongated limbs, swimming in the manner of salamanders was difficult. This shortening of the body and elongation in limbs could have appeared in water (Griffiths, 1963) or been inherited from terrestrial ancestors (Tatarinov, 1953). The development of an ability for synchronized limb movement leads to the appearance of a new method of swimming and establishes conditions for its secondary use during terrestrial locomotion. The retention in frogs of walking and jumping, which can be rather fast, gives witness to this (*Bufo calamita*).[7] During progressive de-afferentations in frogs, swimming retains the greatest stability as an integrated mobile act, whereas jumping disappears rapidly (Chepelyugina, 1950). Maintaining the capacity to swim under "complete" spinal de-afferentation was observed by Gray (1939a). By itself, the occurrence of "asymmetrical" locomotion in lower tetrapods only during a change of habitat, suggest that in the evolution of anurans, there was a period when the model of nerve control was adopted to conditions of equilibrium in the aquatic medium rather than on dry land.

Another solution to the problem is suggested (Howell, 1944; Schmalhausen, 1964; Gans and Parsons, 1966). Gans and Parsons confirm that jumping was developed as a special method of escape from danger in small animals inhabiting the banks of ponds, rivers, etc. For them, jumping from the beginning of their existence provided a fast change from land through air into water. Emerging on land in search of food could be completed with the help of the usual alternate voyage. The gradual evolution of the mechanism of synchronized limb motion could, in its turn, have passed through mobile acts of a non-locomotory character, e.g., by the movement when catching food of the feet remaining in a fixed position in relation to the substrate. Thus, in fact, it is similarly agreed that during progressive movement, asymmetry on the basis of the structure of the locomotory apparatus in amphibians, may not be attained without a change in

[7]The capacity to walk in frogs is mentioned very often (Tatarinov, 1953; Oliver, 1955); for example, in *Bufo bufo, B. calamita* (Barclay, 1946), *Hyla ewingi, H. coerulea, H. aurea, Leiopelma hamiltoni, L. hochstetteri, L. archeyi* (Barwick, 1961) *Microhyla carolinensis* (Anderson, 1954). On the spinal preparations of frog the typical walking reflex (Gray, 1939a) is observed. Consequently, though insignificant, lateral body curves (Tatarinov, 1953) are observed in frogs.

the conditions for the retention of equilibrium.[8]

Closely related to this, is the question about the nature of jumping for the remaining tetrapods. The ability to jump is often observed in salamanders. For example, the gill-less salamander *Aneides flavipunctatus* jumps a distance equal to its body length or a little more (Oliver, 1955). However, its hind limbs are helped by a sudden stroke of the tail upon the substrate.[9] Yet it is not ruled out that the jump of salamanders, like that of lizards which are discussed a little later, is only internally completed by both the hind limbs acting synchronously. The stroke may refer to the sudden retraction of limbs of one diagonal under the passive retraction of the second hind limb. Such a picture is sometimes observed in experiments with spinal preparation of frogs (see below). In other words, as was said earlier, it is possible that movement continues on the basis of a symmetrical sequence of limb work but asymmetry seems to be only imaginary.

Amphibian Tracks and Locomotion

The study of tracks gives a specific clue to locomotion in animals. The frequency of fossilized tracks resulted in the development of an extensive literature (Nopsca, 1926, 1931; Kuhn, 1958). However, paleontologists are more interested in determining the group of animals which left the impressions, rather than interpreting the special aspects of their locomotion. They seem to have their own reasons for this neglect. Even the tracks of recent animals have not been studied. It is not clear if the impressions represent locomotion. These impressions are used frequently to determine the size of the animal.

It must be mentioned that a large number of the impressions from the Permian and Triassic are from quadrupedal animals which cannot be identified accurately. They may belong to Stegocephali and also to primitive reptiles (Schaeffer, 1941). Therefore, paleontologists prefer to speak about the impressions of Stegocephali (or salamander), lacerta, pteromorphids and dinosaurs. These can be differentiated by the nature of separate paw impressions. The stegocephalian has four or five slightly set apart fingers without exerting pressure on any of them. This suggest a symmetrical autopod with an axis close to its middle. In lacertoid impressions, the foot is placed more obliquely, its axis is moved further outside and the outer

[8]Asymmetry according to our definition. Gans and Parsons give meanings to the terms symmetry and asymmetry which contradict that accepted in the present work.
[9]The active role of the tail in the locomotion of plethodontids is wellknown. For example, in *Hydromantes platycephalus,* the tail serves as a support during walking on an inclined surface of rock (Stebbins, 1947). *Pseudoeurycea,* rhythmical strokes by the tail end lead to propulsion for the weaker forelimbs (Taylor and Smith, 1945; Smith, 1947).

fingers, particularly IV, are elongated. Pteromorphoid impressions are characterized by short tracks of compact and thickly-set fingers. The foot is usually five-fingered with a middle axis. A medial axis is also observed in dinosaur impressions, but here the lateral fingers are more or less shorter, and the middle ones carry most of the weight (Heyler and Lessertisseur, 1963).

Individual foot impressions give very little information about the movements of an animal. However, in stegocephalian impressions it is seen that the feet are always placed parallel in amphibians (and are placed thusly even now, excluding frogs) to the direction of the movement. There is no information about the lateral turn of a foot during the limb retraction so characteristic of lizards (Schaeffer, 1941). The depth of the impression depends, in many respects, upon the form of foot (Elftman, 1934). Nevertheless, one can judge the distribution of the pressure in the hand or foot during support: the deepest portion of the impression of the foot lies in the region of the base of fingers II and III; for the hand, in the region of the first three fingers. The internal margin of the impression is always more pressed than the external and hind (Schaeffer, 1941).

The size of the animal and the nature of its locomotion can be identified only in the presence of an impression track, i.e., a series of sequential impressions of all four legs during a few locomotory cycles. However, some idea can be formed about the motion on the basis of the occurrence of groups of impressions (set), i.e., two adjacent impressions of the front and back paws of the same side left during one locomotory cycle.

A system for measuring impression tracks has been worked out by Peabody (1948, 1959). He suggests that the following elements be differentiated: *interpes distance*, the distance between the median margins of impressions of the hind feet ; *overlap,* covering or placing a foot partially or completely on the impression left by the forefoot; *pace*, the distance between similar points of the successive impressions of the two hind or forefeet (in our terminology, simple step, see p. 155); *stride*, the distance between the successive impressions of the same hind or forefoot (in our terminology, double step); *pace angulation*, angle of the step (angle formed by the lines connecting three sequential impressions of both hind feet or both forefeet). The angle of step characterizes, at the same time, the size, stride, and interpes distance. It is greater in long-bodied forms and also during increased speeds. In extant salamander, studied by Peabody, the angle of step varied from 70 to 130° (average 90°). The size of the double step changed from 1 to 7 cm, but *interpes distance*, from 4 to 1 cm. The narrowest track of modern amphibians is observed in *Ensatina eschscholtzii* (angle of step 132°) in view of its "special walking gait" (Peabody, 1959). It is necessary to mention that the narrowness of the impression track, characteristic of many salamanders, is generally not characteristic of the other lower tetrapods with a reptilian type of limb construction. An exception seems to be the impression track of *Chirotherium* described now as *Pseudosuchia* (extinct).

Animal size and the forms of its locomotion should be determined from the group of impressions left by the quadrupodal stage of the cycle. Usually, this does not present great difficulties. However, if the animal's proportions are far from the "norm" as in some gilled salamanders, then it is necessary to consider that the hind limb of long-bodied forms (Peabody, 1948 and 1959) may frequently make not one step to form a natural "groups of impressions." It is important to differentiate primary, secondary, and tertiary covered impressions (Figure 34). According to Peabody, complete coincidence of impressions of the ipsilateral fore and hind limbs or the covering of

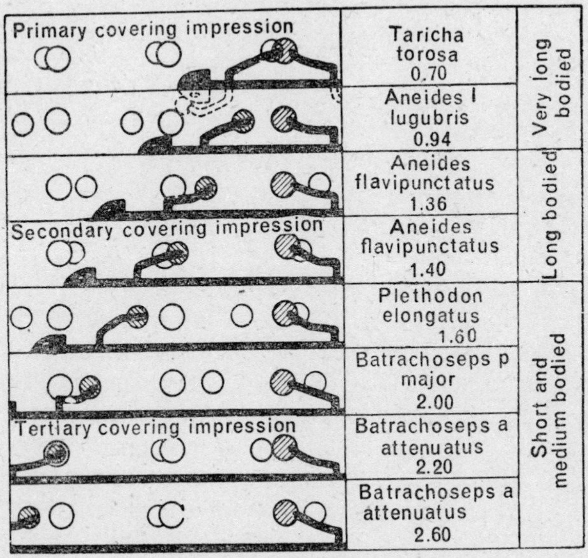

Figure 34. Relationship of impressions of fore and hind limbs in the impression track of tailed ambhibians depending on the "grade of body length" (Peabody, 1959.) The values are the proportions of glenoacetabular distance to total length of fore and hind limbs.

the hind impression by the fore explains the secondary covering or, rarely, tertiary covering (the latter is observed in some species of *Batrachoseps*); since it appears from our study that in primary covering of impressions, there is no real coincidence, then there cannot be any in the existing forms of locomotion in newts and salamanders. For evaluating the degree of body and limb development in salamander, Peabody relates the size of glenoacetabular distance to the total length of the ipsilateral fore and hind limbs and differentiates the short-bodied (or in Peabody's terminology "short coupling" which stresses simultaneous shortness of the body with relatively long limbs), average-, long-, and very long-bodied forms.

Information about the nature of locomotion based on the study of fossil impressions is very rarely seen in literature. Even after his special study of impressions of present-day salamanders, Peabody (1959) differentiates motion only as quadrupedal or bipedal, slow, moderate or fast. For uncovered impressions which, as a rule, appear to be stegocephalian, such an analysis may even be enough. However, the idea of the appearance of covered impressions still remains unclear and subsequently leads to mistakes in efforts to reconstruct the appearance of the animal which left these impressions.

A determination of an animal's size from its impressions is possible by some methods. The gleno-acetabular distance of tetrapods (Soergel, 1925) is equal to the distance from the middle of the line connecting the two consecutive impressions of the hind feet (right and left) up to the level of the impression of the forefoot placed forward. For example, if the impression of the right hind foot is situated in front, but the left toward the back, then the desired forefoot will be the left one. This is inevitably, because the lower tetrapods use a symmetrical-diagonal sequence of limb action. Though as a consequence of Soergel's method, real values are increased, almost one-half of a simple step (Chapter IV); it is used by the majority of authors (for example, Korn, 1929; Abel, 1935). The same value with the same error may be expressed in another way. It is easy to be convinced that three-fourths of a double and uncovered step (Heyler and Lessertisseur, 1963) is exactly equal to the distance calculated graphically by the method of Soergel.

Another method of determining animal size is suggested by Lotze (1928). Here the gleno-acetabular distance is given by formula: $T=3/2\sqrt{L^2-l^2}-E$, where L equals double step, l equals width of the impression track, and E equals uncovered portion. The unjustifiably complicated calculation with lower accuracy results, in part, from using track width, which depends not only on the size of the animal, but on several other factors like speed, etc.,[10] and makes this method less useful (Lessertisseur, 1955).

A more accurate and simpler method is used by Lilienstern (1939) and Baird (1952); the gleno-acetabular distance is defined as the distance between the midpoint of two consecutive impressions of a forefoot on one side and that of two consecutive impressions of the hind foot on the other side. Naturally, in this case, only those impressions of one locomotory cycle are used. According to Heyler and Lessertisseur (1963), this method gives lesser values for the gleno-acetabular distance, because it is affected by the horizontal bend of the body. Our data proves just the opposite. Although the latter method does give accurate animal size, there is no real understanding of the connection between separate elements of the impression

[10]Length of the double step also depends upon the speed, but its increase is compensated for by a decrease in uncovering.

track with its sizes and those factors which determine the nature of movement.

Physiological Mechanism of Locomotion

The physiological mechanism of locomotion in amphibians was studied in connection with the general problem for all vertebrates, i.e., can an animal start moving and use in the course of movement a particular system of coordinating muscular movements without reference to the surrounding world (Gray, 1950). In other words, can there be a characteristic rhythm of muscular activity, which is expressed in a diagonal sequence of limb motion by the phenomenon of a reciprocal innervation of central autonomous origin, or is this rhythm conditioned by the proprioreceptor activity of limbs and body?

Both theories have a long history and many supporters. In 1894, Loeb mentioned that the movement of limbs may be stimulated by skin tension. According to Phillipson (1903), the protraction of limbs in a dog is connected with the pressure of the foot on the ground but retraction by skin tension in the region of the groin. In spinal preparations of *Batrachoseps* (Snyder, 1907), the walking movement of the hind limbs is caused by impulses from peripheral sensory cells and not from centers in the spinal cord. All these facts formed the basis of a hypothesis about the reflex nature of locomotory movements.

However in 1910, it was shown that the de-afferentation of the feet of a cat and the skin of the groin region does not have any effect on movement (Sherrington, 1910). Soon the retention of rhythmical activity was observed in isolated preparation of a pair of de-afferentating muscle antagonists in cat under the condition of well-balanced opposite stimuli (Graham, 1912a, 1912b, 1913; Sherrington, 1913). This formed the basis for considering that locomotory rhythm was an expression of the internal activity of the central nervous system. Thus, there are two theories: one considers animals as having an internally active system which comes to rest only under a halting stimulus; the system happens to be normally at rest and can only be activated by suitably exciting stimulus (Lissmann, 1946a, p. 143).

This problem cannot be discussed here in all its magnitude. However, it is advisable to review the works directly connected with amphibian locomotion.

Gray (1939a) and his several co-workers have presented well-documented evidence for the concept of the reflex nature of locomotion. Several experiments were conducted on amphibians (Gray and Lissmann, 1940a, 1940b, 1946a, 1946b), fishes (Gray, 1936a, 1936b; Gray and Sand 1936a, 1936b; Lissmann 1946a, 1946b), and some invertebrates (Gray and Lissmann, 1938; Gray, Lissmann, and Humphrey, 1938; Gray, 1939b). Two aspects of the role of external and internal factors in amphibian locomotion were studied:

firstly, the effect of deafferentation and deefferentation of limbs and body in different combinations on the rhythm of alternate muscular activity was explained; secondly, the protractor and retractor reflexes of limbs of vertebrate animals, considered closer to stimulus, usually experienced by feet during normal locomotion, or tactile stimuli of considerable force (i.e., painful), were likewise studied.

In the first series of experiments, it is shown that deafferentation of one or two feet does not result in a significant disturbance of rhythm independent of the fall of tone (Bickel, 1897; Hering, 1897; Weiss, 1936; Gray and Lissmann, 1940a). During deafferentation of three and especially four feet, excitation and tone are significantly reduced to such a level that it cannot be explained simply by the sum effect of each deafferent limb (Weiss, 1936; Gray and Lissmann, 1940a). But even here, in some preparations, impressions of normal rhythm may be observed. Only under complete deafferentation of all spinal nerves (II-XI) do the coordination of swimming (Herring, 1893) and walking movements (Gray and Lissmann, 1940a) disappear completely. The appearance of correct rhythms on some preparations of Weiss (1936, 1941a, 1941b) and Gray and Lissmann (1946a) can either be explained by: (a) failure to cut all the sensory nerves, or (b) the progression of stimuli from the labyrinth. They showed that the integrity of a single spinal segment is enough to retain normal locomotory activity, and the position of the segment does not play any large role. But if there is a disturbance in the efferent nerve supply to this segment, coordinating reflexes disappear. During the tactile excitation of a limb with cut effector links during complete deafferentation of the entire body and the three remaining limbs (in the first, afferent connections are retained), all feet respond to only a monophase reaction with the purpose of annulling contact with the source of excitation. Thus, the nature of monophase reaction depends on the place of stimulation (Gray and Lissmann, 1946a; Gray, 1950).

The ideas of Gray and his coworkers are confirmed by the investigations conducted under the guidance of P.K. Anokhin. Chepelyugina (1950) showed that in frogs, the position of the segment retaining its sensory supply plays a particular role in the construction of separate locomotory acts if the latter are not considered as merely coordinative responses of individual groups of muscles connected only with walk. The number of undamaged segments also contribute e.g., during the successive cutting of the dorsal root of the spinal cord, first the capacity for turning on the back disappears and afterwards, the capacity for jumping. The walk becomes more stable. A minimal undamaged region is also enough for swimming and local reaction of muscles to stimulus.

In the second series of experiments, the spinal preparation of the frogs were the objects of the research. It is wellknown that in cold-blooded animals even after cutting the cord anterior to the myelencephalon, locomotory activity is completely retained (Steiner, 1885). But cutting the cord posterior to the myelencephalon significantly changes the functions of many systems in the animal; a more or less deep spinal shock occurs, the somatic musculature weakens, etc. But within a period of time (hours or days in frogs, weeks in mammals) there is some restoration of the lost functions though the strength of spontaneous locomotion is reduced suddenly and irreversibly. The placing of such spinal preparations on the surface of a slow-moving, horizontally situated drum simulates normal locomotion to the extent that passive tension (retraction) in limbs may lead to a response similar to that under active retraction.

These experiments showed that spinal preparations of amphibians are the characteristic models of reflex activity (Gray, 1939a). The flexor (protractile) cross reflex is most clear. The passive stretching of one limb up to a particular moment leads to its protraction if it retains its afferent nerve supply (Gray, 1939a; Gray and Lissmann, 1940b). Simultaneous passive stretching in the hind limbs (this effect is less often observed in the forelimbs), leads to their alternate stepping and not to simultaneous protraction (Bickel, 1900; Snyder, 1907; Cate, 1928; Gray and Lissmann, 1940b). Possibly, in this instance, there exists some degree of independence in the activities of both legs; if both limbs are placed on drums of different revolving speeds, then the protraction will be completed with a frequency proportional to the speed. This may be interpreted as: the protraction activity of one foot stops the analogous activity of the second, and this in its turn will stimulate further the protraction of the first limb (Gray and Lissmann, 1940b).

Passive straightening of all four feet on the spinal preparation leads to a stable diagonally coordinated stepping which suddenly stops at the halting of the drum. The coordinated response of the diagonally situated foot to excitation of the second member of the pair was observed in tailed amphibians by Luchsinger (1880). However, movement for both members of a pair is always at different times: the forelimb passes ahead of the hind. In newts, the opposite is sometimes observed (Gray and Lissmann, 1940b). It is interesting that on rotating the preparation, the outer limbs respond to passive stretching with a greater number of contractions than the inner ones since there is more speed there. Limb protraction cannot begin before the attainment of complete retraction, and for this the foot of the second side should either be resting or in passive retraction. In the coordinated walking of a preparation on the drum, the frequency of contraction in all limbs is similar. This explains the influencing activity of the forefeet on the protraction of the hind ones. It is as if they set the tempo for the work of diagonal limbs: the longer hind limbs are forced to protract when they attain the state of complete retraction. The removal of both front feet from the rotating drum suddenly increases the retraction of the hind limbs and decreases the frequency of their stepping.

Retraction (extensor) activity of the limbs on spinal preparations is observed only during tactile stimulation, for example, at the end of the tail. Pain stimulation of one hind limb, as has already been said, leads to its protraction, but at the same time retraction in the second hind limb takes place (Biedermann, 1909). On withdrawal of the stimulus, the latter is again protracted. In a preparation where the earlier motionless hind foot is placed in a state of retraction, but the second, which is de-afferentated, is in a state of protraction, the pain stimulus acting on the first limb results in a stable retraction of the second (Gray and Lissmann, 1940b). Thus the absence of sensory connections in the latter leads to a disturbance in a natural chain of events: the limb stops responding to the protraction on its own retraction.

Gray and Lissmann (1946b) conducted several experiments, endeavoring to explain to what extent the activity of the muscles or joints of one segment may cause coordinated muscular response in the entire locomotory musculature. If the toad is completely deprived of contact with the substratum, it does not show any locomotory movements, and tactile stimulus causes only a swimming activity, i.e., a synchronized movement of the hind limbs. But if either of the forelimbs meets resistance, a well-defined neotactile, retractive (extensor) reflex is observed which disappears during deafferentation of the foot. Its retraction in turn reflectively causes a retractive response in the diagonal hind limb and a protractive response in the opposite forelimb. These secondary reflexes are observed during deafferentation of the corresponding feet, otherwise they are hidden by their own proprioceptive activity. The protractive response is observed with great difficulty in the ipsilateral hind limb. The protraction of the forelimb with its integrated afferent supply causes responsive protraction of the diagonal hind limb and a retraction of the contra-lateral. Thus, according to Gray and Lissmann, the normal system of coordination of limb movement in animals is established, for example, when the toad swimming in water, comes out on land and starts walking.

The above-mentioned facts led Gray (1939a, 1950) to the following conclusion: there are no proofs for the existence of a centrally, defined rhythm of activity in the movement of animals; the normal locomotory cycle in amphibians should be considered as a series of coordinative reflexes, depending mainly upon the proprioceptive organs of touch (Gray and Lissmann, 1940b, p. 251). However, the physiological mechanisms of swimming and jumping in batrachian amphibians is still not understood. Nevertheless, Gray (1939a) found it possible that their swimming mechanism is centrally controlled, since some completely deafferentated specimens lose the ability to walk, but still retain the ability to swim.

Locomotion in Ontogeny

The study of amphibian locomotion occupies a special place in works relating to the establishment of locomotory functions in ontogeny (Coghill, 1929; Faber, 1956). According to Coghill, even in an immobile embryo of *Ambystoma maculatum* there is a sensory tract in the spinal cord consisting of Rohon-Beard cells which receive impulses from the skin and upper portion of myotomes and the motor neurons which send fibers to the muscles. The connection between the tracts are still absent, but the contraction of muscles is of myogenic origin. Head bending is the first independent movement of the embryo.[11] With age, more and more muscular segments are added into this movement, and after some time, the embryo curves into a loop (loop stage). The loop may bend to the right or left. Furthermore, a loop curved to one side may instantly turn over to the other side. Contraction and relaxation of segments becomes much faster.

At this stage, the basis of future progressive movement is already established—waves of muscular contractions spread from the front to the back. The latter is connected with the presence of interneurons only in the anterior portion of the spinal cord and medulla. With an increase in the speed of curving a second bend in the side opposite to the first is formed before a loop can form. The embryo assumes an S-shape (S stage). Thus, the first locomotory coordination is observed. During a further increase of movement, several bends follow in the body one after the other on either side. The embryo swims. The beginning of active swimming coincides with the contralateral development of interconnection of the anterior portion of the motor tract to the dendrites of cells in the main column of the spinal cord. Consequently, excitation now not only goes back along the motor tract of one side, but is transmitted through the interneurons to the other side causing a contraction of the myotomes there. However, the latter occurs with some delay owing to the large number of synapses. Consequently, a secondary bending, opposite to the primary one in direction, follow the primary after a short interval of time.

The embryo of *Ambystoma* starts swimming before limb formation. With regard to the latter, the forelimbs develop somewhat faster than the hind; their development is completed only with that of the entire body (i.e. they are integrated). The first movement of the forelimbs is concluded in adduction (retraction) and abduction (protraction). During swimming, the limbs are actively pressed to the body. On land, both feet are thrown but simultaneously in front, then retract making the animal move forward

[11]Up to this point, both tracts are connected (left sensory with the right motor and vice versa) through special interneurons lying in the center of the spinal cord and medulla. Only from this moment does the first muscular response appear on lightly touching the skin.

and somewhat raise the anterior portion of the body above the substrate. From such a raised position, the first attempt at walking is made: the head and anterior portion of the body curve inward; the foot protracts on the convex side; on the concave side, it turns back. The first coordination, thus, seems to be the coordination of the movement of the forelimbs with the body and not with each other. The movement of the body during walking should be thought of as a strong, slow, swimming movement by wave-like bends passing from the front to the back.

The first movement of the hind limbs is to stretch them forward simultaneously and hold them in the same position during the stepping with the forelimbs. This leads to their passive following the movement of the body: during the turn of the pelvic region, one foot is in the front and the other in the back. In this, the movement of all four feet resembles coordination in a typical symmetrical-diagonal sequence (Figure 35, C) as the movement of each hind foot follows its diagonal forefoot after an interval of time, i.e., time required for the passage of the body bend from the pectoral to the pelvic region. This explains, as Gray observed (1939a), the dependence of similar movements of diagonal limbs on the speed of movement; during slow movement, the time interval between the forward movement of two limbs is greater than during fast movement as the body waves occur at a slower rate.

Since the local reflexes of limbs appear after the adduction of the latter during the body movement, Coghill considers that they are developed in the process of individualization inside the primary integrated system, but the symmetrical-diagonal coordination of limb movement in terrestrial animals is formed on the basis of the swimming mechanism. The domination of the body over limbs has a simple anatomical explanation; fibers extending from the motor tract do not stop their growth on reaching the corresponding muscular segment, but penetrate further into the developing limb. Thereafter, the first movements of the limbs inevitably submit to the movements of the body. With the development of local reflexes the extent of limb participation in locomotion increases while that of the body decreases. The apparatus of Rohon-Beard cells with the start of metamorphosis, according to Coghill, is reduced and replaced by the apparatus of cells of spinal ganglions, developing from the ganglionic layer. Thus, primary sensory intraspinal cells are replaced by the usual sensory apparatus of higher vertebrates. The locomotory apparatus is also subjected to significant changes.

A clear picture is drawn by Coghill which for all its attractiveness and possibly, correctness in principle (see pp. 27-28) suffers from several substantial shortcomings related mostly to his simplified schematic method of presenting material. A valuable attempt to show a relationship between physiology and anatomy is somewhat discredited due to the absence of exact documentation. The development of *Ambystoma* has not been divided into several consequent morphological stages which complicates the examination of results and a comparison with other amphibians (Faber, 1956). Anatomical constructions are insufficiently based and are, thus subject to doubt. So Zavarzin (1941) rejects Coghill's description of the sensory character of large cells lying in the region of the dorsal roots of the spinal cord in lancelet and sand eels, and Rohon-Beard cells in amphibian larvae, as well as the formation of such cells hidden in the anterior region of the body's sensory and motor tracts. However, Zavarzin's doubt is based only on the large gap between the larval and adult conditions. Zavarzin did not study the nervous apparatus of amphibian larvae.

Sepp (1959) treats the data of Coghill in another way. The primary, sensory, and motor systems parallel to Coghill's, he connects with the snake-like movements of the body since the Rohon-Beard cells are also observed in lamprey and embryonic stages of transverse-mouthed fishes and reptiles. An increase in the role of limbs in locomotion makes it an "insufficient apparatus, automatically conducting stereotyped undulatory movements of the body" (Sepp, 1959, p. 69). In this regard, Sepp draws the following conclusion: "......the automatic motor apparatus of the spinal cord bears reconstruction in view of the fact that the animals change from a pure body-tail undulatory locomotion to appendicular locomotion. This reconstruction relates to the receptory as well as the effector portions of the apparatus. In the receptor part, the Rohon-Beard neuron disappears, i.e., the skin-muscular proprioceptive sensitivity of the body disappears, and the muscular-joint proprioceptive sensitivity develops earlier in the limbs. In the effector portion, the order of formation of the anterior roots and consequently, the order of muscular contractions, based on the principle of a transient axial gradient, is replaced by the order of locomotory units where each peripheral locomotory nerve innervates the particular group of muscular fibers" (1959, p. 70). In the future, the return to pure undulatory movements (on land, snakes; in water, reptiles and mammals) takes place on the basis of the new, functional, and plastic motor apparatus of the spinal cord.

Serious objections were raised by Faber (1956) to the most fundamental points outlined by Coghill; Faber studied the development of locomotion in *Triturus taeniatus* and *Ambystoma mexicanus* (axolotl). It appears that in both forms, the primary movements of limbs are not integrated with the action of the body. Moreover, the primary coordination seems not to be diagonal, but parallel. The findings of Faber require a detailed presentation.

The development of all the three forms described by Coghill, including also *A. maculatum*, differs in anatomical as well as physiological plans. This is related to the shifts in the time of formation of different parts of the embryo. Nevertheless, since the development of the newt and axolotl have much in common, one need to examine only the development of the first.

As usual, the forelimbs of newts develop much earlier than the hind limbs. Their first movement is connected with posture reflex [stage III of embryonical development on the standard system (Glaesner, 1925)]. So, an inclination of the animal in relation to the longitudinal axis leads to a slight raising of the feet (elevation), sometimes with a little protraction. The first reflexor movement of limbs are entirely autonomous and are not connected with the movement of the body. Later on (stage V) placement of the newt on a very slow rotating platform around its vertical axis, may lead to the first coordinated movement of the body and the forelimbs. Rotation causes the head to turn in the opposite direction. Simultaneously or with some delay, the limb on the convex side reacts but the contra-lateral limb is carried forward somewhat (Figure 35, B), i.e., the opposite of that described by Coghill occurs (Figure 35, C). Faber names this mode of coordination as the basic pattern. It is similar to the reaction of an adult animal kept under the same conditions.

Further development (stage VI) corresponds to differentiation of limb movements. Retraction is connected with straightening. Sometimes, as a result of a long turn, a retracted and straightened limb on the convex side of the body makes a single step; it is protracted and slightly curved and after-

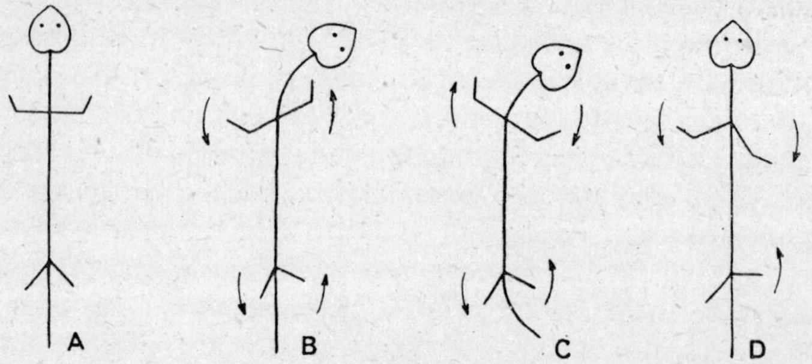

Figure 35. Coordinated models in the development of locomotion in tailed amphibians. *A—immobile embryo; B—main model (basic pattern); C—diagonal model by Coghill; D—parallel model by Faber (1956).*

wards comes to the initial position. At this time, limbs may also be drawn into a catching movement; both feet are retracted simultaneously which causes a jump by the animal. The first unilateral autonomous movement of the limbs (stage VII) concludes with the raising or retracting of the extensor. In stage VIII, the walking movement of limbs becomes stereotyped; foot protraction precedes the flexure at the elbow, followed by a simultaneous retraction and straightening. Tactile stimulation now causes a new reflex-jerk of the foot. The first alternate walking movements of the forelimbs appear only in stage IX. They are completely independent of the body action in spite of the basic model coordination existing in the preceding stages. A synchronized protraction or retraction of both feet is observed very rarely.

Usually, they work at different times. As a rule, retraction of the limbs is prolonged beyond protraction. The hind limbs are not seen at this stage.

The first movement of the hind limbs (stage XII) coincides with flexure of the body. It is possible that like the forelimbs they are also independent of the body, but to a lesser degree. These movements lead to protraction, usually unilaterally on the concave side of the body. However, the observed model of coordination differs from the diagonal symmetrical which is characteristic of the adult animal (Figure 35, C). The protraction of the hind limb is completed at the moment of the simultaneous retraction of both forelimbs. Further, that hind limb is protracted for which the same side forelimb is closer to completion of its retractive phase. At the same time, this movement need not necessarily precede the protraction of the diagonal forefoot. Thus, according to Faber, at this stage the limb action of one side is coordinated, but not of the diagonal which allows him to identify this model of coordination as parallel (Figure 35, D). True, at the same time, other combinations of limb movements may be observed which, according to Faber, support their relative independence.

Hence, if Faber is right and the development of a normal diagonal system of coordination in tailed amphibians is really preceded by a parallel coordination, then some doubt is cast on the development of the mechanics of terrestrial walk on the basis of swimming. At present, conditions do not exist which would permit a summarization on the basis of Faber's observations. Too many contradictions exist between his data and that of Coghill. However, it is clear that further studies along this line promise a good perspective.

2. TURTLES

There are only two methods of locomotion in turtles: quadrupedal walk and ewimming.

The majority of turtles move on land by a diagonal sequence of limb movement. Usually, there are two different forms of locomotion: slow (walking, *pas*) and fast (fast walk, *running*) (Oliver, 1955; Mertens, 1960b). Croix (1929a, 1933a) mentions that the terrestrial tortoises (*Testudo*) move in the form of parerpetico. A selection of several exposures of cinematic film (Figure 5), together with his diagrams, fix the tripodal stage of the cycle. It seems probable that intermediate quadrupedal stages are simply omitted and the tortoise moved with very slow walk. The latter was actually observed many times in our *Testudo horsfieldi* where fastness resolves into a slow trot-like walk. Amphibious turtles perhaps use a slow trot (Casamiquela, 1964), which we observed in *Emys orbicularis*, on land.

It is generally known that turtles are very slow on land, especially terrestrial forms. So Brem (1939) referring to Darwin determined the speed of large *geochelone elephantopus* as about 3.2 km per hour. For *Gopherus*, the speed usually mentioned is from 0.2 to 0.5 km per hour (Oliver, 1955). Maximum speed in *G. polyphemus* (shell length, 24 cm) about 0.8 km per hour, but it does not usually exceed 0.32 km per hour. In smaller specimens (14 cm), the observed speed is from 0.27 to 0.42 km per hour. Freshwater turtles due to their larger limb movements (Sukhanov, 1964a) move faster on land, but there is considerable variation. So, in *Clemmys insulpta* (18.6 cm), maximum speed is considered to be about 0.36 km per hour (Woods, 1945). At the same time, *Chrysemys floridana* (40 cm) moves on the grass at a speed of about 1.7 km per hour (Oliver, 1955).

The presence of the shell chiefly determines the locomotory peculiarity of turtles, in particular the nature of limb movements (Bergounioux, 1955; Sukhanov, 1964). Slowness of movement is also associated with the necessity for maintaining balance in heavy, slow animals. It is mentioned for example, that swift motion may lead to a transition from slow walk to a tired, undetermined gait appearing to be an uncoordinated throwing of the body in the direction of movement (Oliver, 1955). As a rule, the shell does not touch the substrate during movement, however, the tail of long-tailed forms (*Chelydra, Macroclemys*) may leave a twisted trail. The diagram of impressions of *Chelydra* given by Lessertisseur (1955, Figure 54, d) tells about fast movement as the impression of the hind foot covers the impression of the forefoot and the angle of the step attains 90°. Usually in freshwater turtles, the step angle is not more than 80° (Casamiquela, 1964) and for terrestrial tortoises, the angle is 65° (Peabody, 1959).

Walking is mentioned for all turtles, terrestrial as well as aquatic. Webb (1962) observed *Trionyx* many times moving large distances over land. In water, turtles often do not swim, but wriggle on the bottom. In this connection, the typical aquatic turtles like *Chelys* (Oliver, 1959) and *Platysternon* (Mertens, 1960a), generally walk on the bottom and do not swim. Experiments conducted in zoos showed that they learn to swim with difficulty, even when obtaining air is almost impossible while moving on the bottom. The *Chelys*, in this case, does not swim but bouncingly drags itself toward the surface with the help of its proboscis. A no less surprising fact is that in Northern Iraq, *Mauremys caspica* do not swim though in other places swimming is natural (Reed, 1957).

Sea turtles (*Chelonia mydas*) move on land by two methods (Barth, 1962): usually, by alternating the feet in a typical diagonal sequence or by Synchronous movement of the forefeet which are first brought forward and then retracted. The hind limbs work in a similar manner. The impression track left by this second form of movement characteristically resembles a tractor track (Abel, 1935, Figure 134). Undoubtedly, this method of movement is connected with a special method of swimming, sometimes compared with a butterfly stroke and seems to be secondary in turtles. Interestingly, hatchling sea turtles run on the sand in the usual diagonal sequence until their first entrance into the water. This has been nicely depicted in documentary films such as "Big Barrier" (Italy) and "In the World of Silence" (France). In the first days of their existence, hatchling (*Eretmochelys imbricata*) swim by alternate movements of the hind limbs while the front limbs serve as a type of balancer (Deraniagala, 1930) and, only after being in water and swimming by such a method, do the turtles move on land like in the water. Thus we observe for the second time in lower tetrapods, the synchronized work of fore and hind limbs; moreover, this is undoubtedly connected with change from one habitat to another. In turtles such a method of swimming gives higher speed. *Chelonia mydas* (shell size aout 1 m) were clocked at 1.4 to 2.25 km per hour, and *Eretmochelys imbricata* of average size and large *Caretta caretta* at about 1.6 km per hour (Oliver, 1955). The fastest swimmer seems to be the *Drmochelys* which, on unconfirmed data by Deraniagala may attain the speed of almost 36 km per hour. Usually terrestrial and aquatic turtles swim by alternately moving the limbs as in walk (Oliver, 1955). Marey (1901, Figure 235) presents sequential photographs of turtles swimming in this manner.

3. LIZARDS

Lizards, as a whole, because of diverse groups and a large number of locomotory adaptations in them, are unique creeping animals which make it possible to think about the level of locomotory development in reptiles. Neither turtles nor crocodiles with their narrow protective or amphibious specialization, nor snakes, can give as accurate a picture of locomotion in this diverse group of animals. Unfortunately, the lizard locomotion has been little studied except for the special works of Snyder (1949, 1952, 1954, 1962) and Urban (1964, 1965). Rapidity of movement combined with small size is the chief reason why direct observation is difficult. It is natural therefore that literature pays more attention to the more apparent features such as bipedal movement on two legs, crawling, etc. To date, there are no comprehensive methods for studying locomotion in lizards, allowing for analysis of the usual forms. Only Urban (1965) has tried to quantitatively evaluate the locomotion of one family of lizards (Teiidae).

Locomotory Adaptations in Lizards

Methods of locomotion in lizards differ according to the nature of the substrate or medium in which movement occurs; these are swimming, crawling and parachuting, walking and running on land on four or two legs.

Almost all lizards swim well with wave-like body bends or, if the body is short, only the tail. Swimming is characteristic of the sea iguana. This was nicely shown in the film "Galapagos" (FRG). Photographs of swimming *Amblyrhynchus* are given by Hobson (1965). Swimming has likewise been observed in other forms: *Gerrhonotus multicarinatus* (Cowles, 1946), *Iguana iguana* (Swanson, 1950), *Dracaena quianensis* (Vanzolini, 1961), *Crocodilurus lacertinus* (Urban, 1965), our *Lacerta* and *Eremias*. In most instances, the limbs are pressed to the body, but if the movement takes place at the cost of the tail, as in *Iguana,* then they may be stretched passively at the side. However, lizards often try to swim by alternate limb movements in the same sequence as in the gait (Cowles, 1946). But in so doing, the speed of movement is less: in *Crocodilurus* (general length 68.5 cm) about 2 m per second as against 2.8 otherwise (Urban, 1965).

A return to undulatory movement of the body on land is observed in several groups of lizards (Anguidae, Scincidae, Cordylidae, Anniellidae) and is usually related to a partial or complete reduction of limbs (Essex, 1927). As a rule, this coincides with life in grassy areas or a burrowing form of life. This fact is interesting: on tarred road *Ophisaurus* crawls slowly, but on grass it is very active and may move by jumps with a height of 12 to 15 cm completely losing contact with the substratum (Cliburn, 1957). Sometimes, it is considered that it was only the disappearance of limbs which compelled several lizards to change over to a burrowing form of life (Duederen, 1903). However, the majority of authors (Essex, 1927; and others) think that the absence of limbs and their zones is a great advantage for acquiring new ecological niches. On hard soil, serpentine movement is impossible. In such cases (Amphisbaenidae), movement is similar to that of the earthworm (Mertens, 1960b). In Amphisbaenidae, special forms of progressive movement via strokes of the hind portion of the body (as in some snakes) are also observed, due to which their tail is greatly shortened and muscularized.

Lizards climb well on rocks, bushes, branches of trees, even if they do no have any special adaptations for this beyond sharp claws. The majority of geckos have subphalangeal pads, likewise observed in other forms (*Anolis*). In chameleons, a zygodactylous foot and a prehensible tail are seen. A holding function is also present in the foot of the forest iguana, *Polychrus* (Boker, 1935). Several theories exist to explain the activity of the subphalangeal pads of geckos: one describes them as discharging a sticky secretion; another speaks about adhesion by suction; further theories confirm that electrostatic forces act here such as a molecular force of cohesion, or simply friction. Mahendra (1941) considers that an important role is played in lizards by the sharp ends of claws and the cuticular outgrowths of subphalangeal pads which allow the use of surface microrelief. Oliver (1955) confirms the same for the North American forms.

Climbing is usually completed with the help of normal, alternate limb movements. In several cases, however, real jumping is also observed. So in *Eremias scripta*, lizards with long bodies not exceeding 5 cm, the branch to branch jumps, attain 20 to 25 cm (Zakhdov, 1938). But how the limbs act here—simultaneously or successively—is not clear. According to Mertens (1960b), the hind limbs are retracted simultaneously. Such a diagram for *Polychrus marmoratus* was given by Boker (1935, Figs. 48, 49). But it can not be excluded as already said, that one of the limbs is retracted only passively and does not take an active part in the stroke.

As a special form of locomotory adaptation in lizards, it is important to mention sandswimming (Mosauer, 1932b). *Uma notata* living on a friable or loose substrate, while moving at full speed on the surface presses its fore-feet to the body and digs in to the sand by strong lateral movements of the neck and alternate strokes of the hind limbs, as observed in walk. During this, the body shows wave-like bends (Stebbins, 1944; Norris, 1951). Swimmings is continued for not more than a few body lengths (Mosauer, 1935). At the end of such swimming, the hind limbs are protracted and bent at the knee and are ready for suddenly straightening to spring out of the sand (Stebbins, 1944). A large role in digging is played by the sand skis, a series of serrated scales on the fingers with valvular activity (Cowles, 1941). A similar role is performed by the membrane between the fingers in the African gecko *Palmatogecko rangei* which also swims in the sand (Mertens, 1960b). The ability to make a quick disappearance in the sand is also observed in *Neoseps reynoldsi, Scincus scincus* (Oliver, 1955), and in the lacertid *Aporosaurus* (Mertens, 1960b), but this is produced not by the limbs but chiefly by serpentine movements of the body. The burying of our sandy and big-eared, round-headed lizards which bury themselves in the sand not with an inclination like *Uma*, but vertically, does not have anything in common with sand swimming.

Genuine gliding in air among lizards is observed only in *Draco* which has a special fold of skin on the sides of the body; these stretch during flight along the highly elongated ribs (Oliver, 1951; Mertens, 1959, 1960c; Klingel, 1965). The flying dragon is not only capable of directing its movement to a place selected in advance but can complete a full turn in the air (Savile, 1962). The flying gecko *Ptychozoon* which has a skin appendage on the body, limbs, and tail was also earlier considered to glide (Gesse, 1913); but now, together with *Uroplatus* and *Phyllurus*, it is placed in the group of parachuting lizards (Oliver, 1951; Tiwari, 1961). The ability to parachute without any significant adaptations that increase the surface area is observed even in some large forms during a jump from a rock (*Ctenosaura* and *Iguana*). It is still more developed in small lizards such as *Uta* and *Anolis* (Smith, 1946). Cott (1926) mentions that the oriented fall of *Anolis carolinensis* from a height of about 11 m is accompanied by a deviation of 1.8 to 4.5 m (on four specimens) from the vertical plane. Real active flight in reptiles is completely absent. There exists an opinion that even pterosaurs, similar to present-day albatrosses and stormy petrels, hovered in air but did not fly (Savile, 1962).

Bipedalism

Lizards have two forms of terrestrial locomotion: quadrupedal and bipedal. Usually these are considered independent, sharply different methods of locomotion with a passing analogy to that of dinosaurs. However, the recent works of Snyder (1949, 1952, 1954, 1962) and Urban (1965) have successfully negated this assumption. Our own data show that the bipedal run of lizards differs from the quadrupedal fast movement so insignificantly on the basis of biomechanics and physiological details that it is better to consider bipedalism as a variant of quadrupedal locomotion, i.e., fast trot with a dominance of the hind limbs (Chapters VI, VIII). Even then lizard bipedalism is an interesting phenomenon and considerable literature exists on the subject, most of which usually discusses bipedal movement in individual forms.

The first reference to the bipedal run in lizards was related in the seventies of the 19th century when Cope (1875) observed in the Central American iguana *Basiliscus vittatus* the ability to run on only two legs on a water surface. Soon the bipedalism of the Australian agamid *Chlamydosaurus kingii* became clear (Vis, 1884); the movement takes place with an almost horizontally held body (6°), but the limbs touch the soil in a digitigrade position. Since then, the number of bipedal lizard species recognized has greatly increased: 31 genera and 37 species of lizards from five families. The list of these species follows.[12]

Iguanidae :

* *Anolis* sp. (Saville-Kent, 1902).
* *Basiliscus basiliscus* (Saville-Kent, 1902; Snyder, 1949).
* *B. plumifrons* (Snyder, 1952).
* *B. vittatus* (Cope, 1875).
* *Callisaurus draconoides* (Mosauer, 1932b; Snyder, 1952).
* *Corythophanes cristatus* (Van Riper, 1952; Snyder, 1954).
C. hernandezi? (Saville-Kent, 1897).
* *Crotaphytus collaris* (Ditmars, 1933; Snyder, 1952; Van Riper, 1952).
Deiroptyx sp. (Barbour, 1943).
* *Dipsosaurus dorsalis* (Boker, 1935; Van Riper, 1952).
* *Gambelia wislizenii* (Snyder, 1952; Van Riper, 1952).
Iguana iguana (Svihla and Svihla, 1952).
* *Uma inornata* (Snyder, 1952).
U. notata (Norris, 1951).
Uma sp. (Mosauer, 1932b).
Uraniscodon? (Saville-Kent, 1902).

[12]In innumerable cases, bipedalism was observed in lizards of a particular genus, but the species was not mentioned.

Agamidae :

Agama atra (Fitzsimons, 1943).
A. caucasica (Reed, 1956).
A. stellio (Saville-Kent, 1899).
* *Amphibolurus cristatus* (Snyder, 1952).
A. muricatus (Saville-Kent, 1898, 1899).
* *A. rufescens* (Barrett, 1950).
* *Calotes versicolor* (Annandale, 1902; Smith, 1935; Snyder, 1954).
* *Chlamydosaurus kingi* (Vis, 1884; Saville-Kent, 1895; Osborn, 1917; Snyder, 1954).
Goniocephalus sp. (Saville-Kent, 1902).
Grammatophora sp. (Boker, 1935).
* *Hydrosaurus marmorata* (Loveridge, 1945; Snyder, 1954).
Japalura sp.? (Saville-Kent, 1902).
* *Laemanctus serratus* (Barbour, 1934; Snyder, 1954).
Leiolepis belliana (Taylor, 1963).
Otocryptis bivitata (Green, 1903).
* *O. weigmannii* (Smith, 1935).
* *Physignatus cocincinus* (Smith, 1935).
* *Ph. lesueuri* (Saville-Kent, 1897, 1898, 1899; Osborn, 1917; Barrett, 1931).
* *Sitana ponticeriana* (Green, 1903; Smith, 1935).

Teiidae :

** *Ameiva surinamensis* (Saville-Kent, 1899; Urban, 1965).
* *Cnemidophorus maximus* (Van Denburgh, 1922).
* *C. tessellatus* (Burt, 1931)
** *C. tigris* (Urban, 1965).
Cnemidophorus sp. (Mosauer, 1932b).
Kentropyx sp. (Boker, 1935).
Tupinambis teguixin (Saville-Kent, 1902).
** *T. nigropunctatus* (Saville-Kent, 1902; Urban, 1965).

Lacertidae :

Acantodactylus sp. (Judged from the photographs of foot prints: Mosauer and Wallis, 1928).
* *Lacerta viridis* (Rose, 1902; Saville-Kent, 1902).

Varanidae :

* *Varanus giganteus* (Stirling, 1912; Barrett, 1950).

Cases of the forefeet of a lizard in a sitting position, breaking contact with the substrate so that it holds on only with the hind limbs and tail are mentioned in the literature (*Chalarodon madagascariensis* (Petit, 1928), *Basiliscus basiliscus* (Snyder, 1952), *Chlamydosaurus kingii* (Gadov, 1901, Photo), *Calotes* and *Sitana* (Smith, 1935), *Amphibolurus pictus* (Snyder, 1952), *Lacerta viridis* (Rose, 1902), *Varanus gouldi* (Loveridge, 1934; Barbour, 1943).

This unexpected bulk of information about the bipedal run compels one to examine it with particular care. If for several lizards bipedalism may be considered as proven by a photograph, as was done for *Physignathus lesueuri* and *Amphibolurus muricatus* (Saville-Kent, 1898) and *Chlamydosaurus* (Osborn, 1917), then other data require confirmation. The ability for and the use of the bipedal run varies: some constantly take recourse to it even directly from a state of rest (*Basiliscus, Chlamydosaurus*, etc.); in others the forelimbs lose contact with the ground only after running in teiids and varanids. Naturally, it is difficult to correctly judge visually how a lizard runs at fast speed—on two or four legs. On reviewing the list given above, Snyder (1949, 1952, 1954, 1962) felt it was possible to consider bipedalism indisputable in only those lizards marked with one asterisk (*). Also, the subsequent data presented by Urban (1965) and marked with two asterisks (**) do not cause any doubt.

Bipedalism in tetrapods results as a whole, for several reasons (Howell, 1944; DuBrul, 1962). Firstly, this leads to an adaptation in movement with great speed, when the hind limbs are strongly developed but the forelimbs are only an obstacle to the latter's work. Bipedalism in lizards and jerboas appears to be such a case. The second important reason is the necessity to free the front limbs for other purposes (birds and primates). Correspondingly, four main types of bipedal locomotion are identified (Snyder, 1962): (1) reptilian, observed in lizards, pseudo-suchians and dinosaurs in which the body usually moves more or less horizontally and a heavy, long tail serves as a balancer; (2) avian, where the body similarly moves horizontally but the center of gravity lies directly beneath the hind limbs and consequently does not require any balancing; (3) bipedalism in higher primates and man where the body stands semi-vertically or vertically over the limbs; (4) ricochet bipedalism of jumping mammals with very well developed hind limbs and a semi-vertical body and the center of gravity strongly shifted behind.

A similarity of bipedal movement in lizards and dinosaurs should not be cosidered literally, though Saville-Kent (1899) struck by the widespread incidence of bipedalism in lizards considered that this originated from the distant acestors, common with dinosaurs. Lydekker (1912) showed that the bipedal run of the lizard originated independently in lizards and dinosaurs. According to Snyder (1962) bipedalism in the evolution of terrestrial vertebrates originated not less than six times, two times among reptiles (thecodonta-dinosaurs and lizards). It appears to us that even in lizards, the bipedal run developed independently in iguanomorphs and scincomorphs.

The bipedal run in lizards is more economical than the usual quadrupedal movement (Snyder, 1952). Significantly, the length of the step[13] increases,

[13]The length of the step is proportional to the length of limb, angle of swing, and the distance which the acetabulum is carried forward when the hind foot is not in contact with the ground (Barclay, 1946). In its turn, this distance is composed of two values: distance covered for the duration of contact with the substrate of the opposite hind limbs and the distance when the animal is in the stage of free flight.

as a result of which the frequency of movement may be decreased to some extent without a particular loss of speed. Consequently, a smaller expenditure of energy is required during the restoration period of limb action. The forelimbs desist from retarding forward movement at the moment of landing. Nevertheless, bipedalism in lizards is least effective among the remaining types. The hips continue to work in an almost horizontal plane. The distal ends of all segments circumscribe wide elliptical arcs. Apparently, great limitations exist with regard to body weight (Snyder, 1962).[14]

Thus, fastness of locomotion in lizards is attained not by structural peculiarities of the locomotory apparatus, but by a strong development and overstressing of the muscles. The apparatus is almost unchanged. The differences between the quadrupedal and bipedal gaits in iguanomorphs (Snyder, 1954, 1962) lead only to the following. The length of the presacral region is decreased and the tail is increased; in quadrupedal forms, this constitutes 30 to 46 and 53 to 68% respectively; in bipedal, 23 to 33 and 65 to 76%.[15] The pelvis narrows somewhat, the iliac bone elongates, and its pre-acetabular outgrowth is increased. In all bipeds, the length of the forelimbs is significantly decreased, mainly at the cost of the forearms and hands. During this, the length of each segmet in iguanids increases, particularly proximally, in agamids, if at all, there is a growth (usually insignificant), then in the first instant, the foot is increased. In bipeds, the extensors of the shank and the flexors of the foot are strengthened while the extensors of the foot (in iguanids) and the adductors of the hip are weakened. The distal tendon muscles are elongated. In quadrupeds, the flexors of the shank and the adductors of the hip are better developed. In bipedal agamids, the extensors of the hip are better developed than they are in quadrupeds.

Consequently in lizards, no major reconstruction occurs in the locomotory apparatus during the change to partial bipedal movement. Even the above-mentioned adaptive changes are explained readily by movement with increasing speed, rather than by direct bipedalism. The development of bipedalism in archosaurs leads, on the other hand, to a sharp change in the apparatus of movement. In particular, the limbs of dinosaurs worked in plane, close to the parasagittal . Their bipedalism can be considered complete. This is not a variant of one gait, but an independent method of movement where even slow locomotion occurs only on two legs.

The tendency to bipedalism developed in two large ecological groups of lizards (Snyder, 1952). The first group includes terrestrial species, living in open sandy or stony places (*Amphibolurus, Chlamydosaurus, Sitana,* etc.).

[14]In *Basiliscus vittatus*, the bipedal run is often seen in young specimens, but the adult starts running easily and suddenly on two legs from a state of rest (Hirth, 1963).

[15]An even greater elongation of tail is seen in *Takydromus* and some *Calotes;* where it is 4 to 5 times longer than the body, it causes lowering of the speed of movement (Mertens, 1960b).

The second group combines the forms living in forests or bushy zones which may be classified as semiarboreal, semiaquatic or both. These are *Basiliscus, Physignathus, Calotes,* and others. Lizards of both the groups differ in characteristic features: they have short bodies, strongly developed hind limbs, and long, heavy tails. Naturally, under these conditions, bipedalism in teiids, lacertids, and varanids with relatively long bodies, which cannot be raised high above the ground, causes some surprise. Snyder (1952) while including *Cnemidophorus maximus* and *Varanus giganteus* in the list of bipedal forms, does so with several reservations ("if so, then......"). But photographs by Urban (1964, 1965) finally solve the problems: Some teiids really are capable of a bipedal run though, as a rule, the fast movement occurs on four legs. Unlike iguanomorphs, the specialization of fast movement in teiids does not lead to a narrowing of the pelvis, but affects the elongation of the back and front limbs (Urban, 1964).

Forms of Locomotion

During quadrupedal locomotion on dry land, the limbs of lizards work in diagonal pairs or in a symmetrical-diagonal sequence *RH, RF, LH, LF.* Only a casual remark of Snyder's (1952) explains the presence of a lateral sequence in them (*RH, LF, LH, RF*).[16]

The first reference to the specific forms of locomotion in lizards is given by Marey (1901, Figs 223, 224) who presents two successive stills of the common lizard (*Lacerta* sp.) and a gecko moving with one interrupted trot. Judging from the photographs, this should be a slow trot-like walk. The lateral body bends are less observable in *Lacerta.* The hind limb during its protraction does not straighten completely at the knee. According to Croix (1929a) whose views are not widely known, there are three forms of locomotion in lizards: slow walk in the lateral sequence (*meterpetico*), reptilian trot (*calperpetico*) and bipedal run. Howell (1944) projects the idea that the main form of locomotion for lizards is the trot with a tendency for a hind limb to touch down earlier than the diagonal forelimb. But he notes that because of fast movement in lizards, this assumption could not be verified. During slower movement, according to Howell, a tendency is observed toward the sequence of real walk where the hind limb somewhat lags behind the diagonal forelimb.

The Howell's suggestion that the trot is the basic form for quadrupedal fast movement in lizards was confirmed by Snyder (1952) using fast motion pictures. In beginning movement from a state of rest, the stroke is given by

[16]Snyder, studying fast trot with dominance by the hind limbs, considered the order of establishing contacts of limbs with the substrate as the sequence of their work. Figure 22 shows that limbs here work in pair. Disconnection of feet, however, is completed in accordance with the diagonal sequence.

the two hind limbs, one of which starts protracting before having completed full retraction. Thus, only one hind limb is leading which pushes the body forward and to the side over the diagonal forefoot. At this time, the second hind limb moves forward over the ipsilateral foot. It touches down in *Crotaphytus* at the same level or in front of the latter but in *Sceloporus* and *Cnemidophorus* behind. The hind limb touches down earlier than its diagonal forefoot. By placing the latter on the substrate, the animal is supported only by the two diagonal limbs, clearly showing that the main form of locomotion is trot. With increased speed, the body support time on only the hind feet increases as their swing grows and, consequently, the size of the step. The shorter front feet cannot manage to follow them. As a result, the hind limbs not only touch the ground quicker than their diagonal front ones, but also liftoff later from the ground.

Unfortunately, the description of the locomotory cycle given by Snyder (1952) is very confusing and only now has it become clear that he had in mind the gait which we call the fast trot dominated by the hind limbs. At the same time, following the contradictory diagram of Howell, Snyder ascribed to lizards besides trot, movement at higher speeds and in the form of a running walk. In so doing, he was not disturbed that the support plan given by him did not correspond to the running walk of Howell (Figure 17 of the present work). This is the slow trot with dominance of hind limbs which Howell did not know.

Snyder's error is quite significant. The error is not just a matter of an incorrect identification of the form of locomotion. The cycle of the running walk requires the presence of a stage of unilateral support on only two limbs, a stage clearly contrary to lizards. Stages of unilateral support, described by Snyder in *crotaphytus* and especially in *Cnemidophorus* do not actually seem similar. Here only the hind foot functions as the supporting limb, and the forefoot, which has not yet started protracting only passively drags on the substrate. The same mistake is also committed by Urban (1965, Fig. 4) who introduces in his support formulas the stages of lateral support. True, he considers that it is impossible to differentiate running walk from trot in lizards.

Thus, at present (Urban, 1965) it is acceptable to differentiate only three forms of locomotion: quadrupedal walk, slow movement where the diagonal forelimb leaves the ground earlier and touches down earlier; quadrupedal fast movement in which the diagonal hind limb succeeds the forelimb in lifting and touching; and finally the bipedal fast run. However, the identification given by Urban of a quadrupedal fast gait immediately contradicts his own data (however, the author did not notice the contradiction). Not even in a single support plan given by him for this gait or even in the theoretical example, does the hind limb lift earlier than its diagonal front one; it always does so later or simultaneously. In fact this gait is identical to our fast trot with dominance of hind limbs, whereas the quadrupedal walk corresponds to our slow trot-like walk. Moving a step further, it must be noted that besides these gaits, lizards also move in slow trot with dominance of front limbs or, often, the hind ones.

Work of Limbs

In iguanids (*Crotaphytus, Gambelia, Sceloporus*) and agamids (*Amphibolurus, agama*), the hind limbs work almost identically during a quadrupedal run and the bipedal run (Snyder, 1952). Toward the beginning of the propulsive period, the thigh is protracted. The entire leg is straightened (extension of the knee joint and some ventral inflexion in the tarsometatarsal joint). The foot is firmly implanted. Contact with the ground takes place on the whole foot. The fingers are somewhat spread. The direction of the longer axis of the foot at the moment of contact varies: in long-legged *Amphibolurus, Crotaphytus,* and *Gambelia,* it is directed straight in front or somewhat to the side at an angle of 20°, in *Sceloporus* and *Cnemidophorus*, it is turned by not less than 50°. During a stroke, the foot turns laterally (Schaeffer, 1941).

In the beginning of a stroke, some bending takes place in the knee and a significant straightening (dorsal flexion) of the foot. During the propulsive period, the thigh is retracted. The limb straightens at the knee. The foot is bent ventrally so that at the end of stroke, it takes a digitigrade position, and the entire leg is stretched almost in a straight line. All segments of a limb take an active part in propulsion (Snyder, 1949). At the beginning of the restoration period, the thigh is somewhat abducted, and the knee is bent. As a result of this, the foot loses contact with the ground. With the protraction and abduction of the thigh, the entire leg is brought forward.

Movement of the forelimbs does not differ substantially from movement of the hind one. In *Sceloporus* and *Cnemidophorus*, the forelimbs touch the ground with the wrist, but as speed increase in *Amphibolurus, Crotaphytus* and *Gambelia,* the contact is made only with the tips of the fingers. Only at maximum speed does *Sceloporus* also become digitigrade. During a bipedal run, the forelimbs are either immobile or undergo a rhythmical movement in the same direction as that of the corresponding hind limb.

The distal end of the thigh in iguanids makes an ellipsis almost equally stretched in front and back from the transverse plane passing through the acetabulum (Figure 107, D and E). In agamids, *Amphibolurus,* this ellipsis is significantly shifted forward (Figure 107, C). A considerable portion of the corresponding ellipses of the shank and foot in iguanids, is concentrated behind the aforesaid plane. In *Amphibolurus* these planes are equidistant anteriorly and posteriorly (Snyder, 1962). This is considered the most perfect adaptation to run.

As already mentioned, the thigh in lizards act mostly in the horizontal plane. However, with increased speed the thighs are adduced more, though the degree of adduction is small since it is limited by the greater internal trochanter of the femur (Snyder, 1954). According to Snyder, the thigh in all lizards are directed ventrolaterally not more than 40° to the horizontal. While studying locomotion in teiids, Urban (1965) tried to evaluate the degree of thigh adduction accordig to the speed and gait. To do so, in motion pictures the angle between the vertical plane and the line connecting the acetabulum with the end of the longest toe was determined. It is shown that increased speed leads to a significant increase in thigh adduction (up to 11 to 18°) in those forms capable of fast locomotion (*Ameiva, Cnemidophorus tigris*), but it is retained almost without change in slow-moving lizards (*Pholidopolus, Crocodilurus*). The initial degree of adduction during slow movement is similarly high in fast forms.

The work of limbs in the vertical plane increases the effectiveness of a stroke by helping the median stoppage of the foot (Snyder, 1952). This only leads to an increase in the degree of straightening of the limbs during speed. It has been suggested (Urban, 1965) that the latter be evaluated by the ratio of the distance of the acetabulum from the substrate to the body length. As in teiids and also in Callisaurus (*Iguanidae*), i.e., in all the forms studied by Urban, this ratio increases with speedier gaits. This shows that in good runners the body is carried higher over the substrate than in poor runners, even when moving at the same speed (correctly, within the limits of one gait). In bipedal forms, the limbs are straightened more than in quadrupeds (Snyder, 1952, 1962).

The Body During Locomotion

Lateral body bends in short-bodied forms are less often observed. However, in all the cases studied, an increase of speed is followed by an increase of lateral body undulations. This is observed in iguanids, e.g., *Crotaphytus* (Snyder, 1962), as well as in teiids (Urban, 1964).

During quadrupedal locomotion, bodies are arranged almost horizontally. But with an increase of speed the angle of inclination grows; moreover, it is always observed in fast lizards and only slightly so in slow-walking lizards. So in fast *Ameiva* (Teiidae) during slow movement, the angle is equal to 12°; during a fast quadrupedal, 24°; during a bipedal run, 30°; in *Pholidopolus* also, the angle is always about 1° (Urban, 1965). Usually those forms incapable of fast locomotion hold the body more horizontal during slow movement than lizards which move similarly, but probable capable of greater speed. Maximum inclination is observed in bipedal iguanids (Snyder, 1949, 1952, 1962). *Basiliscus* starts its run on two legs immediately from an immobile condition and the inclination of the body is determined by the direction of the stroke and attains 46°. When the movement becomes more uniform, the inclination decreases and varys depending on the moment of the cycle, between 20 and 31°. An angle of 45 to 46° is observed also in *Crotaphytus* and in *Callisaurus* (Barbour, 1934). However, in the latter during a quadrupedal fast run, the angle is equal to 21° (Urban, 1965). The largest angle, 750, is observed in *Gambelia* (Synder. 1952). In agamids running bipedally, e.g., *Amphibolurus*, the inclination is significantly less i.e., in all 25° (Snyder, 1962). This is considered as the most perfect adaptation in running. The head may be raised making a horizontal angle of 45°. In another bipedal agamids, *Chlamydosaurus*, the inclination of the body is observed to be 50° (Schmidt and Inger, 1957), but it is not excluded that the position of the head and not the body is considered.

The amplitude of the intracyclic changes of body inclination and head was determined from the distance from the eyes to the substrate (Urban, 1965). It appeared that during slow locomotion in all the teiids studied and *Callisaurus*, the amplitude is more or less similar, but with an increase of speed, it not only increases but does so differentiatly: in speedier forms it is greater than in slow moving ones.

In view of the primitive position of limbs on the body of lizards, transverse forces are significantly active; these forces are somewhat less during the median position of feet (Snyder, 1952). It is similarly observed that the body rotates on the vertical and longitudinal axes.

Speed of Locomotion

It is wellknown that small lizards develop a phenomenal speed of movement over short distances. The speed is not easy to measure. The most accurate results can be obtained by film under laboratory conditions (Snyder, 1962; Urban, 1965), but to what extent these results correspond to natural conditions is unknown. It is known that animals in circumstances against their will often move slower than usual (Belkin, 1961). In the field, time is usually measured for the portion of the track which the lizard passes, the limits of which are marked by reference points. The margin of error for this, according to Belkin, does not exceed 0.3 seconds. Naturally, the longer the distance covered by the animal, the more accurate are the results. Speed is similarly affected by other factors which cannot always be considered: the ambient and body temperatures, activity, and so on.

Information on the speeds of lizard obtained from the literature is usually characterized by the aforementioned maximum limits. Speed, as a rule, is given in miles per hour and rarely in kilometres per hour, which is hardly advisable as lizards seldom run more than ten or twenty metres at a stretch. In Table 1, all data is given in metres per second.

In each of the three families included in the table, there are species which attain a high speed of movement. The maximum is in the iguanid *Callisaurus*.

Table 1. Speed of locomotion of different forms of lizards

Species	Character of Locomotion	Speed (in m/sec)	Data taken from
Iguanidae			
Sceloporus undulatus	quadrupedal	2.2	Snyder, 1962
Iguana iguana	,,	3.1; 4.5—5.5(?)	Swanson, 1950
Basiliscus vittatus			
juv.	bipedal	1.6	Hirth, 1963
adult.	quadrupedal	2.7	
B. basiliscus			
juv.	bipedal	2.5	Snyder, 1962
adult.	,,	3.0	
Crotaphytus collaris	quadrupedal	4.9	
,, ,,	bipedal	7.1	
Uma notuta	,, (?)	5.4	Stebbins, 1944
,, ,,	,, (?)	6.7	Norris, 1951
Dipsosaurus dorsalis	,,	7.3 (av)	Belkin, 1961
,, ,,	,,	8.5	
Callisaurus draconoides	quadrupedal	2.2	Urban, 1965
,, ,,	?	6.7	Oliver, 1955
,, ,,	bipedal	7.2 (av)	Belkin, 1961
,, ,,	,,	9.7	
Agamidae			
Amphibolurus cristatus	quadrupedal	2.2	Snyder, 1962
,, ,,	bipedal	5.4	
Teiidae			
Pholidopolus montium	quadrupedal	0.13	Urban, 1965
Teius teyou	,,	1.0	
Crocodilurus lacertinus	,,	1.1	
Cnemidophorus tigris	,,	1.6	
,, ,,	bipedal	1.4	
C. inornatus	quadrupedal	2.8	
C. sexlineatus	,,	1.6	
,, ,,	?	8.0	Hoyt, 1941
Cnemidophorus sp.	?	4.7	Oliver, 1955
,, ,,	?	6.7—7.9	Mertens, 1960b
Tupinambis nigropunciatus	quadrupedal	5.1	Urban, 1964
,, ,,	bipedal	4.3	
Ameiva ameiva	quadrupedal	3.0	
,, ,,	bipedal	7.3	

The relationship of speed to a particular gait is little studied. Usually, how the movement took place—on two or four legs—is all that is mentioned. Attention is paid to the fact that though the bipedal run, as a rule, yields high speeds; nevertheless in some teiids (*Ameiva, Tupinambis, Cnemidophorus tigris*), its speed is less than that of quadrupedal locomotion.

A change of speed during an increase is, in the first instance, connected with an increase of step length and only to a lesser degree to an increase in the speed of the cycle. The length of the double step in many iguanids is frequently equal to their body length, but during maximum speed it may exceed that by almost three times. At the same time, the speed of the cycle is increased by only 10% (Snyder, 1962). Urban (1965) tried to express this relationship by graphs where the relative size of the step (to body length) is the abscissa and transport time (valid, with reservations) as the index of the speed of cycle is the ordinate. Urban's error consists not only of the fact that the speed of the cycle requires consideration of duration, transport and support, but also that transport time does not change proportionately to speed; it quickly attains a specific minimum and afterwards remains unchanged. Thus the method suggested by Urban may be used to compare only the lesser speeds of locomotion. However, it was possible for him to show that in teiids capable of a faster run, the size of the step is generally greater, but transport time is less than in the more slow-moving forms. A minimum transport time is similarly observed in *Callisaurus* during quadrupedal slow and fast movements. In the majority of fast forms, transport time during high speed is nearly similar, but in lower speed, differences do appear.

Lizard Tracks

No special works on lizard tracks are available. Some photographs and figures are given by Mosauer and Wallis (1928) and Mosauer (1932b, 1935). In the slow movement of *Acanthodactylus* (Lacertidae), the finger prints and the track of the long tail are clearly seen. The footprint of the forefoot is perhaps covered by the hind one during a very fast run, the tail does not touch the ground, and each separate print of the hind feet is turned into a round cavity. In general, the forefeet do not leave any impression. In *Scincus officinalis* (Scincidae) forms with strongly reduced limbs, the abdomen and tail are dragged on the sand during slow movement. The footprints of the hind limbs do not completely cover those of the front ones and approximately correspond to an extreme degree of secondary covering as in *Batrachoseps major* (Figure 34). In *Uma notata* (Iguanidae) during low speed, there are finger prints in each separate impression, as well as a tail track. Increasing speed results in a growing difference in the depth of the impressions left by the fore and hind limbs and to significant covering. On the basis of similar observations, Stebbins (1944) confirms that *Uma* in fact run on two legs so that the greater portion of body weight is borne on the hind limbs. The impression track of *Uma* is either covered or overlapped. Overlapping is also observed in the impressions of *Callisaurus* (Barbour, 1934, Figure 57).

Some information about the tracks of lizards is given by Peabody. In long-bodied *Gerrhonotus coeruleus* (Anguidae), the impression is characterized by a continuous wave-like line of the tail with considerably incomplete covering: prints of the hind feet are situated slightly posterior to the level of the impression opposite to the forefoot (Peabody, 1948, Pl. 42, A). The angle of the step does not exceed 85° (by forelimbs, 100°). The value of the double step is about 5 cm, and its ratio to the length of foot is 4:1 (to length of hand, 6:1). In *Sceloporus occidentalis,* the angle of step is 90° (132°), double step 7.5 cm. The impressions of the ipsilateral fore and hind feet are situated on the same level, but the hind is more lateral (Peabody, 1948, Pl. 42, C). In bipedal lizards, the angle of the step expands to almost 180° (Peabody, 1959).

4. SNAKES

The locomotion of snakes is outside the principal interest of this work. Considerable literature has been devoted to the topic (Mosauer, 1932a; Gray, 1946; Gray and Lissmann, 1950; Gans, 1962). Therefore, using the reviews given by Gans (1960, 1966a, 1966b) we will mention here only the basic types of locomotion for this extremely specialized group. These are four in all; moreover, a snake may often use one or the other method so the differences between them are not absolute.

The first and main type is locomotion with the help of wave-like bends of the body (undulatory locomotion) which pass from the front to the back and is functionally close to that of elongated fishes. But a uniform resistance to the surroundings, acting on the whole surface of the animal, is replaced here by forces applied only to a few support points on the substrate. The size of bends varies from the beginning of movement, depending upon the unevenness of the ground. In the majority of progressive forms, support points are strictly fixed, waves are "stationary" in relation to the substrate, and each succeeding point in the body repeats the path covered by the preceding one. This can be well demonstrated by the movement of snakes inside a sinusoidal glass tube (Figure 36). Undulatory locomotion is not effective on a smooth surface, or along the straight wall of a trough, i.e., where waves do not have resistance during backward movement. However, movement is possible on quicksand, though with less speed as the body bends passing caudally, gather sand in a small crest, the reaction of which on the body causes the forward progression of the snake. From the impression in the sand made by these bends, the direction of movement of a snake may be identified. A decrease in friction increases the effect of this method of movement. Lateral undulation gives a progressive locomotion among bushes and in tree branches; only the support points are shifted from the lateral position below on the periphery of the animal. The effectiveness of this depends greatly upon the ratio of body length to frequency of branches. Correspondingly, in arboreal snakes, the body becomes longer.

Movement on a smooth surface is possible by another method using the difference between the coefficients of static friction and friction of sliding. Twisting its body like a bellow, the snake fixes the hind portion of its body on the substratum (Figure 37, 1). By straightening, the front portion moves forward (Figure 37, 2 to 4), where a new support point appears (Figure 37, 5). Now the body again contracts into a bellow by drawing the tail region of the body forward (Figure 37, 6 to 7). This method of movement is named concertineo. The speed of locomotion is not great, as speed reduces the difference in the value of the coefficient. Concertine seems to be the main method of locomotion in some arboreal and terrestrial groups of snakes with relatively strong, heavy, and powerful bodies (*Boidae, Colubridae, Viperidae*). On the whole, such locomotion does not require great morphological adaptations and is at best, the solution of movement by behavioral means.

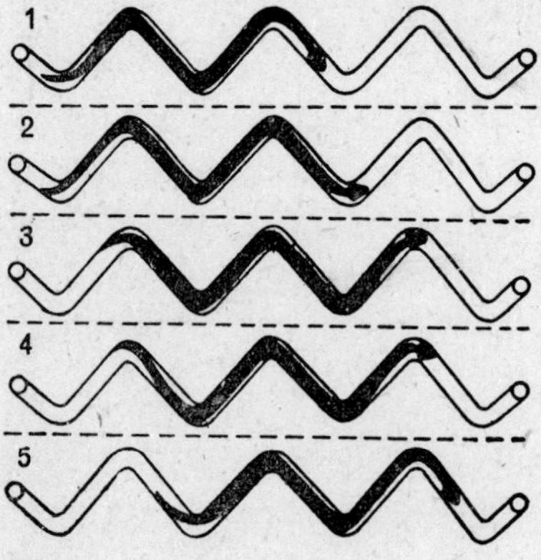

Figure 36. Locomotion of snakes with the help of wave-like body bends (undulatory locomotion). *Tropidonotus natrix* moves inside a sinusoidal tube. From Gray (1953). *1 to 5—successive stages of movement.*

On the other hand, the so-called rectilinear or caterpillar-like movement is not possible without considerable changes, coordinative as well as morphological in character (provision of mobile and elastic connection between the ventral portion of covers and the axial skeleton). Groups of muscles passing from the ribs back to the ventral scales provide a forward movement of separate portions of the skin relative to the substrate and the immobile axis of the skeleton. Afterwards, the moved portions anchor to the substrate and the muscles joining them to the posterior ribs pull the body forward (Figure 38). Movement occurs with less speed but it has several advantages: it allows relatively thick snakes to cross smooth surfaces and to pass through narrow cracks; it makes it possible for short-bodied forms to move in a straight line to their prey. Rectilinear locomotion is observed in Uropeltidae, Boidae and Crotalidae.

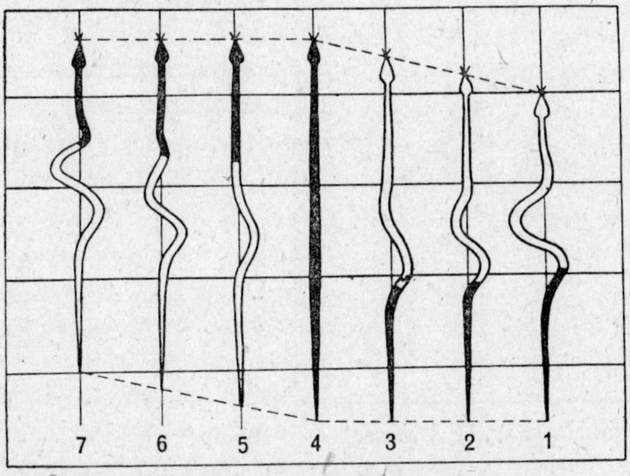

Figure 37. Concertine locomotion of snakes.

Movement of *Tropidonotus natrix* occurs by extending the bellow in the middle of the body (1-4) from a fixed position of the tail region (shown black) after which when the anterior part of the body anchors to the substrate and again forms a bellow (5-7). From Gray (1946).

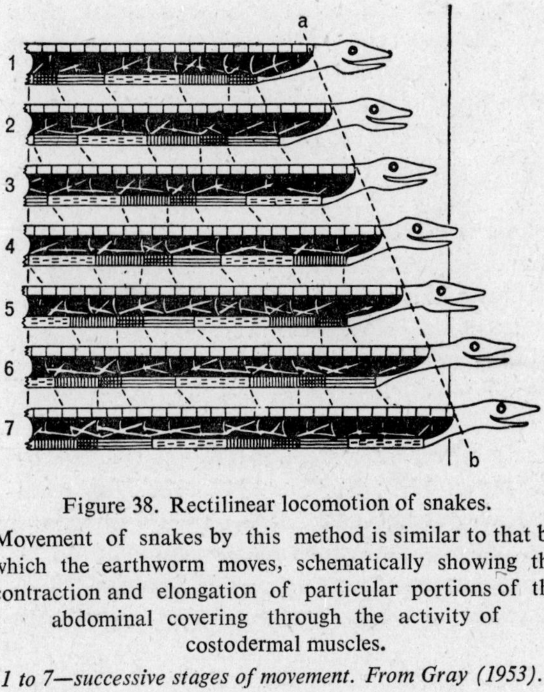

Figure 38. Rectilinear locomotion of snakes.

Movement of snakes by this method is similar to that by which the earthworm moves, schematically showing the contraction and elongation of particular portions of the abdominal covering through the activity of costodermal muscles.

1 to 7—successive stages of movement. From Gray (1953).

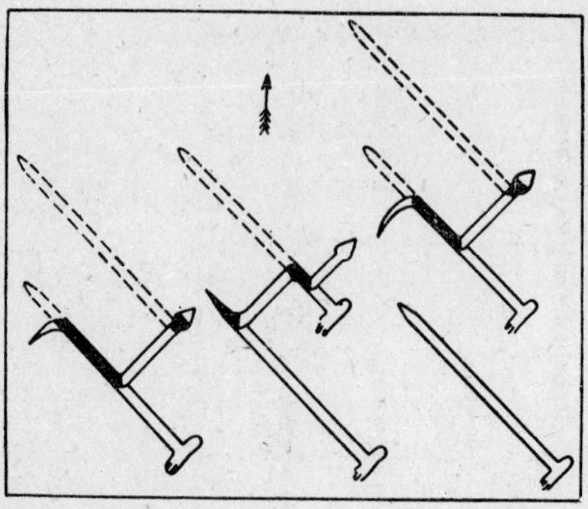

Figure 39. Sidewinding locomotion of snakes. Position of snakes during the course of movement in the direction shown by arrow (each successive stage is replaced in the diagram to the right); black portions of the body are immobile; *dotted lines* show the place to which the body of the snake will be carried; *thin lines* show the impression left by them on the substrate. From Gans (1962).

Allowing the snake to cross smooth surfaces, both (concertine and rectilinear locomotion) have low maximum speeds; the limits are established by the alternate nature of the body movement and by the necessity of strict differentiation of zones of static friction and friction of sliding. A significantly greater speed is attained by sidewinding which, unlike the preceding, occurs only in snakes. Here, the animal does not generate any lateral forces on the substrate but each point of the body pases independently. Movement is uniform but static friction and friction of sliding are used differently. Movement takes place under a sharp angle posterior to the longer body axis (Figure 39). Starting from a stretched position with the body in complete contact, the snake raises its head and afterwards the entire front portion of the body and carries it in the air (sometimes sliding on the surface) to another position on the substrate. Then it does the same with the remaining portions of the body, carrying them section after section to a new position as if rolling out from the stationary portion in front and to the side during the course of movement. As a result, parallel prints of the body situated obliquely to the direction of movement appear on the ground. Lateral movement is often observed in vipers living in sand (for example, *Echis carinatus* or *Cerastes cornuta*) or rattlesnakes (*Crotalus cerastes*). Sometimes, this method is even named crotaline. Gray (1946) observed it in *Natrix natrix* (Colubridae) along with serpentine and concertine.

5. CROCODILES

In the literature, very little attention has been devoted to the locomotion of crocodiles (Huene, 1913; Manter, 1940; Schaeffer, 1941; Kalin and Knusel, 1944; Kalin, 1959; Cott, 1961): they live in water and swim with great dexterity. Movements include the formation of lateral bends which pass as waves from anterior to the tail but the amplitude of the bend is significantly greater in the tail which, therefore, also serves as the main locomotory organ (Manter, 1940).

Terrestrial locomotion is not characteristic for crocodiles; they take recourse to it seldom and usually only when forced (Cott, 1961). Huene (1913) working with *Osteolemus*, and Schaeffer (1941) after observing the alligator differentiate two methods of movement on land. During slower movement, the body is carried quite close to the ground, the tail is dragged, the abdomen sometimes leaves an impression, the limbs act in the manner usual to reptiles i.e., their proximal portions, like lizards', move almost in a horizontal plane. During fast movement, on the other hand, the body is raised high, the limbs are straighter and move closer to a vertical plane. The thigh, for example, forms an angle of about 40 to 60° to the vertical plane (Schaeffer, 1941). Both authors mention that the foot in crocodiles is functionally more significant in their locomotion than it is in lizards, in connection with the development of a wide protruberance on the clacaneus. According to Huene, the foot is oriented parallel to the direction of movement throughout propulsion, but Schaeffer considers that a small lateral turn (20 to 30°) is present during the stroke.

In *Crocodylus niloticus*, Cott (1961) mentions only the second method, referring to it as the high walk: the body is raised, the sacrum is held higher than the humerus, the head is somewhat inclined and only the end of the tail is dragged on the ground. The limbs act in diagonal pairs (quite possibly this is trot); the hind foot is placed on the substrate in the digitigrade position, posterior to the forefoot, until its raising, i.e., in the cycle there are partially covered and guadrupedal stages. In our terminology, this would be perhaps a trot. Evidently, a greater part of the animal's weight is carried by the hind limbs, and the forefeet act at best, simply as mobile supports. Schaeffer (1941) presents some frames from a film on alligators (Figure 18, A) from which it may be judged, though not all stages are covered in the given pictures, that the movement continued as a slow trot with dominance of the forelimbs (frames 3 to 6). The latter is connected apparently with an incomplete straightening of the knees of the hind limbs during protraction (frames 6 and 7). Schaeffer while describing the movement of the hind limbs, mentions that unlike tailed amphibians, in the beginning of propulsion the shank of alligators is not directed in front, but is almost vertical in position. This similarly demonstrates the diagram of trajectory (Figure 107, E) in the distal ends of segments of limbs in alligator (Snyder, 1962, Fig. 21), compiled from the same film by Schaeffer: here the knee in its most protracted position, is situated clearly in a flexured state because of which the greater portion of ellipses correspond to the distal ends of shank and the foot lies posterior to the transverse plane passing through the acetabulum. Snyder considers the latter significantly more effective than that observed in lizards.

Information on the speed of movement for crocodiles is practically absent in literature. Only Oliver (1955) mentions that a young alligator passes 0.96 km in an hour.

Cott (1961) mentions two more forms of locomotion for crocodiles on land. One, belly run, is connected with movement along the slope of the bank toward water. The crocodile returns to a creeping movement, sliding on its abdomen with the help of the laterally stretched limbs acting much like paddles. The slide on the abdomen occurs with a greater speed than a high walk. The second gait, gallop, is met extremely rarely and only in small animals (1 to 2 m) suddenly moving from a state of sleep. In this, a relatively higher speed is developed, about 11 to 13 km per hour. Here the fore and hind limbs act in pairs. The body is pushed forward by both hind limbs whereas the forelimbs are stretched in front for support; while the latter are still in place, the hind feet are carried forward. The author compares the crocodile moving to the gallop of a squirrel. It might be added that *Osteolemus* may jump, springing with all four limbs simultaneously, but in this instance it lands not on the forefeet but on the abdomen (Huene, 1913).

Extant reptiles constitute a very small part of this once widespread group and to arrive at any conclusion in regard to the locomotion of fossil forms is very difficult indeed. The study of locomotion for the latter is, at present, the same as studying the morphology of the locomotory apparatus and its evolution. Several interesting investigations were conducted along this line (Huene, 1908; Abel, 1912; Watson, 1917; Gregory and Camp, 1918; Romer, 1922, 1956; Miner, 1925; Schaeffer, 1941; and several others). However, mainly the biomechanical peculiarities of the skeleton are described without reference to the forms of movement. Only a very limited number of works touch specially on the gaits of extinct reptiles (Dollo, 1905; Hay, 1910; Soergel, 1925; Gilmore, 1927; Peabody, 1948; Howell, 1944; Gregory, 1951; Bock, 1952) and on their other locomotory adaptations (Dechaseaux, 1959; Fletcher, 1959; Wilfarth, 1949; Watson, 1951). A part of these is based on the study of fossilized impressions, and some on the similarities to extant animals which can be observed from the study of the skeleton. For our purpose, there is no necessity to give a review of works of this kind.

* * *

In concluding this review of literature, it is necessary to state that from what has been mentioned earlier, one might get a false impression about the relative success of the research done on locomotion of animals. In fact, much of the data could obtain its due significance only in the course of preparing the present book. On the basis of general systems of symmetrical locomotion (Part I), it is clear that the disconnected comments by several authors should be interpreted as remarks that for salamanders, two forms of walk are characteristic (slow and fast); these correspond to our very slow and slow trot-like walks. But for reptiles in addition to the walk, there is the trot with a tendency for the hind limbs in the diagonal touch down earlier and liftoff later than the forelimbs (our fast trot with predominance of hind limbs).

Now it is clear that it is a mistake to ascribe the movement of a trot to amphibians and a running walk to lizards. In fact, the following should be considered as proven earlier. Locomotion in lower tetrapods seems to be symmetrical and accomplished, as a rule, on the basis of a diagonal sequence. However, it can change under experimental conditions and alteration of natural habitat, as in the case of sea turtles, flying lizards and birds. The reasons for the analogous acquisition of asymmetrical locomotion by frogs are still subject to much discussion. It is solidly established that an increase in speed of locomotion by the walk is followed in amphibians and reptiles by some change in gaits toward the trot.

CHAPTER IV

THE MATERIAL AND METHODS OF ANALYSIS

The basis of our material is field diaries kept for 1954, 1955 and 1959 containing observations on locomotion of lizards in the Kara Kum; the results of a special study conducted on impression tracks, speed of movements, and size of lizards in sandy deserts (1961), motion pictures of lizards under field conditions (1959) and salamanders and lizards in the laboratory (1965); and finally, an analysis of the movement of Komodo monitor filmed by a special expedition of the French National Museum of Natural History ("Dragon of the Island of Komodo") and the films of I.S. Darevskii (Zoological Institute, Academy of Sciences, USSR), at the time of an expedition to Indonesia (1963).

Study of Lizard Locomotion Under Field Conditions

The main problems in studying impression tracks of lizards and the methods for doing so are discussed in detail in Chapter V. Speed of movement is determined by clocking the time of a run with a stopwatch and measuring the distance from the impressions on the substrate. Separate portions of impression tracks were photographed and measured. The number of double steps were counted for the entire distance covered (locomotory cycles; this makes it possible to determine the average indices of non-uniform movement, the average duration of cycle, and so on. Animals, as a rule, were caught and measured in advance. The period of captivity for the animals was never more than one day. Only slow moving lizards could be measured directly by clocking locomotion.

Errors in measurements of speed by such methods are not great. The duration of cycles counted from impressions is similar to those counted in motion picture stills. Factors which alter locomotion in lizards and which are important considerations in studying locomotion under field and laboratory conditions have already been discussed (see p. 122). However, it is important to mention that errors in measuring speed are inversely proportional to distance, but these need to be neglected as the run of lizards often does not exceed 2 to 3 m. However, it is necessary to always keep in mind the relative nature of the data obtained.

Filming in the Field

For shooting under field conditions, a "Kieve-16 S" camera was used with a film speed of 64 frames per second. This apparatus has several advantages: lightness of weight, a significantly higher speed of photography, 16 mm film, and fewer shortcomings such as parallax, lack of confidence that the film speed exactly correspond to the given value, and the generally known inefficiency of the shutter during increased speed of film, etc. Some shortcomings in field shooting are in general difficult to overcome. These are an absence of a suitable scale for counting absolute speed of locomotion in connection with the movement of lizards at an angle to the apparatus and the movement of the apparatus after the animals which changes the position even of accidental orientators. This is also the problem of photographing animals from above which frequently does not permit complete deciphering of the limb movements as the latter are masked by the body. The advantage of field shots is the possibility of recording on film significant portions of the movement of lizards under natural conditions, and not just one or two locomotory cycles. However, shooting with a telephoto lens (and deciphering the film needs a larger scale), makes it very difficult to capture the very fast movement of lizards. Usually, it is possible to photograph only the beginning or the end of the run where the speed is non-uniform. The basic disadvantage of shooting in the field is insufficient film speed which causes a blurred image[1] and, secondly, increaes significantly the possibility of error

[1]In deciphering the film, lack of focus plays a particularly positive role: distal segments of limbs are somewhat blurred during the moment of protraction when the

during the calculation of the duration of the stages in a cycle. It is enough to mention that the duration of one cycle of a fast run for toad-headed lizards is estimated as 0.1 to 0.2 seconds, i.e., when the speed of film is 64 frames per second, one cycle occupies 6 to 12 frames. In this connection it becomes necessary to consider several figures by which we will operate only tentatively. For future work, it is desirable that cameras with a shooting speed of 200 to 300 frames per second be used.

A series of pictures capturing the movement of Komodo monitor obtained by Darevskii were taken with 8 mm film, using an "Admira" movie camera with a film speed of 64 frames per second. The size of the *Varanus* was sufficient for a large-sized image on the film and thus adequate for a detailed deciphering. However for smaller animals, an 8 mm camera should not be used. The shooting speed of the French film was perhaps 24 frames per second.

Filming in the Laboratory

A portion of the laboratory films were also made with a "Kieve-16 S" camera at a speed of 48 or 64 frames per second. A very detailed scale was used for the determination of absolute speed of movement: filming was done from above on a light field with a grid of 0.5 cm divisions. A part of the filming was conducted by P.P. Gambaryan (Zoological Institute, Academy of Sciences, USSR) with a scale less suited to such small animals (10 cm); however, the use of a special "Pentaflex-16" and "Pentaflex-16 SP" made it possible to not only obtain film with high speed (from 70 to 90 frames per second), but to get a time scale with an accuracy of about 0.01 seconds. Based on the time calculations in Gambaryan's films, the accuracy of corresponding calculations in the field shootings may also be determined.

Other advantages of laboratory filming are: the positioning of the apparatus at the level of the moving animal which permits a comparatively accurate fixing of the moment of liftoff and touch down of the limbs;[2] and the possibility of photographing the animal from above and from the side simultaneously on the same film by using mirrors. The disadvantages of the laboratory method are clearly: the artificial nature of the substrate; use of animals kept in captivity for quite some time; an insufficient space for running with the result that usually the movement of the animal is somewhat un-uniform

speed of their movement much exceeds the speed of displacement of the body. On the other hand, during retraction they become sharper.

[2]Since it is not always possible to make lizards walk in a particular direction, Snyder (1949, 1952) and Urban (1965) with the purpose of restricting the course used a special box with transparent walls, the floor of which was covered with emery paper or sand. This made it possible to shoot from the sides, the top, the back and the front. The basic inconvenience was that the running track could not exceed 1 to 3 m. In our work, we did not have such an adaptation.

in the camera field; the impossibility of swiftly swinging the camera after the animal and fixing in this way a few successive locomotory cycles; variations in the film speed (increase after switching on, etc.) leading to a disproportionate number of frames to absolute time which greatly disturbs calculations and leads in the last analysis to a large consumption of film.

All this requires careful attention for future work; selection of a suitable movie camera (with a time unit), maximum closeness to field conditions, and so on. It is necessary to take into account Snyder's experience (1952); he shot lizards at a speed between 1,000 to 1,500 frames per second. Only in this case, is it possible to observe the work of each segment of the limbs.

Preliminary Processing of Motion Pictures

Processing of motion pictures is presently very simple. The film is cut into series of consecutive stills representing the movement of any one animal. Each series is indexed; this consists of words corresponding to the type of animal, figures showing the number of specimens, and the numerical order of the series.[3] Each tenth still is numbered, each fifth one is marked with a dot.

Defining Locomotory Forms

By studying each series of film with a magnifying glass, the plan of support for each still can be described in a sequence. On the basis of an entire series, a conclusion can be made about the form of movement according to the system suggested in the first part of this work. During this, it is important to bear in mind that the film examined still does not present the complete plan of the locomotory cycle. Very often, particularly with low-speed film, short periods of tri- or quadrupodal stages fall out, but as a rule, not for the whole series. So, in the film given by Urban (1965) and Snyder (1952), plans of support for this or that gait represent not the stages of one cycle sequence, but rather stages fixed by the movie camera. In identifying gait, it is necessary to remember that the occurrence of secondary uni- or tripodal stages somewhere in the series, makes it possible, almost without error to identify the fast trot with predominance of hind limbs, slow trot-like walk, or slow trot with predominance of fore or hind limbs. At the same time, the first uni- and tripodal stages themselves may still serve as an argument in favor of one of these gaits. Sometimes missing stages may be restored during a comparison of adjacent stills; for example, a frame wherein one of the diagonal limbs occurs in the air close to the substrate, followed by a frame

[3]B—fast barb; D—long-legged scink; K—Komodo monitor; C—scinco gecko; Y—toad-headed lizards; S—spotted salamander.

wherein both feet are already in contact with the ground. In this case, it may be confidently said that the missing support stage is that of only one limb. In practice, the continuity of such reconstructed stages was thought to be equal to a half frame.

After reconstruction, if it is necessary and sufficiently justifiable, the continuity of each stage in the row of successive cycles, consisting of a series, is determined. In all events when the speed of film is uniform, the continuity of stages at this point is better expressed in number of frames. If the speed of the film changes, calculations are complicated. During shooting by special camera in the laboratory, time is determined by the timer unit which leaves dark and light intervals at the rate of 50 frames per second on the margins of films.

Drawing Locomotory Diagrams

By roughly writing the plans of support for successive stages where their continuity is shown, the series is constructed on graph paper by the method suggested in Part I. Depending, upon the length of the series and the continuity of the shortest stages of the cycle, which on the diagram should not be less than 0.25 cm, a scale of two or four frames per centimeter is used. Diagrams of series represent the main form in which material on animal locomotion is shown. It reflects the duration of support and transport of each limb, duration of each stage of the cycle, their order of change, etc. All further calculations are done directly from the diagram.

The entire series is divided in such a way that the maximum number of complete cycles can be determined from it. The latter are counted from the beginning of any stage. The order number of the cycle is showing Roman numerals standing over the diagram to the left of the vertical arrow, which separates each cycle (Figure 40). Small Arabic numbers over the diagram represent the order number of a frame (each 10th and occasionally the 20th are shown). Arabic figures on white portions inside the diagram on the white portion of the notation line characterize the rhythm of limb action. It is calculated in relation to the preceding support time to the subsequent transport time, on the portion of which stands the index of rhythm and is given with accuracy up to 0.1. The values of the rhythms of locomotion are shown above and below the diagram in percentages. To calculate these, the entire series is broken into portions (not shown on the diagram) limited by the middle sections, characterizing the transport time of the hind limbs. Each portion corresponds to the duration of half a locomotory cycle: *LH-LF-RH* or *RH-RF-LH*. During this, it is necessary to consider that the division of a series into full cycles and half-cycles does not coincide with each other. The rhythm of locomotion is determined by the ratio of interval between the movements of diagonally situated limbs (similarly, for average times

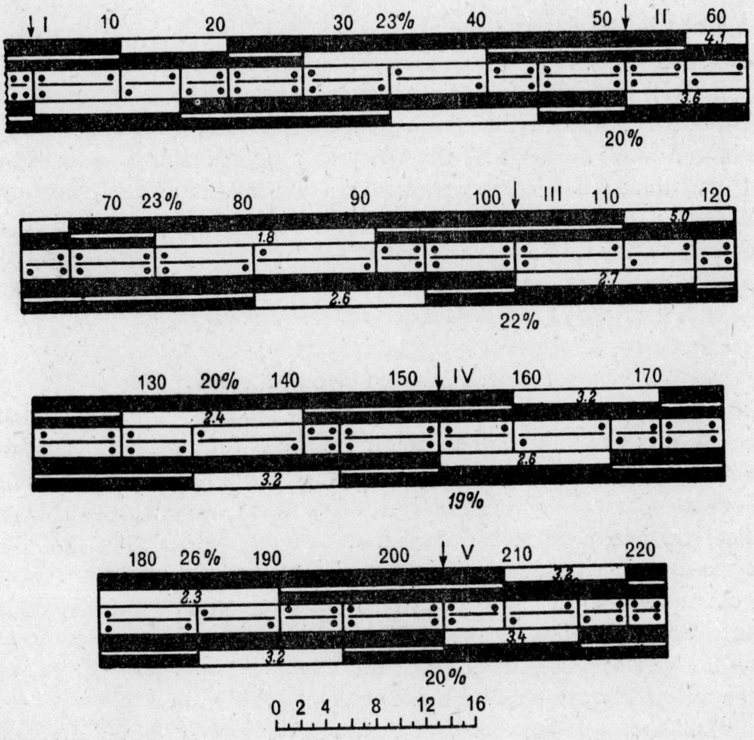

Figure 40. Diagram of a slow trot-like walk of salamander (*Salamandra salamandra*) during an approximate speed of 0.06 to 0.08 m per second. *In the diagram are reflected 1 to 222 frames of series S2-No. 3; scale shows the number of frames per unit length; film speed, 64 frames per second;* arrows—*limits between separate cycles;* Roman numerals—*order number of cycles;* Arabic numbers above the diagram—*order number of frames;* inside the diagram—*rhythm of action of corresponding limbs;* percentages—*given rhythm of locomotion.*

of transport) to the continuity of the half-cycle. The index of the rhythm of locomotion stands at the beginning of the transport time of the forelimb on that side of the diagram where the work of two of the three limbs taking part in the given half-cycle is registered. The negative value of the rhythm of locomotion points to the disturbance of the diagonal sequence in the limbs action and to a change to lateral sequence.

The rhythms of locomotion and limb actions shown on the diagram reflect the real course of locomotion. Hence from the diagram and speed of film, the absolute value of support-transport time, etc., are easily calculated.

Cyclic Analysis of Locomotory Diagrams

To obtain the general picture of changes of the major characteristics within a film sequence, it is important to calculate each cycle separately. In the special table, the following indices are shown to characterize locomotion for the cycles of a given series of motion pictures: speed of locomotion; duration of cycle; duration of secondary quadrupodal stages, stages of free flight, and diagonal support expressed in percentages of the entire cycle, but the latter also in seconds (total of both stages of cycle); degree of predominance of any limb in each diagonal pair; rhythm of work for each limb separately; rhythm of locomotion divided into the first and second half-cycle. At the end, the form of locomotion used in both halves of the cycle is shown. Throughout this, it is necessary to keep in mind that the locomotory cycle similar to that accepted on the diagram layout, corresponds to the full cycle of work for only one of the four limbs. The remaining extend into adjacent cycles. As it is not advisable to count the cycles for each limb separately, more so since the portion of increase characterizing the movement may be obtained only on considering the work of all limbs together, then one must calculate the time of support, transport, and so on, conditionally presenting the cycle as an elementary unit in the uniform process of locomotion. In such cases, the real duration of time is not considered, e.g., of transport, but the general duration in the cycle of time during which the given limb does not touch the substrate. Thus, the numerical data forming the basis of the additional suggested tables, are entirely relative. It is likewise important to add that separate indices may change depending on the method of separating the series into cycles. All this is important to remember, considering what questions a given figure may answer, and where their accuracy is insufficient. The magnitude of error in different diagrams of the tables varies depending on the interval of time between two frames and the speed of movement. The calculation of duration of cycles and stages of diagonal support are most accurate. Here the margin of error in several cases may possibly not exceed 0.01 seconds. The less accurate figures are the ones reflecting in percentages the duration of both stages of free flight and, during very fast movement, of both stages of diagonal support in regard to the entire cycle, and degree of predominance of any limb in the diagonal pair. The latter is determined as the ratio of difference in support time for two limbs of a pair to the support time of the limbs which predominate.[4]

Sequential Drawings from Motion Pictures

A diagram of a series together with the results of its cycle analysis gives

[4]Predominance of forelimb in a diagonal pair is conditionally shown with a minus sign (—).

a sufficiently complete analytical picture of the animal's locomotion. However, it is not less important to imagine how the animal looks during the course of locomotion, how the limbs work during different stages of a cycle, and so on. Therefore, considerable attention in the suggested work is given to sequential drawings prepared with the help of a drawing apparatus and attachment FMN-2. The almost total absence of similar data in other literature underlines the value of this material. Separately taken stills of motion pictures are not worth printing as the image on them is seldom sharp. In connection with this, preference has been given to outline diagrams though separate details are given in schematized form. Special attention to the pictures of stills taken in field conditions, is paid to the animal's shadow as this helps in determining whether the limbs are in contact with the substrate or not.

For this study, quite a wide range of forms of amphibians and reptiles have been used. It is advisable to list them as they occur in the material discussed.

Chapter V

THE LOCOMOTORY FEATURES OF SALAMANDERS
(Spotted Salamander Used as an Example)

As the locomotion of amphibians is easier studied, as a whole, than that of reptiles, the main stress here is given to clarifying questions connected with the forms of locomotion which may throw light on the origin of locomotion for reptiles. The single object of this research was the spotted salamander (*Salamandra salamandra*) as this form is more photogenic than newts, moves better on dry land, and furthermore, is more readily available. The movements of four specimens of salamander were studied exclusively with the help of high-speed motion pictures under laboratory conditions. In all, eleven series of cinema shots were analyzed. Shooting speed varied: in series S1-Nos. 1-3 and S2-Nos. 2 and 8, 48 frames per second; in series S2-No. 3, 64 frames per second; in series S3-Nos. 1-2, about 70 frames per second; in series S4-Nos. 1-3, 67 frames per second. Animals moved on a solid substrate, a wooden platform, or on a paper covering the glass of the copying table. Unfortunately, during the preparation of the present manuscript for publication, the number of photographs had to be much reduced. Large portions of diagrams of series were omitted (see Sukhanov, 1967b). Nevertheless, the results of the cycle analysis of these series are given in Table 2.

Forms of Locomotion

Salamanders move at a speed of 0.03 to 0.1 m per second. The cycle duration during this reaches 0.7 to 1.6 seconds. In all cases, limbs act in a

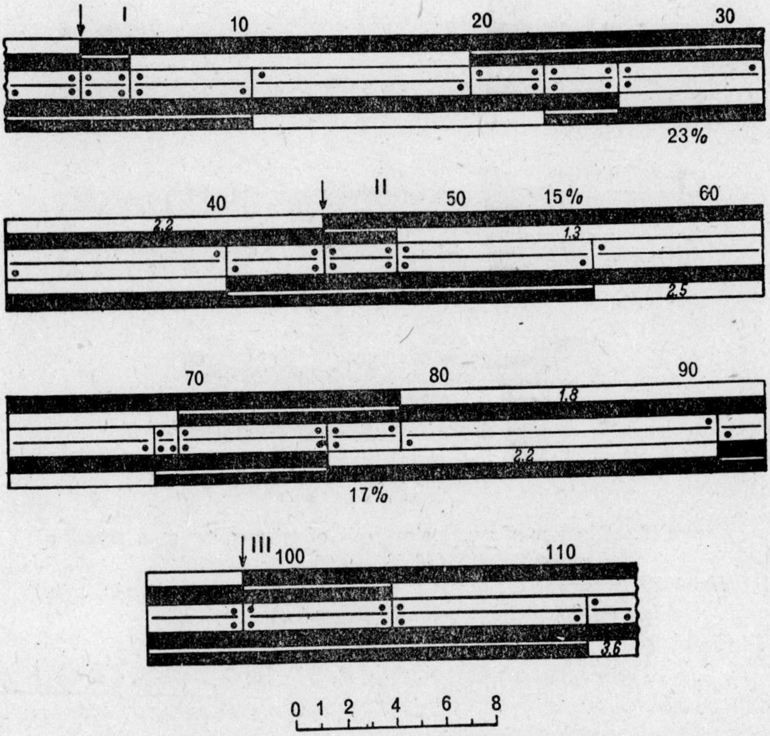

Figure 41. Diagram of a slow trot-like walk of salamander at a speed of movement about 0.09 to 0.1 m per second.
The diagram represents 1 to 113 frames of series S4-No. 1; shooting speed of about 67 frames per second. Legend same as in Figure 40.

symmetrical-diagonal sequence. However, if we force the salamander to walk backwards (walking on heels) by blowing air on it from the front, then the typical lateral sequence is used (see p. 24). Diagonal sequences often disturb acts of motion which are non-locomotory in character. So, during an attempt to force itself into a narrow crack, a salamander may push with both hind limbs simultaneously. When confronted by an obstacle, the animal gets over with the forefeet, the hind ones being kept immobile.

An analysis of the diagram shows that the main form of locomotion for salamander is a slow trot-like walk (Table 2): series S1-No. 2, S1-No. 3,

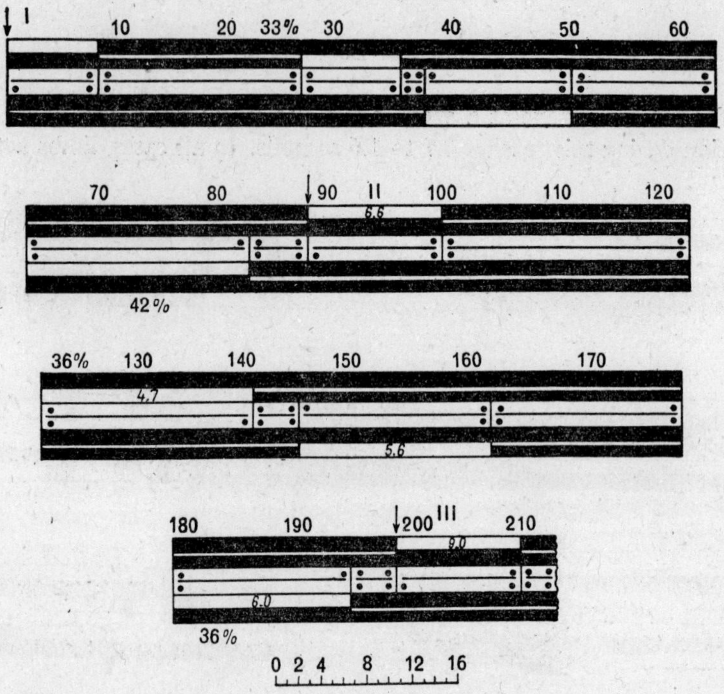

Figure 42. Diagram of a very slow walk of salamandar at a speed of movement about 0.03 to 0.03 m per second.
The diagram represents 1 to 213 frames of series S3-No. 1; shooting speed close to 70 frames per second. Legend same as in Figure 40.

S2-No. 2, S2-No. 3 (Figure 40); S2-No. 8, S3-No. 2, S4-No. 1 (Figure 41); S4-No. 2, S4-No. 3. At lesser speed, a very slow walk is used: series S3-No. 1 (Figure 42). Sometimes a mixed movement is observed: series S1-No. 1 (Figure 43). Thus, the trot is not characteristic of amphibians. This conclusion is supported by photographs and drawings from cinema shots of moving amphibians, whenever these are given in the literature (Schaeffer, 1941, Fig. 5; Barclay, 1946, Figs. 2 and 9; Evans, 1946, Fig. 4; Gray, 1953, Fig. 29). A portion from these is reproduced by us (Figures 30 and 31). However, only Gray's material (Figure 44 of the present work) gives a sufficiently clear picture about the true nature of the locomotory cycle: the newt in his study moved by a slow trot-like walk with the rhythm of locomotion about 30% and the rhythm of limb action from 2.2 to 2.7 (calculations were done from the diagram in Figure 44), i.e., somewhat slower when compared to the norm of the gait and in this form it is closer to a real walk than to a trot (Figure 5). Consequently, references in literature to movement by a trot are misinterpretations. These might be cleared by recognizing the

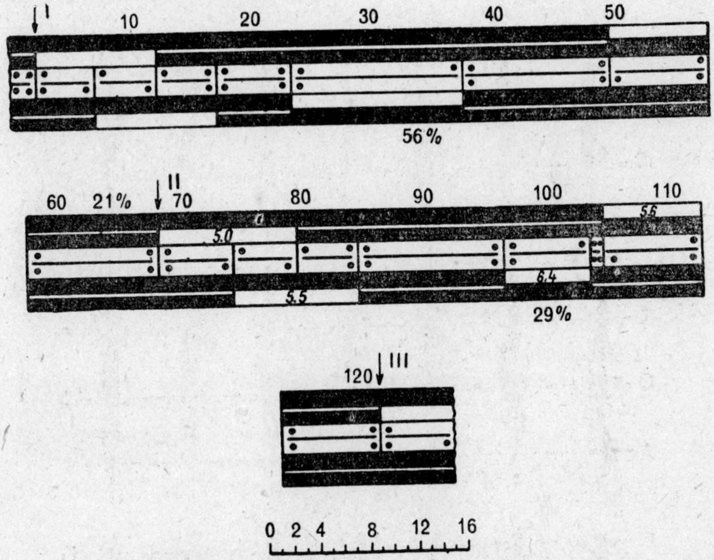

Figure 43. Diagram of movement of salamander during which very slow and slow trot-like walks alternate at a speed of about 0.05 m per second.

The diagram represents 1 to 226 frames of series S1-No. 1; shooting speed was 48 fames per second. Legend same as in Figure 40.

tendency to decrease the interval in the action of diagonal limbs during an increase of speed, insufficient accuracy of observation, and the absence of correctly identifying what ought to be considered a trot. Refusal to use the limbs at maximum speed that was observed in the newt (Evans, 1946) and poorly coordinated faster movement of gill-less salamanders (Peabody, 1959), were first of all caused by the "inability" of amphibians to walk by a trot.

An increase of speed leads to some lengthening of the step. However, as may be judged by our material (series S4-Nos. 1-3; Figure 41 and Table 2), the duration of the cycle during this decreases almost inversely proportional to the speed. Thus, speed in salamanders depends to a greater extent on the frequency of movement of limbs than on the size of the step.

Transposition of the distal regions of limbs takes place at a speed much exceeding the locomotion of the animal. So in series S2-No. 3, the double step varies from 6.2 to 7.3 cm. Transport time during this is 0.23 to 0.29 seconds, i.e., the speed of foot transposition with regard to the substrate is, on an average, equal to 0.2 to 0.3 m per second. This is four to five times greater than the actual speed of movement of the animal. When the animal slows down in the series S1 No. 1, foot transport speed is determined as

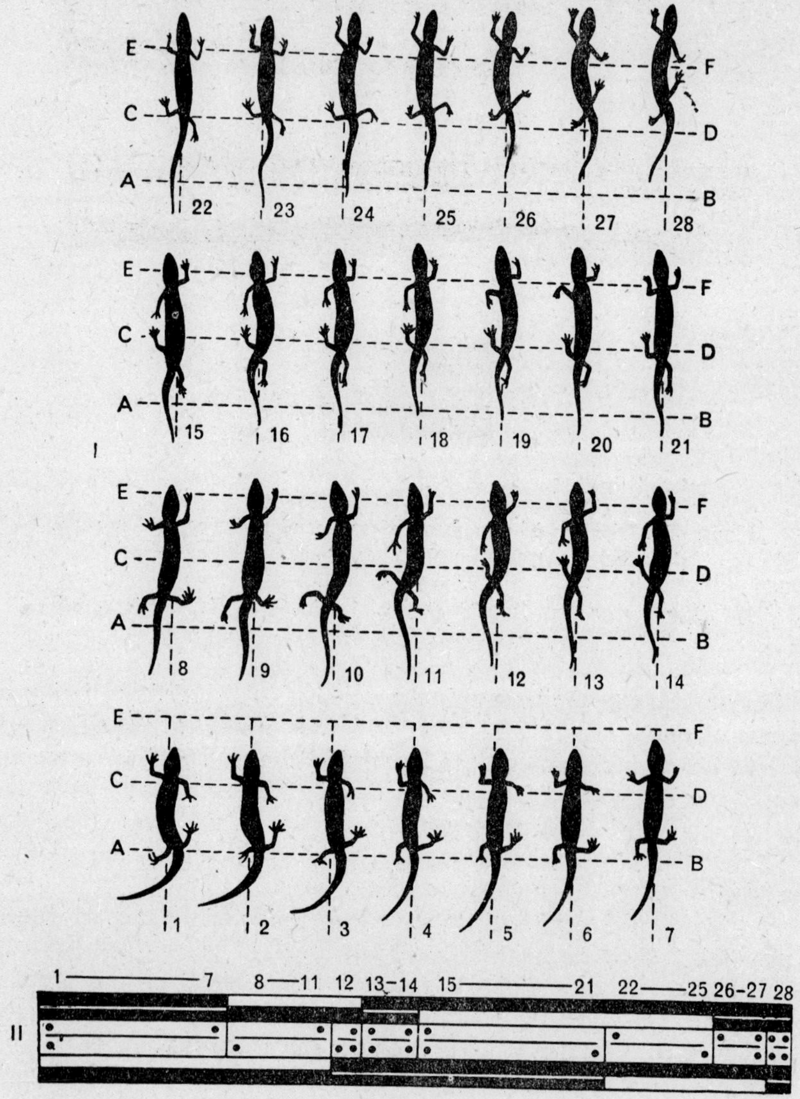

Figure 44. Slow trot-like walk of a newt (*Triturus vulgaris*).
A—28 successive moments during the course of one cycle of movement of newt, according to Gray (1953); B—diagram representing the ratio of different stages in the cycle of movement given in A.

Diagram number	Cycle number	Speed (in m/sec)	Duration of: Cycle (in sec)	Support diagonal (in sec)	Support diagonal (in %)	Secondary four-support stages (in %)	Degree of predominance (%) LH-RF	RH-LF	Rhythm of work of limbs (in conditional units) LH	RH	LF	RF	Rhythm of locomotion in halves of cycle (%) I	II	Form of locomotion in halves of cycle I	II
S1-No 1	I	~0.05	1.38	0.1	8	18	10	0	7.1	5.6	5.6	3.8	15	70	STW	VSW
(43)	II		1.08	0.1	10	2	—2	2	5.4	4.1	3.7	6.7	21	31		,,
S1-No 2	I	~0 05	0.86	0.32	36	—	3	3	4.1	3.1	2.7	3.5	7	12		STW
S1-No 3	I	?	0.79	0.12	16	—	9	—3	8.9	3.2	3.7	4.3	13	24		
S2-No 2	I		1.0	0.4	33	—	3	8	3.3	3.0	2.2	3.0	19	19		
	II		1.02	0.36	35	—	0	8	3.1	3.1	3.1	2.3	18	16		
	III	0.06 average	1.04	0.34	32	—	0	—3	3.2	2.6	2.9	3.2	22	20		
	IV		1.02	0.38	37	—	0	3	2.8	2.5	2.3	2.8	16	20		
	V		1.1	0.36	32	—	7	3	3.8	2.8	2.6	2.8	17	21		
	VI		1.21	0.34	28	—	7	—4	3.8	3.2	3.8	2.9	16	22		
S2-No 3	I	0.08	1.0	0.27	27	—	8	8	4.3	3.0	2.2	2 9	23	23		
(40)	II	0.07	1.04	0.31	30	—	2	11	4.5	2.6	1.8	4.0	18	24		
	III	0 07	1.06	0.32	30	—	14	8	4.6	3.2	2.4	2.4	24	18		
	IV	0.06	1.06	0.32	30	—	5	8	3.2	3.2	2.4	2.7	20	26		
S2-No 8	I	0 08	0.95	0.41	43	—	2	12	3.3	2.4	1.6	3 1	15	15		
	II	0.07	1.14	0.55	48	—	5	2	4.0	1.7	1.6	3.1	11	12		
	III	0.09	0.92	0.28	31	—	7	7	3.6	2.7	2.1	2.7	19	32		
	IV	0.07	1.05	0.53	51	—	6	7	3.6	1.8	1.5	2.8	13	8		
S3-No 1	I	~0.04	1.26	—	—	8	15	—5	11.0	6.8	9.8	4.4	30	43	VSW	VSW
(42)	II	~0.03	1.59	—	—	7	4	2	9 3	6.5	5.8	7.0	40	33	,,	,,
S3-No 2	I	0.07	0.91	0.11	13	—	—5	—4	4.3	3.9	4.8	6.1	19	27	STW	STW
	II	0.06	0.91	0.13	14	—	—9	4	3.6	4.8	3.9	6.1	22	23		
	III	0.05	0.97	0.11	13	—	—2	0	4.2	4.7	4.7	4.7	24	25		
S4-No 1	[	0.1	0.61	0.28	44	—	7	7	2.2	2.4	1.9	1.7	20	24		
(41)	[I	0.09	0.79	0.38	48	—	—8	23	1.8	3.1	1.4	2.3	13	17		
S4-No 2	I	0.08	0.7	0.23	34	—	11	9	2.9	2.9	2.2	1.9	28	21		
	I	0.06	0.85	0.21	23	—	19	7	3.1	3.7	2.9	1.6	37	28		
S4-No 3	I	0.06	1.0	0 18	18	—	0	19	3.8	4.1	1.9	3.8	28	35		
	II	0 06	1.09	0.12	11	—	—3	5	4.2	3.5	2.9	5.1	30	29		

NOTE: STW—Slow trot-like walk; VSW—Very slow walk.

0.3 m per second which is six times greater than the speed of the salamander. Consequently, the slower the locomotion, the greater the difference between the speed of progressive movement of the salamander and the transposition of its limbs.

Locomotory Cycle and Movement Speed

An increase of speed causes several characteristic changes in the locomotory cycle (Figure 45). Within the limits of a very slow, more or less uniform walk, the absolute and relative durations for the majority of stages are reduced, but the secondary quadrupodal stages are decreased much faster. During the transfer to a slow trot-like walk, they disappear completely and are replaced by stages of diagonal support (compare series S3-No. 1 and S3-No. 2). Within the limits of a slow trot-like walk, reduction in the majority of stages continues but the stages of diagonal support grow absolutely and relatively. All this is easy to explain on the basis of Part I in which gaits were considered as the functions of speed and rhythm of locomotion. Increasing speed leads to the change of ratio of support/transport: the relative duration of transport time is increased. Correspondingly, the index of the rhythm of limb action is decreased (Table 2). During movement by a very slow walk

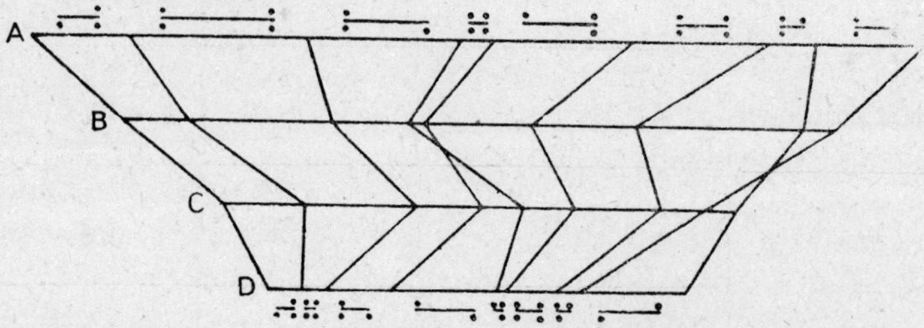

Figure 45. Dependence of relative and absolute duration for separate stages of cycles for salamander on the speed and form of movement.

On the horizontal lines in a fixed scale is given the duration of one locomotory cycle during movement with different speeds: A and B correspond to very slow walk (series S3-No. 1; duration of cycle in frames 111 and 88); C and D correspond to slow trot-like walk; in C, cycle there are 63 frames (series S3-No. 2); in D, 51 frames (series S4-No. 1); above and below the diagram is shown the plan of support for corresponding stages.

this should have led to a uniform reduction of all quadrupodal stages, but the tripodal stages would have been left unchanged (pp. 39-40). During a slow trot-like walk, tripodal stages also would not have been changed but the relative duration of the primary quadrupodal stages (p. 48) would have been reduced. Consequently, increasing speed by itself does not answer for the changes mentioned above in the cycle (Figure 45). They are conditioned by a simultaneous increase of speed and a change of the rhythm of locomotion toward the side of a trot.

Rhythm of Locomotion and Speed

Direct calculations of the rhythm of locomotion (Figures 40-43, Table 2) confirm the conclusion made above. During the slowest movement in the series S3-No. 1 (Figure 42), the rhythm of locomotion is extremely close to the rhythm of walk (30 to 40%). Judging from the rhythm of action for the hind limbs, speed is closer to the norm of a very slow walk. In isolated cases, for example in series S1-No. 1 (Figure 43), the index of the rhythm of locomotion is equal to 56%. But perhaps it is higher because of a change in form of movement during the course of the cycle. This is particularly evident during the analysis of the cycles (Table 2). With an increase of movement up to the level of norm of slow trot-like walk in series S3-No. 2, the rhythm of locomotion in the same animal comes closer to the rhythm of a half-trot. During maximum speed in series S2-No. 8 (Table 2) and S4-No. 1 (Figure 41), the rhythm of locomotion is still closer to the rhythm of a trot, but its index, as a rule, does not exceed the 10% limit. Usually, salamanders move with a rhythm of locomotion in the limits of 15 to 25%. Increase, not connected with the change of the rhythm of locomotion to the side of a trot, is not observed in salamander. The fore and hind limbs of the salamander do not act similarly. As a rule, support time for the hind limbs in the diagonal in relation to transport time is more than for the forelimbs (Table 2). However, the degree of predominance under normal conditions does not exceed 10%. In isolated cases, one of the forefeet may predominate, for example in series S2-No. 2 (Table 2). It is possible that during slower movement, this happens very often.

Variability of the Fundamental Locomotory Parameters

From the diagrams (Figures 40-43) and Table 2, it is clear that the basic characteristics of the process of locomotion are extremely variable. The latter does not seem to be so uniform and coordinated as it often appears. Of course, variation exists within limits, beyond which the movement is improbable, but their range is very high. Besides the orderly changes of basic indices, connected with rhythm and speed, there still exist many accidental variations; their causes are unknown. For example, in series S1-No. 3 (Table 2) judging from the rhythm of limb action, the left diagonal appears slower than the right; in the first half, the predominate role is played by the hind feet, but in the second, by the front one. In the second half of the cycle, the rhythm of locomotion almost corresponds to the norm of a slow trot-like walk, but in the first half, it is significantly closer to the rhythm of a trot, though the duration of this half-cycle is not less than the second. Variation can also extend to the other indices of locomotion. Though on an average, steps of the fore and hind feet during symmetrical locomotion are equal to each other in a given cycle, this condition may be disturbed. Sometimes, it is completely unexplainable beyond its link with the change of speed of movement; one of the limbs may be held in the air longer or, on the other hand, on the ground than the other limbs. The last, for example, explains a sharp upward jump of index of the rhythm of action of the left hind limb in the same series (S1-No. 3). Such examples may be found in countless numbers for lizards as well as salamanders. However, it is important to mention that the limbs of one diagonal are usually more coordinated in their action than the limbs of the other diagonal pair.

Some variations are quite stable and individually characterizable. In one salamander photographed in series S2-Nos. 2, 3, and 8, the index of the rhythm of limb action for the one diagonal (*LH-RF*) is invariably higher than in the other (Figure 40, Table 2). In the other animal (series S1-Nos. 1-3), the rhythm of locomotion calculated from the movements of the right and left hind limbs is invariably closer to the rhythm of walk than the rhythm of the same half cycle where both left and right hind feet (Figure 43, Table 2) take part. One gets the impression that the right hind limb follows after the left one slightly ahead of time.

As a result, the problem remains to discover in the mass of figures (Table 2) the orderly variations of the basic characteristics of the locomotory process, to give reasons for them, and to compare these with those brought forward in theoretical discussions. In a given case, it is advisable to express the dependence of any index of locomotion upon this or that factor through the system of coordination. This has already been broadly done (Part I). It is most important to show on the maximum generalized figured material, how the tendency in the change of basic indices among accidental variations is realized.

Accidental non-uniformity in locomotion is not a new phenomenon. Often an adaptive significance is discovered in it. Thus, Nursall (1958) determined such non-uniformity in fishes as a continuous adaptation of the animal to fast changing environmental conditions. But the question naturally arises: are we not ascribing excessive adaptations to many animals. In attempting to explain any morphological structure in the locomotory apparatus, we always start by saying that they should provide the ideal movement, maximum economy, maximum uniformity, and so on. But it appears correct to consider that the degree of adaptation itself is laid during the course of evolution. In this case, some variation in the movement of lower tetrapods should be considered as the sign of a relatively low organization.

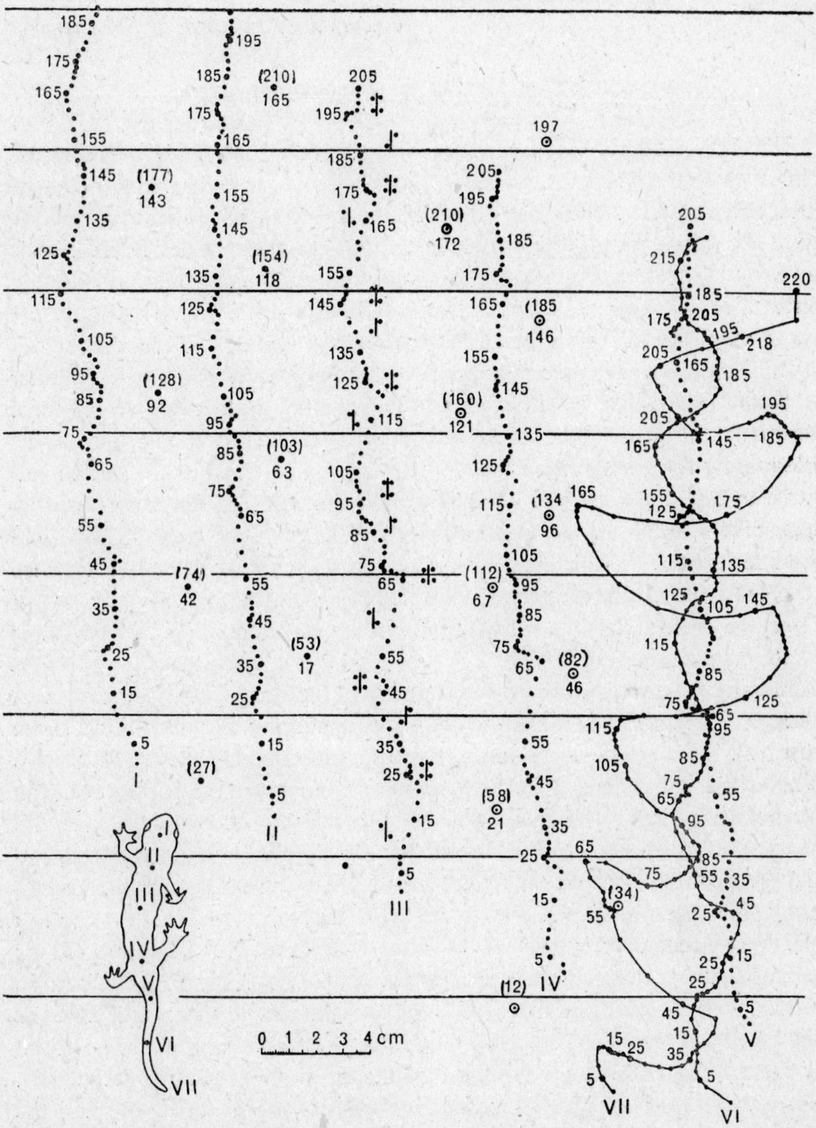

Figure 46. Trajectories of displacements relative to the substrate of 7 dots situated on the axes of the body of a salamander, during its movement by trot-like walk (series S2-No. 3).

Dots : I—in the middle of the head; II—in the pectoral region; III—at mid-body; IV—over the pelvis; V—near the base of the tail; VI—in the middle of the tail; VII—tip of the tail taken as the dot. Each successive trajectory of the first five dots is replaced relative to the preceding, to the right so as not to complicate the general picture. Each trajectory consists of dots marking the position of corresponding dots on the body through one frame (order number of frames in the series are shown for each tenth frame; if the count starts from five : 5th, 15th, 25th, and so on). Place of contact of fore and hind limbs (position of the main II finger in the forefoot and IV in the hind one is shown by the circles of relative trajectory displacement of dots in the pectoral region and pelvic region respectively; figures under *these show the moment of landing (number of frame* above *these—in brackets—the moment of disconnection from the substrate). For orientation of several with the trajectory dot standing in the middle of the body, the support plan of stages is given in which the animal is situated at the moment.*

Speed Alterations During the Locomotory Cycle

The salamander's speed of locomotion changes are orderly during the cycle. It decreases when the animal is supported on four limbs and is increased at that stage where at least one foot is in the air. This is well demonstrated in Figure 46 where transference relative to the substrate (series S2-No. 3) is shown by separate points on the body of the salamander. Before filming, several dots of white poster paint were dabbed on the animal between the eyes, in the pectoral region, at midbody, over the pelvis, and two on the tail (which divided the animal into approximately three equal portions). Filming was done from above against a grid background (graduation of 0.5 cm). Afterwards, the image from the motion picture was projected on graph paper. Subsequently for each second frame, the position of the dots on the animal relative to the substrate was marked on the diagram. In order to keep the diagram from becoming too complicated, the trajectory of the successive dots was shifted to the right (except for the tail dots, including its tip). The place on the substrate of the supporting forelimbs (in relation to trajectory dot in the pectoral region) and that of the hind limb (dot on the pelvis) are similarly marked on the diagram.

Judging from the nature of the trajectory, the dot at midbody displaces the largest distance in comparison with the remaining dots excluding those on the tail. During this, the points on the diagram making the trajectory are situated either more densely or farther apart. Comparing the outline with the corresponding diagram (Figures 46, 40), it may be concluded that the concentration (of points) in the trajectories correspond in time to the quadrupodal stages of the cycle, the sparseness to stages of diagonal support. Consequently, the speed of movement in the cycle decreases twice and increases twice. This peculiarity in the locomotion of animals may be explained by referring again to the material given by Barclay (1946). Figure 33, C, shows the change of longitudinal forces developed separately by the right and left limbs on the substrate during the cycle.[1] The diagram (Figure 33, D) shows how these force changes are combined with the support plan of stages of a cycle, starting with the quadrupodal stage where the right hind limb and the left forelimb have just landed. The latter exert a stopping action, more than the hind limb and much exceeding the propulsive strength of the left hind foot, which already begins liftoff before the end of retraction, and by the forelimb which just lifts from the substrate. On the curve (Figure 33, B) showing the total force, the quadrupodal stage corresponds to the deep dip. Maximum increasing force is observed toward the beginning of the diagonal support

[1]Barclay resolves this situation by saying that the limbs of both sides work similarly. As has already been mentioned, this seems to be more an exception than the rule. But introducing these changes in the diagram does not change the essence of the work.

when the right hind limb gives acceleration to the animal. To do this, it is helped by the left forefoot. In the second half-cycle, the limbs of the other side act exactly in the same manner. Thus, if the functional axis of the limb (line connecting the acetabulum with the center of support in the foot) lies anterior to the transverse plane passing through the acetabulum (normal plane), then this limb stops the movement. If the limb is taken back behind the normal plane, then it, on the other hand, acts as the one which increases speed. Barclay (see p. 94) describes the variations of increasing and decreasing forces as being of another nature.

The Body's Work During Locomotion

Trajectories of transference of separate dots on the body of the animal (Figure 46) are more or less sinusoid-like lines which add up the progressive movement of each dot in front and its transverse displacement during the bending of the body in the horizontal plane. The amplitude of the transverse variations is minimum in the movement of the pectoral and pelvic region, and maximum in the dots standing at equal distances from the fore and hind limbs and in the tip of the tail. Trajectory of dots at midbody most resembles a sinusoid; however, because of the intracyclic non-uniformity in the speed of movement, the peaks of the sinusoids are slightly sharpened. In each given moment, the direction of the lateral displacement, irrespective of the variations of amplitude, coincides in the head and pectoral area on one side, and at midbody and pelvis on the other. The entire tail bends to the same side as the head. During this, the amplitude of the lateral displacement of the proximal portion is less than the distal.

Thus, an analysis of trajectory confirms the observations of Roos (1964) on the movement of newts: during movement with the help of limbs on land, lateral bends in the body of salamanders are characteristically stationary waves, in the bends of which there is no transverse displacement, but the maximum turning is around the vertical axis. As in newt, the bend of the waves in the spotted salamander lies slightly posterior to the pectoral region and on the base of the tail. However, in the head and the region of the tenth vertebra of the tail, zero nodes are absent in the salamander. Correspondingly, at the moment of maximum bend, the body of the salamander has an appearance of a simple round bracket. In view of an increase in number of nodes, the form of the bend in the newt's body is significantly complex.

In series S2-No. 3, the salamander uses a slow trot-like walk at relatively high speed. Consequently, the interval between the movements of limbs in one diagonal is less here than in a very slow walk. Because of this, and similarly in connection with the complicated accidental deviations of trajectory form, there is no possibility in the given material of establishing authentically, i.e., the difference in time when successive dots on the axis of the animal attain the maximum inclination. However, it seems that the inclination of the head outstrips the body. Consequently, a wave is formed from the front to the back. In the beginning, the front portion of the body bends to the side and one of the forefeet is put forward. Afterwards, the posterior half of the wave is formed and the diagonal hind limb is protracted. A real standing wave, when its formation starts from the bend in the middle is, in principle, possible only during movement by a trot with a simultaneous carrying forward of both limbs of the same diagonal.

Thus, the relation of speed to the formation of stationary waves with the magnitude of interval in the action of diagonal limbs, or in other words, the relation of the speed of movement with the rhythm of locomotion (p. 147) is the result of a primary integration of limb movement and of wave-like bends of the body, i.e., the type of movement seen in fish (wave passing from the front to the back).

The trajectory of displacement of the pelvis is characteristically oriented in relation to the place of contact of the hind limbs with the substrate. The dot in the region of the pelvis passes the peak of the sinusoid for two to three frames up to the release of one of the hind limbs in the moment when the second hind limb, while retracting, passes the normal plane. As a rule, the peak of the sinusoid lies on the line joining the place of contact of right and left limbs. During this, the pelvis is extremely removed from the place of contact for any just-landed forelimb in the position, but closer to the contact of the second. Thus, during retraction of the first limb, the pelvis shifts parallel to the place of contact, but it does not depict an arc with its center in the latter as would be expected; moreover, its movement is continued in the same direction even after liftoff of the second hind limb from the substrate.

On the whole, the activity of the body and limbs of the salamander in the course of one locomotory cycle may be presented in the following manner. In the beginning of the stage of diagonal support, both the body and the tail are straightened to the maximum. While the right foreleg and the left hind one move forward, the body forms a bend, the peak of which is directed toward the right. The head and tail during this are displaced to the left. An active turn of the head via the muscles connecting the skull with the pectoral girdle provides a maximum protraction of the forefoot. The tail is immediately displaced passively because of the protraction of the hind limb and also the strain of the *mm. caudi-femorales*. The moment of maximum bend of the body follows after the landing of the forelimb, but before the landing of the hind one, i.e., it coincides in time with short duration secondary tripodal stages and precedes the quadrupodal one. With the retraction of both limbs, the bending of the body toward the opposite side starts. The turn of the head toward the right allows the right forefoot to retract more than it could have when the head was immobile. The turn of the tail toward the right strengthens the activity of the left *mm. caudi-femorales*, the main retractors for the hind limbs. This turn is completed actively as otherwise, under the influence of contraction by the *mm. caudi-femorales*, the base of the tail could have been drawn in the direction of retraction of the hind limb. The latter is readily observed but occurs at the end of retraction.

* * *

Salamanders, moving with the help of limbs on land, use only the very slow or slow trot-like walk, but not the trot. An increase of speed is followed by a change of support/transport ratio (rhythm of limb action) to the advantage of the latter. The rhythm of locomotion during an increase is always changed toward trot, but its index, as a rule, does not cross the limits of the line corresponding to 10%. The support time of the forelimbs is usually somewhat less than that of the hind ones, i.e., locomotion is completed with small, not more than 10%, predominance by the latter. Besides accidental non-uniformity of movement in the cycle, the reduction of speed at the time of quadrupodal stages is twice observed with its subsequent increase. During the course of locomotion, the body of the salamander forms a bend which may be compared to a stationary wave, the nodes of which are located in the region slightly posterior to the pectoral girdle and in the base of the tail. However, wave formation is from the front to the back such as seen in the breaking of a moving wave. There are only two dots in the body of the salamander which do not experience transverse displacement during bending. The body is straightened in the beginning of the stage of diagonal support. Maximum bending comes in the secondary tripodal stages.

CHAPTER VI

LIZARD TRACKS AS AN INDEX TO THEIR FORMS OF LOCOMOTION

A systematic description of lizard tracks is not given in the available literature despite the fact that this would have been very useful to field zoologists. Similarly, it is not my goal to specifically describe the characteristics of impression tracks of the different forms of lizards but several photographs given below may be useful for field identification. Our main purpose is to explain how the basic elements of tracks change during an increase in speed and to what extent these changes are related to the change in the form of locomotion. The latter is of considerable interest in connection with the study of fossil tracks and the reconstruction of biological characteristics of extinct animals. How speed affects impression tracks is not fully explained. It is generally known only that a rise in speed is connected with an increase of step lengths, as a result of which an uncovered impression may become covered or even overlapped in mammals. Only the increase of a limb swing is put forth to explain an increase of the double step in the track. The effects of other factors are, as a rule, ignored.

The Track and Its Components

The system of measuring the basic components of tracks and the corresponding terminology suggested here (Figure 47) were developed as a result of several years of field work during which it was established what elements reflect more accurately the forms and speed of locomotion. Compared to similar systems used in studying fossil tracks (Peabody, 1948, 1959), it may be mentioned that our system introduces the concept of a *constant step* (*const*) and the *main constituents of a constant step*. The first represents the distance between the impressions of the fore and hind feet of one diagonal left in the course of the locomotion cycle; the second, distance between various impressions but only in the course of movement of the animal. In Figure 47 it can be seen that the basic component is determined as the total of simple step and uncovering during slow movement (A), or as the difference between simple step and the overlapping during fast movement (B).

During the field study of tracks, particularly in sandy deserts where they are extremely short-lived, it is important to remember that there are some measurements which must be recorded in the field, and other important measurements for the complete characterization of locomotion may be obtained later from the field measurements. The field measurements are related to the double step, diagonal step, constant step, *uncovered* or *overlapping*, and *width of tracks*. The derived values are *simple step* (two simple steps consisting of one double)[1] and *lateral support* (total of double step and uncovered or difference of double step and overlapping) and, as already mentioned, the principle constituent of the constant step. The angle of step being a function of the size of the double step and the width of the track is easily determined geometrically and may likewise belong to the derived values.

Research Material

Study of the locomotion of lizards by their tracks determined the selection of specimens. These were inhabitants of sandy deserts—plate-tailed geckos (*Teratoscincus scincus*), retinal barbs (*Eremias grammica*) and toad-headed lizard (*Phrynocephalus mystaceus*), and representatives of the three main systemic groups of our desert lizards—*Gekkonidae, Lacertidae* and *Agamidae*. Additionally, several other lizards were studied from *Agamidae*—toad-headed desert lizard (Phrynocephalus *interscapularis*) and steppe agama (*Agama sanguinolenta*); from *Lacertidae*—striped and fast barbs (*Eremias scripta* and *E. velox*); from *Gekkonidae*—cristadigital gecko (*Crossobamon eversmanni*), Syrian and Caspian ground geckos (*Gymnodactylus russowi*

[1]Here it becomes necessary (from the example of salamander) to neglect the already wellknown and often observed in the field, non-uniformity in the movement where two simple steps may not be equal to each other.

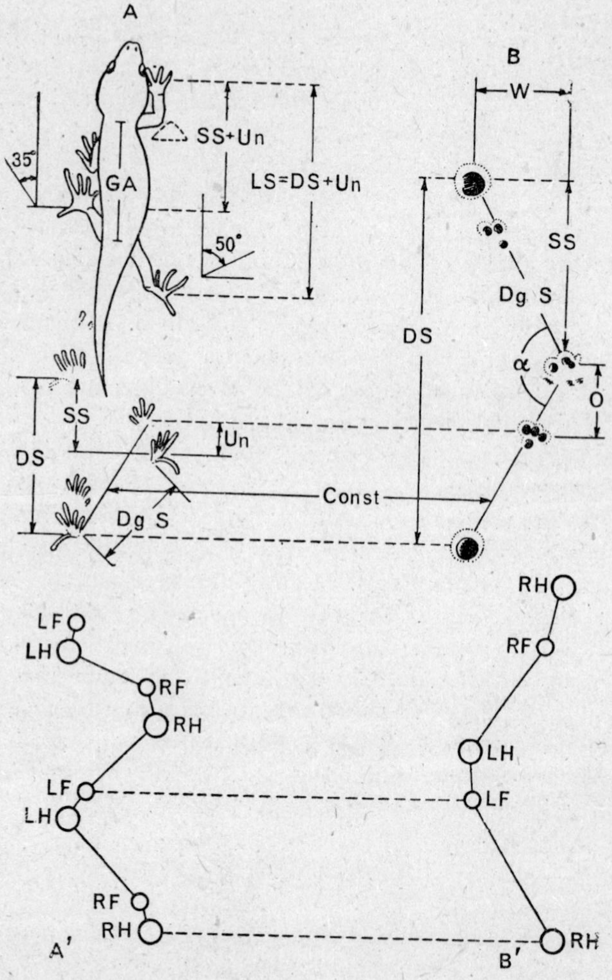

Figure 47. Basic elements of lizard tracks and their ratio during slow and fast movements.

A—track of scinco gecko in slow movement. (A¹—same in schematic form); B and B¹—in fast movement; LS—lateral support; GA—gleno-acetabular distance; DS—double step; Dg S—diagonal step; Un—uncovered; O—overlap; SS—simple step; SS+Un—principle element of constant step; W—width of the impression track; Const—constant step; α—angle of step. The position of the longer axis of finger IV of the hind limb in relation to the direction of the movement in the beginning and in the end of the propulsive period, is indicated in degrees. The remaining legend same as in Figure 1.

and *G. caspius*); from *Scincidae*—long-legged scink (*Eumeces schneideri*) and golden mabuya (*Mabuya aurata*); from *Varanidae*—desert monitor (*Varanus griseus*).

A special study of body and limb proportion was not conducted. Nevertheless, it is advisable to give (Table 3) some tentative figures on several lizards.[2] For our purposes, it is important to underline that in geckos and barbs, the limbs in relation to the body are significantly shorter than in agamids. In plate-tailed geckos, differences in the length of fore and hind limbs are minimum but pro- and epipodial elements are almost equal. However, in the more mobile cristadigital geckos, the hind limbs are longer. Consequently, the

Table 3. Proportions of limb segments to the gleno-acetabular distance (GA) in some lizards

Species	Proportions of limb segments to GA (%)				Relative difference between length of front and hind extremities (%)
	Femur	Shank	Humerus	Forearm	
Teratoscincus scincus . . .	31—34	29—31	26—30	25—30	5—11
Crossobamon eversmanni .	33—37	32—40	28—32	26—29	12—17
Eremias grammica	27—33	30—35	24—28	19—24	13—29
E. velox	30—35	31—40	27—35	23—35	10—20
E. scripta	29—36	31—41	24—30	20—23	13—24
Phrynocephalus mystaceus	37—44	43—53	33—43	31—35	11—22
Ph. interscapularis	43—50	49—60	33—42	26—35	23—40
Agama sanguinolenta . . .	32—36	36—39	32—33	26—28	9—16

NOTE: Differences in the length of both pairs of limbs is evaluated from the length of only the proximal segments.

difference is also greater between the fore and hind limbs. A considerable difference between these is observed in barbs where this is related to the elongation of shank and a shortening of the forearm. The most mobile among them are the striped barbs. The relative length of hind limbs is maximum in it. In agamids, an elongation is apparent in all segments of the limbs but more in the shank and less in the humerus. The differences in length of fore and hind limbs are similar to those in barbs, but in some fast and small forms (desert toad-headed) they may attain a phenomenal size.

Parallel measurements were conducted on the three main groups studied: the speed of movement, the main elements of the track, and several size characteristics of the animal (overall length and length of the body, gleno-acetabular distance, and maximum extension of hind limbs and limbs of one diagonal). Some of the data obtained are summarized in Table 4.

[2]Data obtained on only ten specimens of each species.

Table 4. Speed of movement and basic elements of lizard tracks

Species	Number of specimen	Animal sizes	Speed (in m/sec)	Conditional speed	Duration of cycle (in sec)	DS	Dg S	W	(α) deg	O	Un	Ratio of MSHL to Dg S (in %)	Ratio of LS to MSDL (in %)	const.	Ratio of const. to MSDL (in %)
Phrynocephalus mystaceus	1	SV=10.7, TL=21.5,	3.03	0.19	0.10	30.0	21.3	8.8	120	9.3	—	59	125	11.3	69
		GA=6.6, MSHL=12.5	1.10	0.26	0.22	24.0	15.0	7.5	116	5.8	—	84	110	9.5	55
		MSDL=16.5													
	3	L=8.6, TL=18.9	2.24	0.19	0. 35	30.4	17.5	8.0	128	9.5	—	61	149	8.2	59
	4	L=10.2, TL=21.0	1.80	0.29	0.18	33.0	16.0	8.2	128—136	7.0	—	78	162	9.3	58
	5	L=9.4, TL=20.0	2.05	0.34	0.12	25.1	12.0	?	?	4.0	—	92	144	9.5	65
	6	L=9.8, TL=20.0	2.70	0.21	0.12	33.0	18.5	6.5	136	9.5	—	63	157	9.5	63
	7	L=10.2, TL=21.5,	3.70	0.16	0.11	40.0	21.5	7.5	136—142	13.5	—	54	171	9.0	58
		GA=5.6, MSHL=11.7	3.56	0.15	0.11	39.6	23.0	6.3	142—150	14.0	—	50	165	9.3	60
		MSDL=15.5	2.18	0.18	0.15	32.6	18.0	5.8	136—146	10.5	—	65	143	8.0	52
			1.28	0.29	0.20	26.3	14.0	6.3	124—138	5.5	—	82	134	8.5	55
			1.10	0.31	0.22	24.0	13.0	5.8	124—134	4.5	—	90	126	8.5	55
Eremias grammica	1a	SV=5.2, TL=11.4,	2.4	0.26	0.08	18.7	11.5	4.5	128	4.5	—	72	161	5.5	61
		GA=3.1, MSHL=6.8,	1.46	0.14	0.10	15.3	11.0	5.0	114	5.5	—	62	109	5.0	57
		MSDL=9.0	1.20	0.19	0.14	16.9	9.5	3.5	134	5.3	—	59	126	5.0	57
	2	SV=9.6, TL=26.2	1.35	0.3	0.13	18.0	13.0	6.5	109	3.6	—	62	121	7.5	64
	3	SV=8.8, TL=24.0	3.1	0.2	0.07	22.0	11.0	5.0	130	6.5	—	62	145	7.5	70
Eremias grammica	4	SV=9.3, TL=25.8	2.4	0.28	0.10	24.5	14.0	5.0	136	5.5	—	105	173	9.5	86
		GA—4.8, MSHL=7.6,	0.3	1.00	0.24	7.3	6.0	3.0	100	—	3.8	146	101	7.8	71
		MSDL—11.0													

	5	SV=9.5,TL=26.0	3.48	0.24	0.08	28.4	16.5	4.5	144—146	7.5	—	53	185	7.0	62
		GA=4.8, MSHL=7.6,	0.53	0.55	0.17	9.1	6.0	3.0	114—120	—	0.5	127	85	7.0	62
		MSDL=11.3	0.53	0.50	0.17	8.8	6.5	3.0	111	—	0.5	117	82	6.0	53
			0.51	0.56	0.18	9.0	6.0	?	104	—	0.5	127	84	6.5	58
			0.40	0.59	0.21	8.8	4.5	2.5	?	—	0.8	167	47	6.6	58
Teratoscincus scincus	1	SV=8.9, TL=13.7,	0.21	0.86	0.33	7.0	5.0	3.2	94	—	2.5	123	93	6.2	61
		GA=4.6, MSHL=6.3,	0.19	?	0.35	6.6	4.1	2.8	98	—	?	154	?	5.5	54
		MSDL=10.2	0.15	0.9	0.42	6.3	4.8	2.7	91—98	—	2.5	131	86	6.0	59
	2	SV=8.1, TL=12.5,	1.13	0.35	0.14	15.5	8.5	3.7	130	2.3	—	74	132	6.1	61
		GA=4.2, MSHL=6.2,	0.80	0.31	0.17	13.7	8.0	2.6	138	2.6	—	79	111	5.3	53
		MSDL=10.0	0.68	0.44	0.14	9.2	5.3	3.3	106—114	0.6	—	117	86	5.8	58
			0.65	0.55	0.16	10.2	6.0	3.5	110	—	0.5	104	107	5.8	58
			0.56	0.56	0.16	8.8	5.8	3.5	103	—	0.5	107	93	5.8	58
			0.27	0.74	0.23	6.2	5.0	?	?	—	1.5	124	77	?	?
			0.19	0.65	0.34	6.5	4.5	3.4	94—116	—	1.0	138	75	?	?
	4	SV=7.8, TL=12.8,	1.75	0.25	0.09	16.4	10.0	4.1	122—132	4.0	—	60	130	5.5	58
		GA—4.0, MSHL=6.0,	0.47	0.56	0.18	8.4	5.2	3.6	92—106	—	0.5	115	104	5.2	55
		MSDL=9.5													

NOTE: SV—distance from the tip of snout to vent. TL—distance from the tip of snout to the tip of tail. GA—gleno-acetabular distance. MSHL—maximum swing of hind limbs. MSDL—maximum swing of diagonal front and hind limbs. For remaining designations, see Figure 1. All linear sizes are given in cm.

Speed of Locomotion and Foot Imprints

An increase in speed of locomotion leads not only to a proportional change in the different elements of the track (discussed below), but also to a change in the foot imprint on the sand. In plate-tailed geckos, during slow movement on sand (Figure 48), the prints of each finger of the fore and hind feet are seen. There is a similarly complete print in the tracks of cristadigital geckos (Figure 50), of retinal barbs (Figure 51), and even of toad-headed lizards (Figure 55). As a rule, a speed increase leads to a deepening of the print, the disappearance of prints for separate fingers, and a change of imprint to a round hole (Figure 52, C; Figure 57, B) often with a small similar round hole somewhat toward the back and outside of the main impression. Perhaps this is left by finger V.[3]

It is important to mention that the depth of prints during a speed increase is greater in the hind limbs than in the forelimbs. For example, for scinco geckos (Figure 49, C) at a speed of 0.8 m per second, the impression of the hind limbs already presents a deep cavity, but the forelimbs still retain the imprints of each finger. At a speed of about 1.75 m per second, the impression of the forefoot becomes more general, though it consists of separate cavities (Figure 49, D). In other forms with greater speeds, the prints of the forefeet may similarly present a round hole, differing from the impression of the hind limb only in size and position (Figures 52, C, 43, 56, B, 57). It is interesting that during slow locomotion in plate-tailed geckos the prints of the forelimbs are sometimes more observable than the prints of the hind limbs (Figure 49, A). This bespeaks something about the greater role of the forelimbs compared to the hind ones during slow movement.

Speed and Disposition of Imprints in Track Conditional Scale of Speeds

An increase in speed of locomotion causes an increase of double and diagonal steps (Table 4) which in its turn leads to a change of ratio between the remaining elements of the track. The imprint of a hind limb initially lies posterior to the imprint of the ipsilateral forelimb (Figure 47, A); the hind foot imprint starts approaching the latter and, eventually, covers it. A further increase of speed may lead to an overlapped impression (Figure 47, B).

[3]Sometimes this hole has an outline with different lengths (Figure 54) depending upon the speed of movement, height of raised limbs over the substrate, etc. The presence of such outlines does not show the great contrast of finger V in comparison with the usual imprint in the form of a round cavity. Such a mistake was perhaps committed by Peabody (1948) in giving the reconstructed limb of *Rotodactylus* the appearance of an archosaur though its impressions are completely lacertoid.

Figure 48. Track of slow moving plate-tailed gecko (*Teratoscincus scincus*), corresponding to the diagram in Figure 47, A.

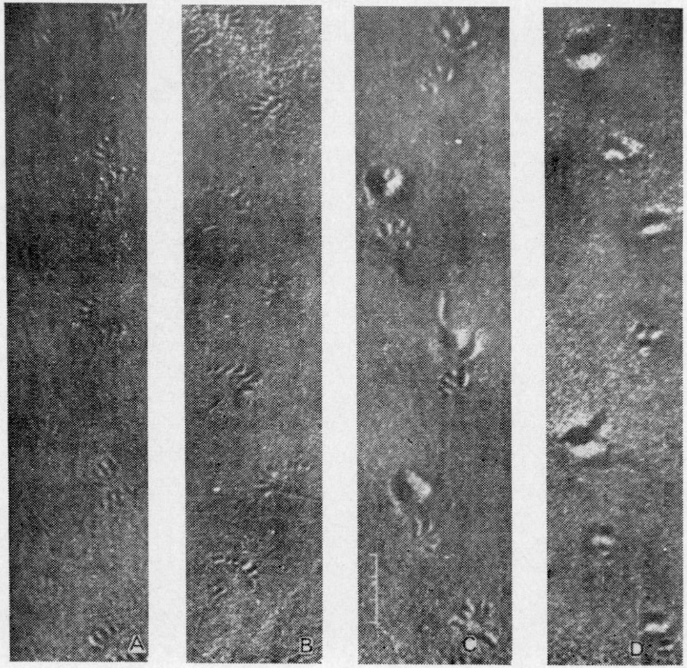

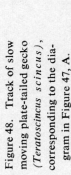

Figure 49. Change of track of plate-tailed gecko during an increase of speed.

A—0.15 m per second (Spec. No. 1); B—0.56 m per second; C—0.8 m per second; (B and C Spec No. 2); D—1.75 m per second (Spec. No. 4). Scale of all photographs is the same. Sizes of animals are shown in Table 2; here and in the next figures each division of the scale corresponds to 1 cm.

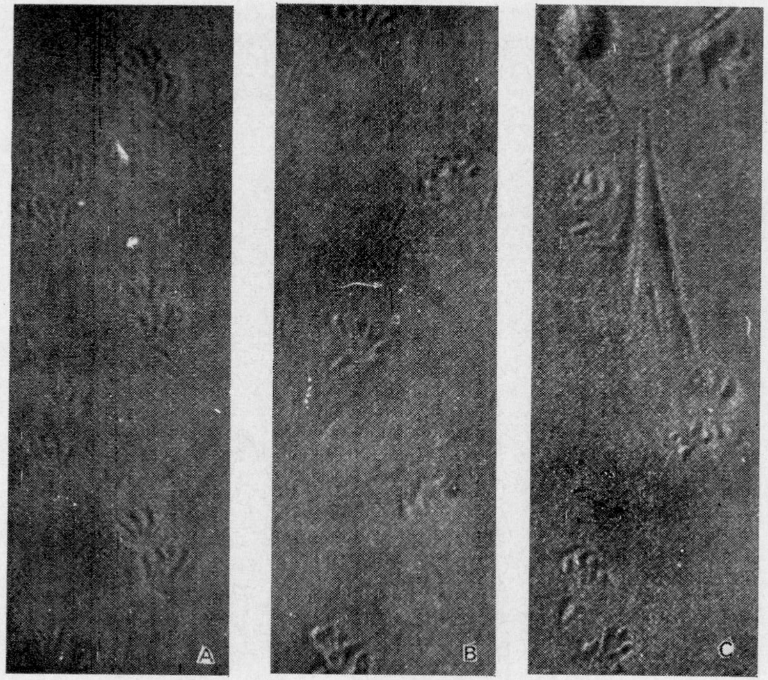

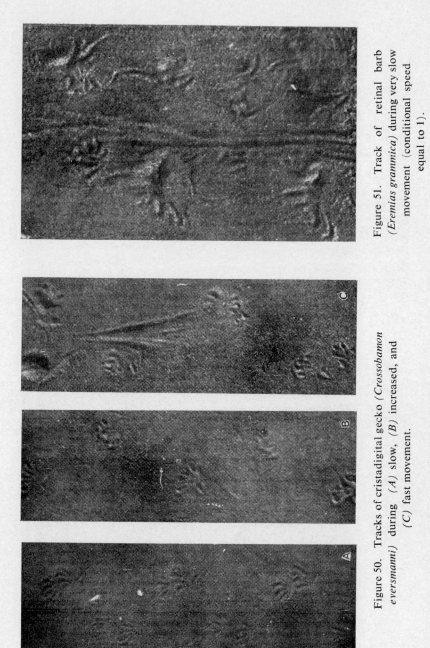

Figure 50. Tracks of cristadigital gecko *(Crossobamon eversmanni)* during *(A)* slow, *(B)* increased, and *(C)* fast movement.

Figure 51. Track of retinal barb *(Eremias grammica)* during very slow movement (conditional speed equal to 1).

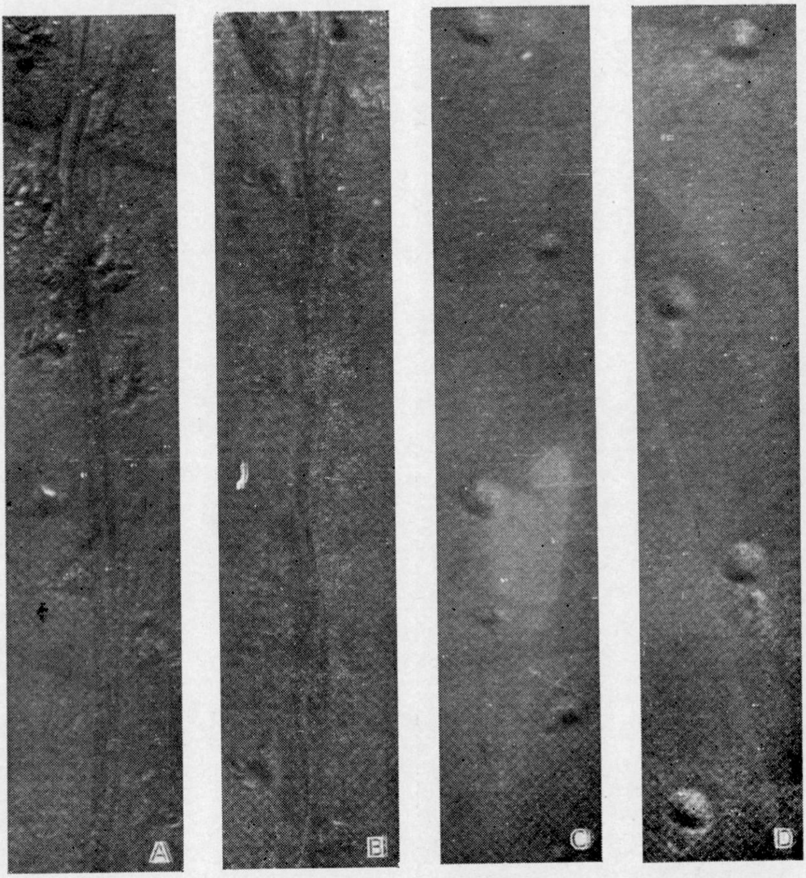

Figure 52. Change of tracks of retinal barbs during increase of speed. *A—0.4 m per second; B—0.53 m per second; C—3.5 m per second (quadrupedal run); D—3.5 m per second (bipedal run). (Spec. No. 5.) Sizes of the animals are given in Table 2.*

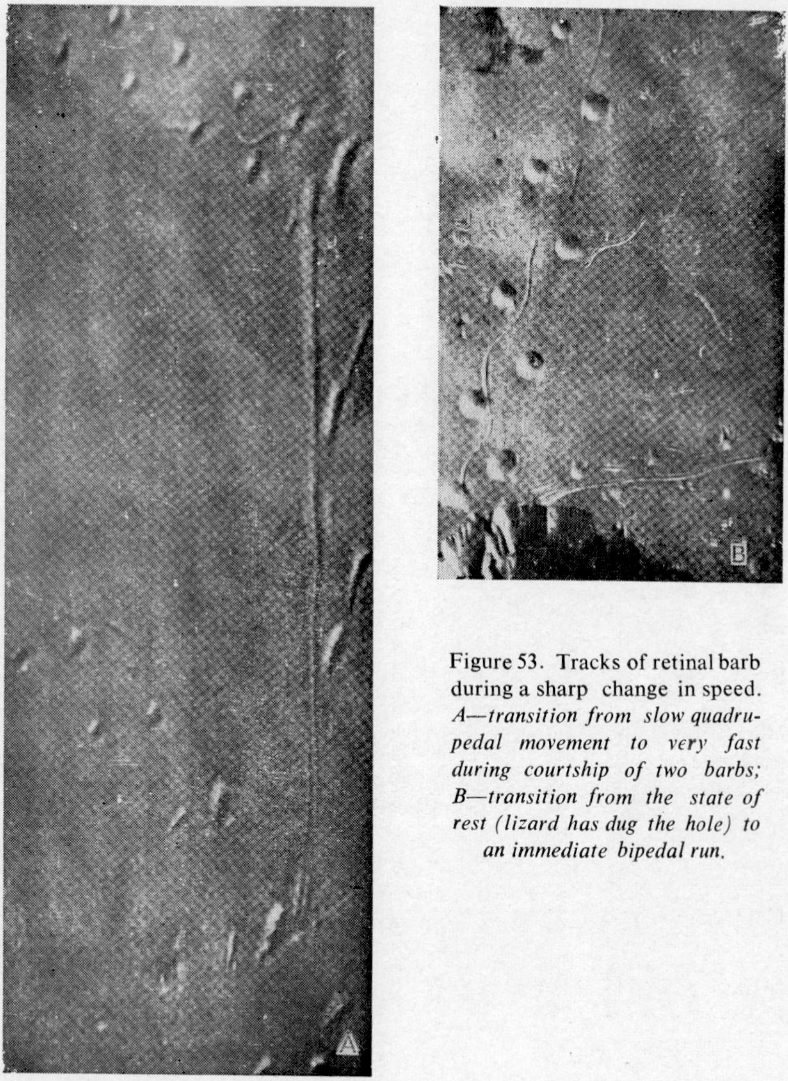

Figure 53. Tracks of retinal barb during a sharp change in speed. *A—transition from slow quadrupedal movement to very fast during courtship of two barbs; B—transition from the state of rest (lizard has dug the hole) to an immediate bipedal run.*

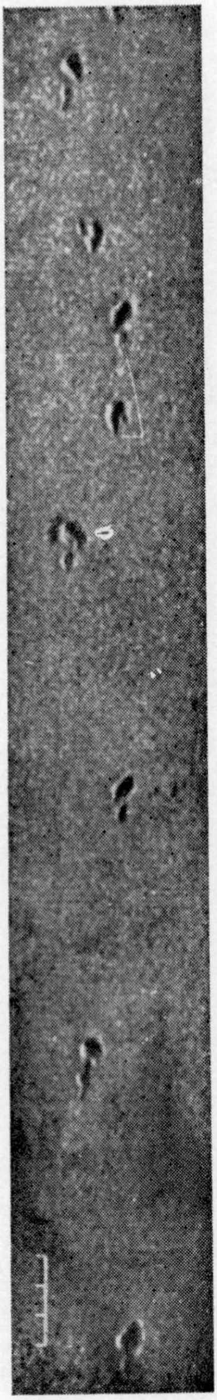

Figure 54. Track of striped barb *(Eremias scripta)* during transition from bipedal run to quadrupedal.

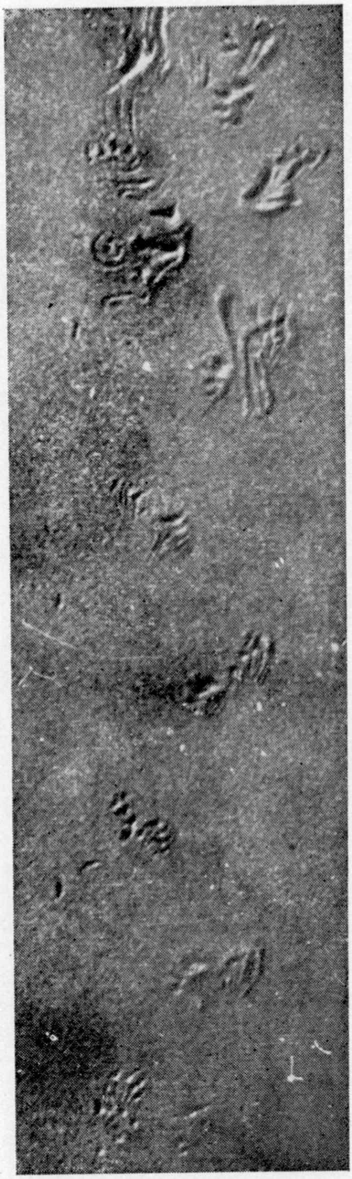

Figure 55. Track of toad-headed lizard *(Phrynocephalus mystaceus)* during speed reduction prior to a stop.

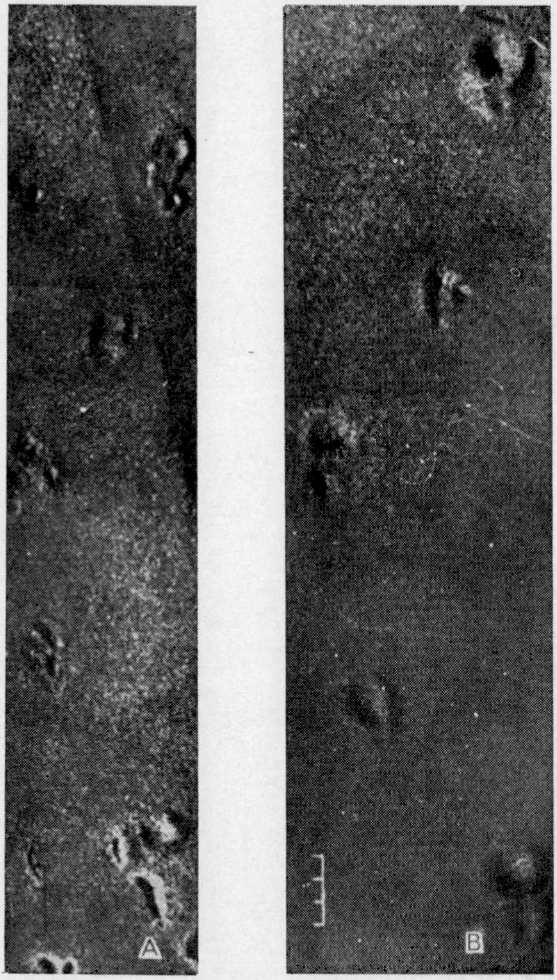

Figure 56. Change of track of toad-headed lizard during an increase of speed.
A—1.8 m per second (Spec. No. 4); B—about 2.6 m per second (Spec. No. 6). Sizes of animals given in Table 2.

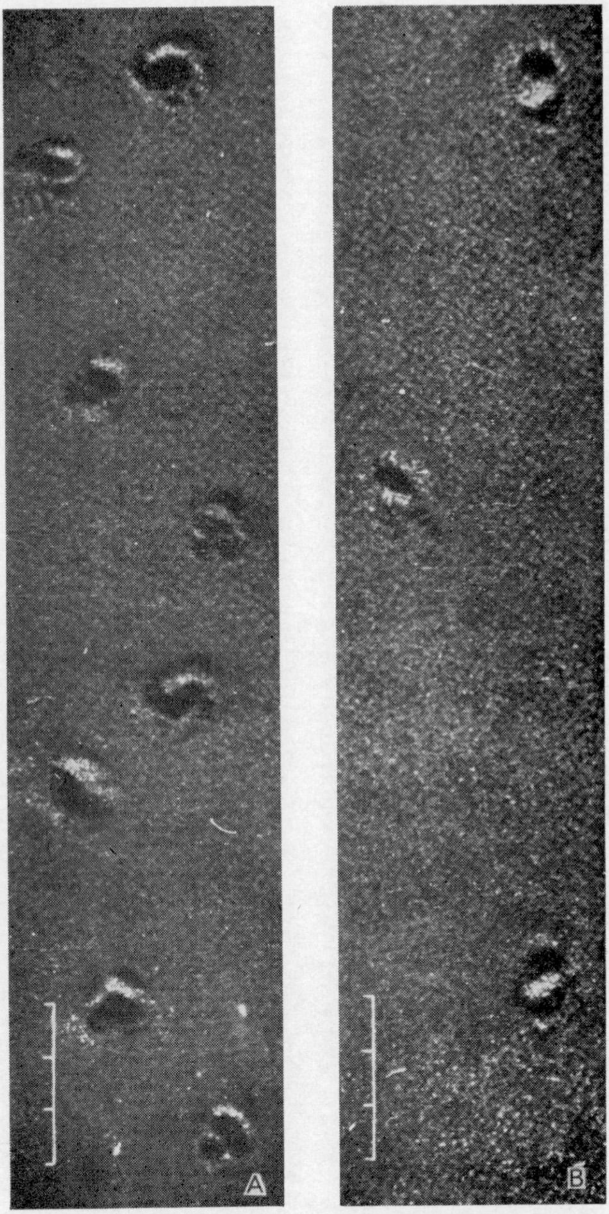

Figure 57. Track of desert toad-headed lizard *(Phrynocephalus interscapularis)* during *(A)* fast quadrupedal, and *(B)* bipedal run.

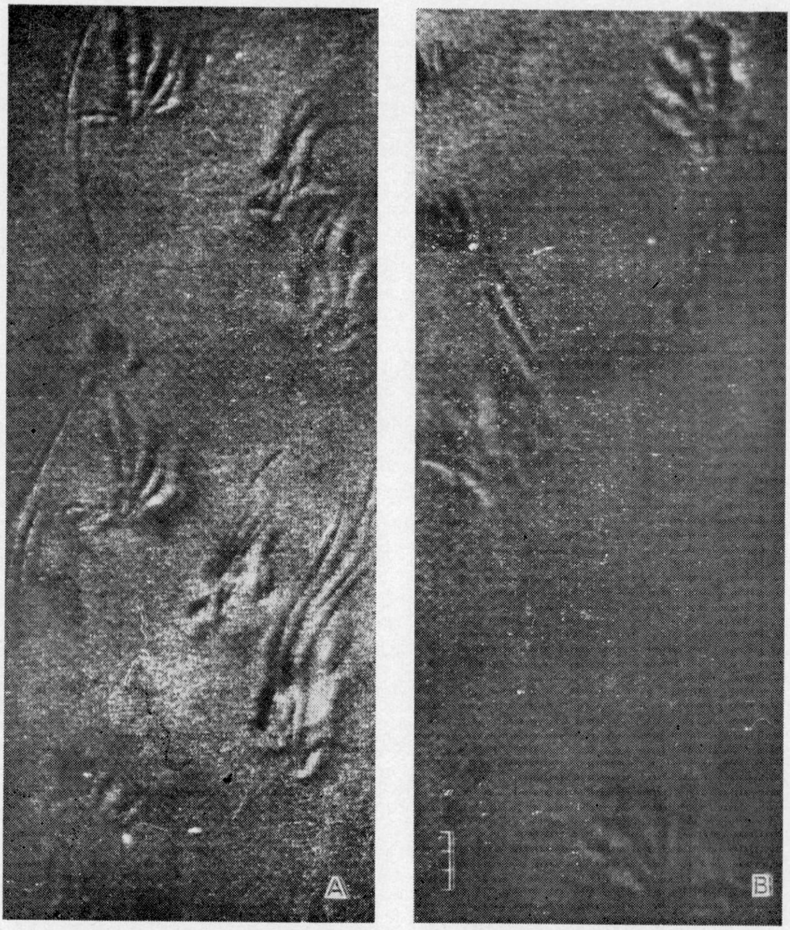

Figure 58. Track of desert monitor *(Vatanus griseus)* during *(A)* slow, and *(B)* fast movement.

However, the relative position of prints of diagonal limbs remains almost unchanged, giving rise to a constant walk.

Following this principle, the speed of the movement may be expressed by the ratio of the basic constituents of the step to the double step (conditional speed). With an increase of absolute speed, the conditional speed decreases as the double step increases. In Table 4, the absolute speed of movement and the conditional are shown simultaneously. The use of a conditional scale of speeds is justified in field conditions as it permits an evaluation of the use of this or that speed during the normal life activity of the animal; for example, during tracking of its impressions in night or dusk activity. In several events, conditional speed may be compared in different forms of almost equal size and proportion. Thus, in plate-tailed gecko and retinal barb (Table 4) similar conditional indices correspond to more or less equal absolute speed.

In lizards used for experiments, conditional speed varied from 0.14 to 1.0, i.e., during maximum speed of double step it is almost seven times the basic constituent of the constant step (or three to four times the body length). Maximum registered speed in absolute units attained 4.0 m per second in retinal barbs and 3.7 m per second in long-eared round-headed lizards. Photographs clearly show how the tracks of different forms of lizards changed during an increase in speed.

Lizard Tracks

The movement of plate-tailed gecko is normally completed without much speed, valued at about 0.75 to 0.6 conditional units (Figure 49, A). Fastness leads to the appearance of covered impressions (Figure 49, B). All dragging foot imprints on the sand, which are observable during slow movement, disappear during protraction (Figure 49, A). During normal activity, very fast movement with overlapping was never observed in the scinco gecko, but this could be caused by artificially carrying the animal into bright light and sun-scorching the surface of the sand. In this case, the gecko developed a speed attaining 0.8 m per second (Figure 49, C) and even 1.75 m per second (Figure 49, D); angle of walk became almost 140° (Table 4).

In cristadigital gecko, a slow movement with uncovering is similarly observed (Figure 50, A) but normally it has fast movement, covered imprints (Figure 50, B) or overlapping (Figure 50, C); conditional speed about 0.5 to 0.4, angle of step, 100 to 110°. Even faster movement is wellknown: speed, 1.2 m per second; conditional speed, 0.18; angle of step about 130°; constant step is equal to 3.5 cm. During the slowest speed (conditional speed, 0.8) of the same animal on sand, an imprint of dragged feet was seen (Figure 49, A). Increased speed is likewise observed in Syrian (conditional speed, 0.27; angle of step, 130°) and Caspian gecko (0.29 and 122°). Slow movement by the latter continues during a conditional speed of about 0.86 and an angle of step,

70°. In all, our geckos are comparatively slow animals. Speed in them never attains the values usual to toad-headed lizards or barbs. Adaptations in the family gekkonidae tend toward those of climbing and because of this, additional structures are present. In our geckos, sub-digital pads are absent, perhaps secondarily. If the cristadigital and supradigital geckos still retain the ability for climbing (bushes, trees and rocks), then scinco gecko is completely changed in the plains habitat, mostly quicksands, but they did not achieve a special adaptation to speedy locomotion, remaining nocturnal animals like the majority of other geckos. The absence of any specialization for fast movement perhaps explains the unspecialized limb proportions of the scinco gecko, and their closeness to primitive conditions.

In retinal barbs, the minimum speed of locomotion is observed (in conditional units of 1.0) with an angle of step about 90 to 100° (Figure 51). However, the norm for them seems to be movement at a speed close to 0.75 (Figure 52, A). Higher speed leads to a covered imprints (Figure 52, B). Some photographs of tracks made by the same retinal barbs (Spec. No. 5) were taken during different speeds: 0.4 m per second (Figure 52, A), 0.53 m per second (Figure 52, B), 3.5 m per second (Figure 52, C,D). During maximum speed, the angle of step in barbs attains 150° (Table 4). Fast movement with overlapping (Figure 52, C) is used very often by retinal barbs, for example, during rushes to prey, in the breeding place (Figure 53, A) and when sliding from danger. In fact, by absolute speed, this is the fastest of our desert lizards. Change to movement by overlapping in retinal barbs takes place almost during the same speed, such as seen in scinco gecko (Table 4), i.e., within the limits of 0.6 to 0.7 m per second. Fast movement is characteristic of the striped barb (Figure 54) and fast of the plate-tailed gecko though the latter's habitat on compact ground makes it impossible to identify its speed by tracks. As a whole, barbs are characterized by a very wide range of speeds which are not available in other forms for study.

In long-legged scinks, only slow movement on sand (which is not its usual substrate) with a conditional speed of about 0.7 and 0.5 was observed. During movement, tracks of specimens whose bodies were 13.8 cm long and overall length 35.5 cm, the speed attained was 1.3 m per second. Mabuya under these very unusual conditions, developed a conditional speed not exceeding 0.5 (covered imprint).

Unlike all other lizards, slow movement is generally not characteristic of our agamids. They, as a rule, move with short fast runs from one stop to another. Only under special conditions, for example, early in the morning when toad-headed lizards dug out from night shelters, were placed on a cold substrate and compelled to move, could a track be obtained with a conditional speed of about 0.5 where the imprint of the hind limbs are arranged almost on the level of imprints of the forefeet (Figure 55). The animal moves clumsily in this, moving each foot in turn. Under natural conditions, a speed below 1.1 m per second was never observed (Table 4). However, even here there is a significant overlapping (in large specimens, not less than 4 cm). The track of toad-headed lizard inscribed during slow speed of movement (Figure 56, A—1.8 m per second) can easily be differentiated by the individual print from the track of a same sized retinal barb. During a further increase (Figure 56, B), it is difficult to differentiate their tracks (cf. Figure 52, C).

Fast tracks of desert toad-headed lizards and striped barbs are similarly identical: both forms are more or less of the same size, but the first is somewhat more massive and its impressions during slow movement are deeper (Figure 57, A). During the fastest movement this difference also disappears (Figure 57, B and 54). Small sized desert toad-headed lizards (length of body almost a third less than toad-headed lizards) attain high speeds to 2.5 m per second and also to 3 m per second. Their angle of step is likewise a large—140 to 155°. Their minimum speed is not below 0.7 m per second with an angle of step about 100°. In desert soil under laboratory conditions, the filmed speed of the toad-headed lizards varied from 0.5 to 1.2 m per second. The track of a steppe agama on quicks and (substrate somewhat unusual for it) is difficult to differentiate from the track of the toad-headed. Maximum speed observed in this case was 2.7 m per second, angle of step, 142°.

Comparatively speaking, the monitor represent a slow-walking group. Desert monitors usually move with uncovered (conditional speed about 0.75) (Figure 58, A), but during some increase the imprint is covered (Figure 58, B). In one small monitor with a long body (about 39 cm; overall length about 90 cm), the following speeds of movement were observed: 0.4 m per second (double step 28-29 cm), 1.45 m per second (double step 41-42 cm, angle of step 116°), and 1.7 m per second (double step about 43 cm). In the latter two cases, the movement continued step by step. Rarely is movement completed with overlapping in gray varanus, but its size is comparatively small. In the Komodo monitor, judging from motion pictures, no overlapping was observed.

Locomotory Abilities in Different Lizard Groups

The method given above makes it possible to differentiate three groups of lizards. First, the comparatively slow-moving forms with a small range of speed changes; these include geckos and possibly varanids. The second group consists of lizards capable of very fast and very slow movement. These comprise lacertids and according to the literature, teiids. The third group is represented in the Soviet Union by agamids whose speciality is the fast run of lizards and in whom the ability to move slowly is almost lost. The place of scincids is not completely clear because of limited material, but possibly they would be included in the first group. On the whole, their specialization did not continue in the direction of fast movement, but locomotion in dense vegetation or through the substrate.

Table 4 permits a comparison of the representatives of these groups (plate-tailed geckos, retinal barbs, and toad-headed lizards) in regard to their locomotory abilities. In geckos, speed may increase from four to six times (Spec. Nos. 4 and 5) during which the step is increased in equal degree and the duration of the locomotory cycle is decreased. In retinal barbs (Spec. Nos. 4 and 5), speed increases more than eight times; however, the duration of the cycle is reduced only 2.4 to 2.7 times, while the walk is increased 3.2 to 3.4 times. On the other hand, in toad-headed lizards during an increase of speed (Spec. No. 7, No. 1 and No. 1a) relatively 3.4, 3, and 2 times, the duration of cycle is reduced to 2, 2.2, and 1.8 times, leaving the increase in step a significantly lesser role (1.7, 1.3, 1.1 times). Thus, in each of the three groups, adaptation to fast movement went a different way. At the same time, a comparative analysis of the data in Tables 3 and 4 shows that while attaining a particular minimum length in the hind limbs, the index of high specialization in this direction seems to be not the ratio of length of limbs to body, but the difference in the size of the fore and hind limbs. Thus, very fast locomotion to some extent is possible in such different habitats as that of toad-headed lizards and barbs. Increase in the length of the hind limbs relative to the forelimbs in striped barbs is comparable to that in retinal, but in desert toad-headed lizards compared to the toad-headed lizards, determines the appearance of a more frequent form of locomotion, the bipedal run.

Tracks and Form of Locomotion

The system of symmetrical locomotion suggested above makes it possible to establish by tracks the kinds of locomotion employed by lizards.

Tracks in lizards during any locomotory speed have a completely regular unchanged pattern: prints of four feet from a characteristic trapezoid (Figure 47) joined by their following lateral sides.[4] The absence of any breaks in this diagram, the regular equality of walk for fore and hind limbs, and other data, denotes the presence of an intracyclic rhythm of locomotion and, consequently, a symmetry of movement in all the lizards studied.

As direct observations and motion pictures (see below) have shown, so also changes in tracks during increase of speed do show that within a single sequence, the limb action of lizards seems to be symmetrical diagonal. However, as with other support patterns, this sequence may be disturbed. For example, during burrowing, a lizard may act with one forefoot, then with the other. But afterwards, with one hind foot followed by the other. In another case, a lizard raked back the sand with his forefoot, but afterwards the sand was thrown away by the hind foot. The limbs of the second side were

[4]During slow movement in the pair of impressions in which small bases of "trapezes" were formed, the impression of the forefoot was placed anteriorly, but during fast—the hind one.

not included in the movement, but the lizard itself lay on the substrate.

The relative permanence of the constant walk is the main speciality of tracks in lizards. Its size usually does not exceed 50 to 80% of the maximum swing of the diagonal limbs (Table 3). In other words, in the movement of lizards, there must always be stages where the diagonal limbs make simultaneous contact with the substrate. Since the distance between the imprints considerably exceeds the gleno-acetabular distance, it is evident that the forelimb in this moment cannot be in an extremely retracted position, and the hind limb in the extremely protracted which is characteristic of movement in the lateral sequence. During support on both diagonal limbs, the latter must be more or less in the same phases.

The simultaneous contact of diagonal limbs indicates the possibility of three stages being present in the locomotory cycle: quadrupodal, tripodal, and diagonal support. However, during movement with high speed and lateral support (in the steps), all lizards greatly exceed the maximum swings for one-sided limbs,[5] i.e., a one-sided contact by an ipsilateral limb of one side is not possible during fast movement. During this diagonal walk, the hind limbs likewise exceed maximum swings. It is clear that fast movement in lizards requires the inclusion of without-support stages, stages of free flight, in the locomotory cycle.[6]

For these three conditions of fast movement, i.e., presence of stages of diagonal support, free flight, and the absence of tripodal stages, the only solution is the fast trot (either main form or variant with predominance of hind limbs) and the fast trot-like walk. The last named is not possible for lizards, as from Figure 5 it appears that a change to this form from any slow movement is completed compulsorily through normal and fast walk, i.e., gaits in which there are stages of support on only two one-sided limbs in the cycle. While these stages are present, a significant change to lateral support during an increase of speed is simply not possible. All the forms of the amble, amble-like walk, and fast forms of real walk are excluded.

Thus, fast movement in lizards should take place (and does take place as shown by motion pictures) in only one form—the form of the fast trot. Some

[5]It exceeds even the swings of diagonal limbs (Table 4).

[6]From Table 4, one can determine approximately what distance is covered by the lizard during the period of without-support stages. In toad-headed lizard (Spec. No. 7) during a speed of 3.7 m per second, this distance is equal to not less than 10 cm; in retinal barbs (Spec. No. 5) during a speed of 3.5 m per second, not less than 7 cm; in scinco gecko (Spec. No. 4) during a speed of about 1.7 m per second, not less than 5 cm; in striped barbs with body length 4.4 cm during a conditional speed of 0.25 (Figure 54) not less than 5.0 cm; in desert toad-headed lizard (body length, 3.2 cm) during bipedal run (Figure 57, B) not less than 4 cm. Thus, smaller lizards fly in the air to a distance exceeding their body length (excluding the tail). Given values are even lower since in calculating them the maximum but not the inherent swing of hind limbs was considered.

increase in constant walk during an increase of speed (Table 4) suggests that the majority of lizards during the fast run use a form of the fast trot with predominance of hind limbs. In fact, during the real trot when the limbs of one diagonal simultaneously touch the substrate, the increase of speed may perhaps change the constant walk, but increase of predominance (and this will be shown from motion pictures hereafter) leads to a long delay in the landing of the forelimbs in the diagonal when compared to the hind limbs. The latter at this moment seem already to be somewhat retracted which may affect the constant walk.

Table 4 shows that the change to the fast trot with predominance of hind limbs always coincides with the change of the tracks from uncovered to overlapping, i.e., it may be considered that in all cases, movement with overlapping takes place in the form of a fast trot with predominance of hind limbs. A diagnosis of slow movement on the basis of partially covered impressions is actually impossible. It is clear only that support stages on only ipsilateral limb pairs are impossible in lizards in relation to their general habitat and the horizontal position of the proximal portions of limbs. Their presence would have attracted, especially during slow movement, an inclusion in the cycle of extremely unstable conditions when the center of gravity lies at a significant distance from the line of support and would have been moved parallel to it. From Table 4, it is clear that if the maximum swing of one-sided limbs exceeds the latter support, then it is always combined with an excess of maximum swing for the hind limbs over the diagonal walk. In other words, stages of tripodal or quadrupodal should be here in the cycle but not stages of lateral support. This slow movement with uncovered imprints may occur only in the form of a slow trot-like walk and slow trot (with variants) or during very slow speed, very slow walk. Motion pictures of nature (see below) confirm the possibility. Because of stages of lateral support in normal and fast walks, the evolution of locomotion in lizards, as in all lower tetrapods, must have gone only to the side of slow trot-like walk and real trot. Only mammals which often change limbs in the parasagittal plane reached a potentiality for using the many forms of symmetrical locomotion (Figure 5).

Tracks and Animal Size

A study of tracks for lizards shows that the real size of an animal is reflected only in the constant walk, the size of which is actually not associated with the speed of movement. The main constituent forming the constant walk calculated from the data in Table 4 is very close to the gleno-acetabular distance of the animal. From this, a scientific basis can be laid for appropriate methods of identifying animal size as suggested by Lilienstern and Baird (see p.100). At the same time, the calculations are greatly simplified, not requiring advance diagrammatical presentations. Thus, to identify by the tracks, the distance between the pectoral and pelvic regions of the animal moving on four legs, it is enough to measure the size of the double step and uncovered prints during slow movement or overlapping during fast, then divide the double step by two and add to it uncovered or to delete the overlapping.

Bipedal Run

The bipedal run in the lizards of our fauna was first mentioned by me (Sukhanov, 1963, 1964b). It has already been stated (Part I) that the fast trot with predominance of hind limbs seems to be potentially the bipedal run as the role of the forelimbs in the support of the animal is reduced to a minimum. This is emphasized through a comparison of two portions of the tracks for striped barbs (Figure 54): the change from a bipedal run in the beginning of the track to a fast quadrupedal in the end (possibly the movement continued with lesser retardation) did not cause any substantial changes in the size of the double step and its angle. The entire fixed portion of the track was 140 cm long (in Figure 54 the second half is given); the lizard ran mainly on two legs but the advance momentum was formed by all four. Thus, after the momentum load from the forelimbs was removed, they stopped touching the ground in stages of diagonal support. The movement now took place on only the two hind limbs. The tracks of striped barbs (Figure 54) corresponds to the speed, very close to the bipedal run, the forefoot sometimes still touching the soil.

In retinal barbs the bipedal run may be started directly from a state of rest or during a sharp speed increase from slow movement (Figure 53, A, B).[7] So in the event of being frightened by man, barbs (body length nine to ten cm) will suddenly run on two legs from a state of rest beginning the movement with a double step of 14 cm. To the end of the first 5 m run (23 double steps) the double step will increase up to 25 to 28 cm. The entire distance passed by the barbs on only two legs reached 25 m (90 double steps). The quadrupedal run in retinal barbs often alternates with the bipedal run without disturbing the continuity of the movement. So in a series of 17 double steps in barbs (Spec. No. 8, body length 9.7 cm), the first step was made on four legs (double step equal to 17 cm; overlapping, 3.5 cm), the following 8 on two, afterward 2 on four, 5 on two, and the latter again on four. The average speed in all portions was 3.4 m per second but the average length of double step was equal to 40 cm. Retinal barbs (Spec. No. 9; body length, 9.2 cm) on a portion 9.5 m in length, ran with an average speed of 2.8 m per second; the first 30 steps passed on four legs, but the last 8 on two in which the double steps at the end were reduced to 15 cm (average on a portion of 20 cm).

[7]Perhaps this occurs in a third form striped barbs and desert toad-headed capable of a bipedal run (Figure 57, B) but in connection with larger sizes, a greater length of run and other specialities of such changes is easy to observe in retinal barbs.

Short fast runs of desert toad-headed lizards often pass on only two legs. Maximum observed size of the track made by a specimen when on two legs was 6.6 m (body length, 3.2 cm; 36 double steps, average of 18 cm; angle of step about 148°). In adult toad-headed lizards, a clearly defined bipedal run is not met though one to two steps may be done without support of the forefeet, but in small toad-headed, the bipedal run is observed. For example, Spec. No. 1a (body length, 5.2 cm) ran from a state of rest some steps on two legs (body during this was quite unnaturally raised almost vertical at 60 to 70°) and only afterwards changed to the usual trot. Double step in the beginning did not exceed 12 to 13 cm (diagonal step for more than 1 cm exceeds the maximum swing of the hind limbs), but during trot attained 18 cm.

Jumping in Lizards

Jumping leading to free flight during the course of fast movement of lizards are completed only at the cost of strokes by one of the two hind limbs. In nature, not a single track was observed wherein the prints of both hind limbs were situated at one level or were situated opposite to the imprints of the forefeet. Thus, the symmetrical character of movement in lizards is never disturbed. In fact, sometimes in beginning movement, for example in the laboratory with steppe agamid, some similarity between the present jump and a single retraction of both hind limbs could be observed. However, in the beginning of the jump, one of the feet is more forwardly projected. It is also seen to be important in the stroke as the latter loses contact with the substrate. The second foot starts protraction long before attaining the maximum retractive position. Consequently, the beginning movements already indicate the different phases in the action of the hind limbs. Possibly, the retraction of one of them is completed passively, similar to the feet of frogs in a special preparation on the revolving drum (p. 102). It is clear that here there is no similarity to the asymmetrical locomotion of the desert lizard or of jerboas. All is completed on the basis of symmetrical-diagonal sequence of limb action. Arising out of this, it seems that a change to movement with a simultaneous stroke by the hind limbs as in frogs should be related to the inhabitants in surroundings with other conditions of equilibrium.

Fossil Tracks and Origin of Fast Trot with Hind Limb Predominance

Many tracks of lower tetrapods are wellknown from the deposits of Carboniferous, Permian and Triassic formations, left advantageously during slow locomotion as they are mainly uncovered. Tracks are extremely rare where the prints of fore and hind limbs are situated on one level. However, the fast trot had appeared in the Permian; tracks discovered in Texas of small creeping *Microsauropus clarki* (Moodie, 1929), were related to microsaurus without adequate justification, already had an overlap of about 1.5 cm with length of double step 10 to 11 cm and an angle of step of 130°. In Arizona, on the bottom of the Middle Triasic, tracks of other fast-running *Rotodactylus* (Peabody, 1948) were found in which overlapping almost did not lead to better runners among modern lizards. Judging from photographs of a *R. cursorius* specimen with a gleno-acetabular distance not exceeding 12 to 15 cm, locomotion continued by a double step of 46 to 53 cm, angle of step 131 to 143° and overlapping about 10 cm (conditional speed about 0.25). Tracks of this type specimen seem to be the result of alternation of quadrupedal and bipedal locomotion; it is similar to the track of striped barbs (cf. Peabody, 1948, Fig. 16; and Figure 54 of the present work). Correctly rejecting the suggestion by Brady (1935) who analogously described the tracks as jumps of a small primitive dinosaurs, Peabody nevertheless failed to state clearly which form of locomotion corresponded to the tracks of the *Rotodactylus*. One of the reasons for this may be the absence of well-described tracks for present day lizards. Considerable overlapping made Peabody suggest that the animal had very long limbs which were carried in front after the forefeet. Peabody indicates that this type of track is left during a fast gait in which all four limbs never touch the ground at one time (Peabody, 1948). It is clearly sufficiently characteristic as under this identification may be placed all symmetrical gaits except the very slow walk, slow amble-like and trot-like walks, and slow ambles and trots. The degree of overlapping in *Rotodactylus,* according to Peabody, exceeds all that is known in modern tetrapods, except for specialized gaits (gallop) of fast running mammals. In lizards, for example in the iguanid *Sceloporus,* there is little overlapping. It is considerable in *Callisaurus* and *Uma,* but nonetheless not so great as in *Rotodactylus*. Peabody surprisingly indicates that there is overlapping already in the slow gait of *Rotodactylus*.

However, the tracks of toad-headed lizards described above where there is always overlapping attain in fast run about 15 cm during an angle of the step up to 150°[8] and more so, retinal barbs with overlapping up to 17 to 18 cm show that there is no basis for reconstructing *Rotodactylus* or any dinosaur-like creature although it has longer forelimbs than the real bipedal dinosaurs. If we base our assumptions only on the tracks, then the best we can think of is a smaller pseudosuchian. Peabody was right in this assumption for he thought of a pseudosuchian with a face similar to the present day round-headed ones with elongated hind limbs and a relatively shorter body. Possibly, that group of Triassic pseudosuchian including *Rotodactylus,* being quadrupedal similar to the round-headed ones, moved with overlapping in the form of a fast trot with a predominance of hind limbs, changing with enough momentum into a bipedal run. Tracks of *Rotodactylus* indicate that by the lower middle Trias on the basis of a fast trot with predominance of hind limbs, a bipedal

[8]Long-eared round-headed lizards are almost twice as small as *Rotodactylus*.

run similar to that of modern lizards had already appeared which perhaps was the beginning of real bipedal locomotion in dinosaurs. This would indirectly confirm that it is doubtful if bipedalism in dinosaurs, the characteristic peculiarity of which seems to be the possibility of movement on two legs, fast as well as slow (caused by the transference of hind limbs in the parasagittal plane, a more vertical orientation of the vertebral column, etc.), appeared before dinosaurs passed the stage of small fast-running animals. Actually, the lacertid's bipedal run would perhaps appear contradictory to large forms.

Parallelism in the Development of Bipedalism in Lizards

As fast movement of lizards always appears as a fast trot with a predominance of hind limbs, it is completely natural to think that bipedalism may be met in any lizard capable of running at high speed. The principal similarity between both forms of locomotion leads to the conclusion that the differences between the locomotory apparatus of bipedal iguanids, agamids, and other quadrupedal forms are insignificant (Snyder, 1954). It is natural to also find in the list of bipedal forms such systematically distant groups as lacertids and teiids on one side and iguanids and agamids on the other. Thus, not only is it an interesting fact that bipedalism is a potential capability possessed by the majority of lizards and has appeared under many conditions. In our fauna this was no doubt caused by an open landscape habitat. The agamids of our fauna developed a fast run in deserts. However, this is linked in them with greater losses, especially noticed in such specific open landscape (sand and talus) forms as the group of round-headed lizards. The loss of the ability to move slowly decreases their ecological niches as compared to the agamids which could be seen in open places (for example, on compact soils with gentle undulations) in saxaul clumps, on cliffs, etc. Toad-headed lizards, by their extreme degree of specialization, give a good example of unadaptive evolution.

In other words, the acquisition by higher forms of fast locomotion, bipedal run, proceeded in scincomorphs. In this group extreme fastness, exceeding even what we see in agamids with relatively short bodies, is combined with retention, but maybe also by the acquisition of elongated bodies and consequently, an increased aptitude for horizontal body bends essential during movement in thick vegetation. This may be considered as adaptive evolution. Scincomorphs in reality are a biologically evolving group. Out of it, individual representatives in open landscapes undoubtedly evolving later than agamids and iguanids, show that on a morphological basis, bipedalism is likewise completely attainable in conditions of dry sands (retinal and striped barbs) and also in dense soils with rate vegetation (fast barb).

Special Adaptation to Slow Locomotion in Scincogeckonomorphs

The necessity to associate faster movement, for which longer limbs are necessary, with slower movement when longer limbs always disturb led to a life of special adaptation permitting a decrease in the functional length of hind limbs during the transition from faster movements to slower ones. The effectiveness of this adaptation in retinal barbs requires comparison: the size of their double step is changed three to four times (actually somewhat more; as a rule, the slowest movement passing with frequent stops could not be fixed) as against 1.7 times in toad-headed lizards. Reduction of the functional length of hind limbs is related to fixation of a permanent curve in the knee of the limb during the course of the entire cycle, i.e., during its protraction and during retraction. As the degree of flexion and extension of the foot is likewise limited, then the proportion now is identified only by the movement of the limbs at the hip joint. Resulting from this, the position of the foot is changed in the beginning of protraction. If during fast movement, the foot is arranged under a very small angle toward the direction of movement, now it is placed under an angle of 60 to 70° to it, which is well seen in the tracks (Figure 51; Figure 52 A, B). Observation shows that during very slow movement, the limb at the hip joint is moved on 100°; at the knee, all on 45°; at the intertarsal, on 20°.

A reduction of functional length of hind limbs takes place also in geckos (Chapter VII). Thus in scincogeckonomorphs we rarely observe this phenomenon in nature—the appearance of an adaptation to slow locomotion—despite the widespread concept that all fast running animals may move equally well slowly. This assumption is based on a very direct deduction of Gregory's (1912) who declared the dependence of structure of the locomotory apparatus on maximum loads during maximum possible speeds for a given animal.

It is important to mention that in lacertids and geckos, identical adaptations caused the identical change in morphology also; responsible for the fixation of the knee, *mm. tibialis internus et ilio-fibularis* are stregthened and appreciably complex (Sukhanov, 1961). On the other hand, in agamids these muscles are developed extremely slowly. In geckos the limited foot mobility results in a sharper decrease in its basic flexure—*m. gastrocnemius.* This does not exclude that the complexity described earlier (Sukhanov, 1957) of *mm. pubo-ischio-femoralis externus et internus* in both groups, is also associated with adaptation to slow movement.

* * *

As another method of measuring speed of movement from the main elements of the tracks and sizes of animal, we studied the effect of speed and forms of movement on the tracks of geckos, barbs, toad-headed lizards, etc.

With an increase of speed, the depth of imprints of the hind and, to a lesser extent, the forelimbs, is increased. Prints of separate fingers are brought out. Imprints acquire the shape of a round hole. In the track, double and diagonal steps are increased and the ratio between their main elements is changed. The imprint of the hind foot gets closer to the imprint of its ipsilateral forefoot, covers, and afterwards overlaps it. However, the distance between the imprints of diagonal limbs (constant walk) remains practically unchanged, reflecting the actual size of the animal. By relating the value of the basic component of the constant walk to the double step, these can be compared through conditional units of speed of locomotion for different lizards. By their locomotory capabilities, three groups of lizards are distinguished. Geckos, possibly scincids, and varanids move comparatively with less speed and a smaller range of change. Lacertids and teiids are capable of very slow as well as very fast movement. On the other hand, several agamids, such as the toad-headed, did not lose their ability for slow movement. These lizards start running with great speed immediately leaving an overlapped impression.

An analysis of changes in tracks during an increase of speed shows that the fast movement of lizards with overlapping is only possible in the form of a fast trot with a predominance of hind limbs. Movement with uncovered prints may lead to a form of very slow and slow trot-like walk and slow trot. It is impossible to differentiate these walks by tracks. Some lizards of our fauna (desert toad-headed lizards, striped, retinal, and fast barb) are capable of moving on their hind legs only after an advance momentum or immediately from a state of rest. The basis of the bipedal run of lizards seems to be the fast trot with a predominance of hind limbs where the role of the forefeet in supporting the body is reduced to a minimum. Judging from fossil tracks, the time of origin of the fast trot with a predominance of hind limbs is thought to be the Permain where tracks with overlapping first appeared. Some reptiles of the Middle Triasic already ran after advance momentum with a bipedal run of the type used by lizards. The appearance of a bipedal run in lacertids, available to animals of only small size, preceded bipedal locomotion in dinosaurs perhaps, including locomotion on two legs during less speed. Consequently, the ancestors of dinosaurs should have passed through a stage when they were small, fast-running animals. The bipedal run of lizards is thought to be available to all forms capable of fast locomotion whose living conditions are an open landscape. Unquestionably, it appeared independently in scincomorphs and iguanomorphs during the course of their adaptation to movement with high speed. The wide range of speed variation observed in scincomorphs is provided by an adaptive ability to change the functional length of the hind limbs. Because of this special development, the muscles fix the limb in a constantly bent knee position. A similar adaptation has developed also in geckos.

CHAPTER VII

SPECIALITIES OF LIZARD LOCOMOTION BASED ON MOTION PICTURE DATA

Our study of tracks showed that the possible forms of running locomotion in lizards is limited. Only one gait corresponds to fast movement, to slow, a few, but to differentiate them by tracks is impossible. We tried to analyze slow forms of locomotion with the help of high speed motion pictures. The materials obtained made it possible to describe how the process of locomotion operates, to compare the peculiarities of different forms of movement in lizards, often to see the working of the limbs, etc. Unfortunately, not all questions could be studied with thoroughness and accuracy. Many of the films were incidental, especially those in the field. The material seems to be fragmentary and hence difficult to compare. Nevertheless, the attempt itself to study locomotion of reptiles via motion pictures deserves attention. In this line very little has been done. Therefore, each new, though single, fact is of interest as a contributory factor to future work.

The movements of the following forms were studied: scincogeckos (in the field and laboratory), fast barbs and long-legged scinks (laboratory), toad-headed (field). The locomotion of Komodo monitor (*Varanus komodoensis*)

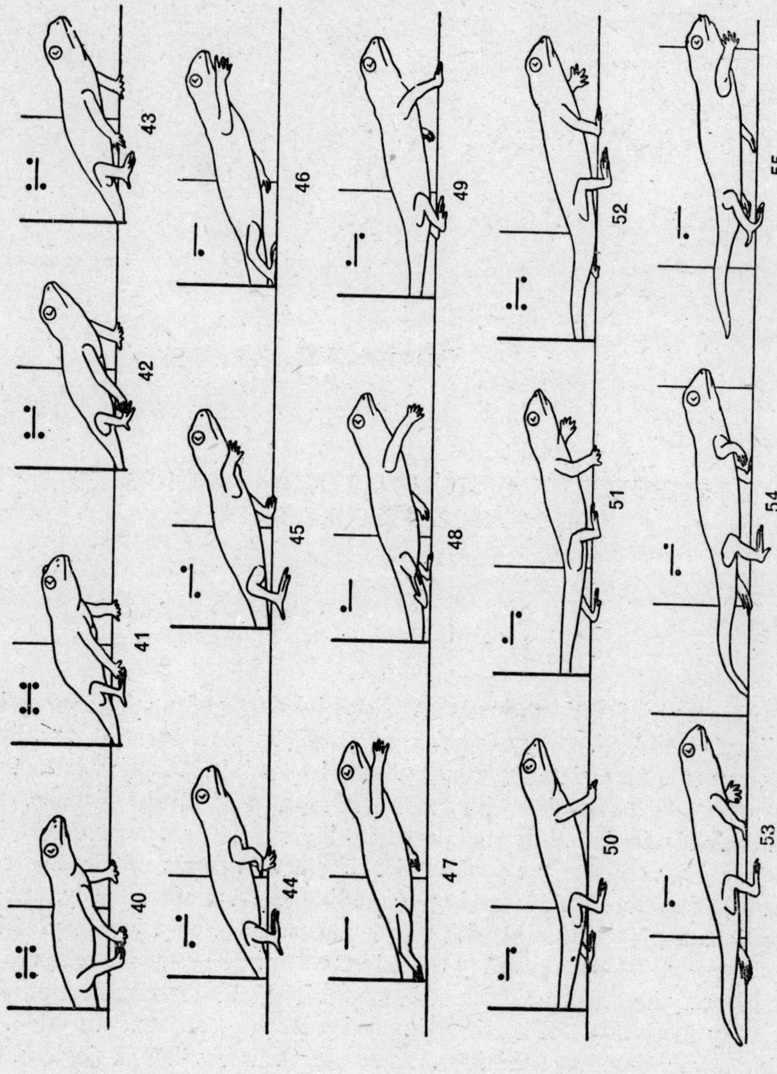
40
41
42
43
44
45
46
47
48
49
50
51
52
53
54
55

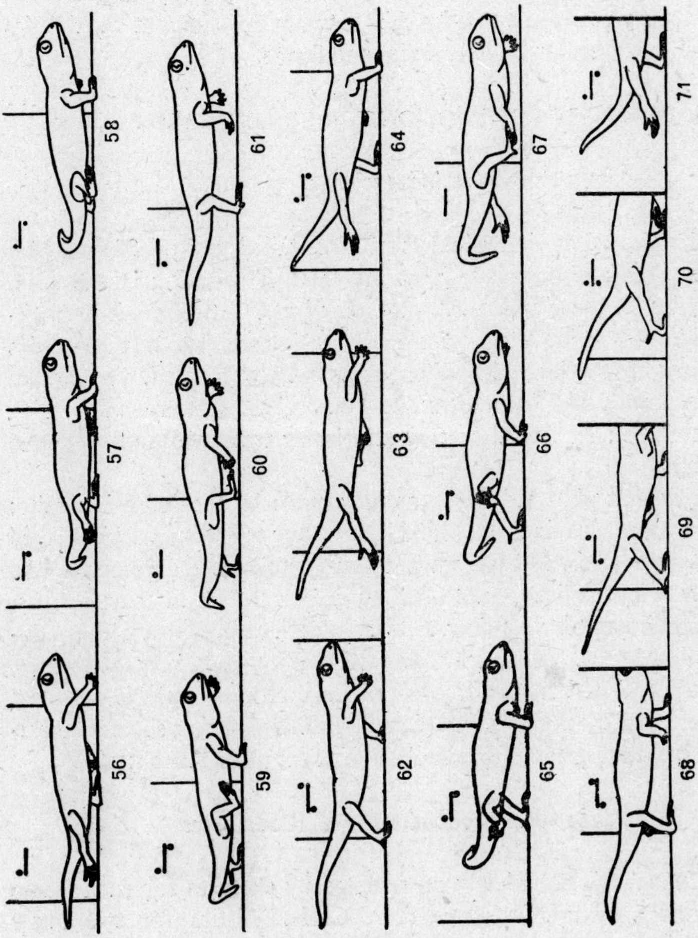

Figure 59. Jump and fast trot with predominance of hind limbs for plate-tailed gecko.
Sketches of frames 40 to 71 of series C28-No. 6; for convenience, the plan of support corresponding to each frame is shown; distance between the vertical lines on the backdrop is equal to 10 cm.

was studied from the materials of the French film "Dragons of the Island of Komodo" and motion pictures of I. S. Darevskii. Some results were obtained on the movement in the laboratory of the takyr toad-headed lizard and steppe agamas. The material is presented in the form of figures for each frame from motion pictures, diagrams of locomotion and tables which include data analyzing diagrams in cycles.[1] It seems advisable to first review the material according to the forms of locomotion for each lizard, then the characteristics of each, and finally to see the relationship between the different capabilities of locomotion and changes in its speeds and forms.

1. FORMS OF LOCOMOTION FOR SOME LIZARDS

Teratoscincus scincus

From 36 series of motion pictures of plate-tailed geckos, 28 could be completely analyzed. Unfortunately, at the time of shooting in the field, the order number of the given lizard was not written. Therefore, it is conditionally considered that in all the series (the exception seems to be those series where there are no big intervals) different animals were used. These were given numbers from 5 to 27 (numbers 1 to 4 carried the specimens for which tracks were studied). In the laboratory all filming was done on one gecko (Spec. No. 28).

Films show that plate-tailed geckos may move by the following gaits: fast foot trot with predominance of hind limbs, slow trot with predominance of hind or forelimbs, slow trot-like walk, and very slow walk. In other words, all the gaits available to lizards are used by geckos but in different degrees. Most of our specimens showed slow trot-like walk and slow trot with predominance of hind limbs. Though increase of movement is very often met, nevertheless the real fast trot with predominance of hind limbs is observed only in one series of motion pictures (C28-No. 6). This being so, it is convenient to start the description of locomotion with the plate-tailed gecko.

Fast Trot With Predominance of Hind Limbs

Series C28-No. 6 is completely represented by sketches for each frame (Figure 59) and a diagram (Figure 60). Characteristics for two latter cycles from the three are given in Table 5. In the first half of the series (stills 40 to 54) we have two sequences of jumps with the help of the right hind limb. The remaining feet play mainly a secondary role. The initial pose of the gecko standing immobile on a wooden platform

[1]During the preparation of this work for the press, part of the illustrated material was released; so also were several series of diagrams and stills (see Sukhanov, 1967b).

(Figure 59, still 40) corresponds to the position of the animal at the moment of a quadrupodal stage of the cycle (Figure 103, B) but not a state of rest (Figure 103, A). On touching its tail, the gecko reacted sharply by a jump in which the leading limb was the right hind, leaving the substrate later (Figures 59, 60, still 46) than the left forelimb (still 45) and the left hind one. The latter is not seen on frames 40 to 47 but as it is already off the substrate in frame 48, there can be no question about one-time and synchronized striking by both hind limbs. The left hind limb should have moved in front no later than the frame 44 (Figure 60).

The stroke of the right hind limb was so powerful that without any momentum the animal was in the air (Figure 59, frame 47). During this, the angle of the jump was more (about 20°) than during real free flight in the course

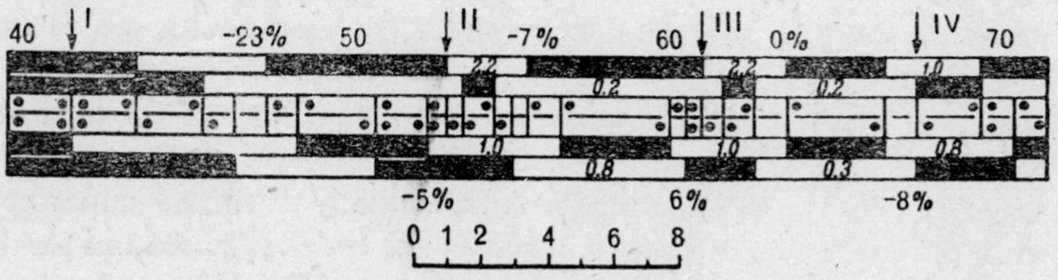

Figure 60. Diagram presenting movement of plate-tailed gecko in Figure 59. *Series C28-No. 6, film speed 70 frames per second. Designations same as in Figure 40.*

of fast movement (still 63). The inclination of the body was retained on the first stage of locomotion even during diagonal support (stills 49 to 51). This resulted from landing after the jump on a curved knee of the left hind limb which makes for a very small walk (cf. frames 46 and 48). Afterwards, on the substrate, the right forefoot touches (frame 49). Both limbs in the left diagonal[2] losing, possibly, too much strength on the softening of the first jump, do not have a strong propulsive action. Therefore, after the stage of diagonal support follows the tripodal support, the right hind foot enters (frame 52) making an already significantly large step. Now one would have thought that the animal would wait for the landing of the left forelimb, but because the inclination of the body delays that so much, it is compelled to start retraction even in the air (frames 51 to 54). The right hind limb secondarily produces a strong stroke. This leads to a lift off initially by the right forelimb but afterwards also by the left hind one. The left forelimb nevertheless touches the substrate, but only on one movement (frame 54). The short stage of diagonal support is changed to a secondary unipodal stage. The change from the latter to a primary unipodal stage was not caught by the camera but it cannot be excluded that these were divided by a very short-timed stage of

[2]Here the limbs of the right and left diagonals have been differentiated depending on which of the hind feet is put forth in the given diagonal.

free flight (Figure 60; frames 55 and 56) or support on only two hind limbs which more certainly takes place later (frame 61). Such a bipodal stage was fixed in frame 70 (Figures 59 and 60). The third cycle of the series is already more uniformly completed although in the beginning the limbs of the right diagonal have an unnaturally short support time.

Though the form of movement of geckos in the series C28-No. 6 is externally less similar to fast trot with a predominance of hind limbs (Figure 19), the identity of both does not appear to be doubtful. In support of this are the presence of a stage of free flight (frames 63 and 67), primary (frames 53, 56, and 61), and secondary (frames 48, 55, and 60) unipodal stages. The movement in the series took place in all with no large increase. The speed in the latter cycles was close to 1.1 m per second (Table 5). For geckos, this is not their fastest movement (Chapter VI). Here speed is not attained by the level of norm of the fast trot, but even then the rhythms of limb action, are, as a rule, below 1. During this, the rhythms of limb action for the left diagonal are somewhat higher than the right. The degree of predominance of the hind limbs is quite high. Attention is drawn to the inclusion in the cycle of stages with support on only two posterior limbs but a similarly negative significance for rhythm of locomotion in some portions of the series. The reasons for these peculiarities will be clarified later as they are met with in all lizards.

Slow Trot with Predominance of Hind Limbs

This walk is best illustrated in series C28-No. 10 (Figures 61 to 63). In Figure 61, the movement of the gecko is shown in the beginning of the series with a speed of about 0.3 to 0.4 m per second; in Figure 62 at the end of the series, the speed is closer to 0.7 to 0.9 per second. In spite of the increase, the same form of movement is used throughout the duration of the entire series, a slow trot with predominance of hind limbs. On this the rhythm of locomotion is close to zero (Table 5) and a resemblance exists in support plans for primary and secondary tripodal stages (Figure 63). This is attained in the following way.

The limbs of one diagonal work synchronously, but the shorter forelimb lifts earlier than the hind one (Figure 61, frame 8) on two frames. It similarly touches down later than the hind foot (frames 14 and 15), as its time of transport is increased at the cost of a high raising of the foot during protraction which is easily seen in Figure 62 (frames 87 to 89). By this, the slow trot with predominance of hind limbs is differentiated from its similar variant of fast trot during which the hind limbs come into contact earlier with the substrate mainly because of a maximum increase in its swing or, as in the case of toad-headed lizards, simply in connection with its considerable length compared to the forelimb. The predominance of the hind limbs in series C28-No. 10 is considerably less than during the fast trot in series C28-No. 6

Table 5. Characteristics of locomation of plate-tailed gecko

Series (sketch number)	Cycle number	Speed (in m per sec)	Duration of: Cycle (in sec)	Duration of: Diagonal support (in sec)	Duration of: Diagonal support (in %)	Duration of: Secondary four support stages (in %)	Duration of: free flight (in %)	Degree of predominance (in %): LH-RF	Degree of predominance (in %): RH-LF	Rhythm of limb work (in conditional units): LH	RH	LF	RF	Rhythm of locomotion in half-cyles (in %): I	II	Form of locomotion in half-cycles: I	II
1	2	3	4	5	6	7	8	9	10	11	12	13	14	15	16	17	18
C5-No 1 (72)	I	?	0.25	0.16	63	—	—	—10	8	1.3	2.9	2.1	1.6	6	6	STW	ST
	II		0.21	0.13	62	—	—	13	20	1.6	3.1	1.6	1.2	15	8	STW	STW
	III		0.25	0.11	44	—	—	0	0	2.1	2.9	2.9	2.1	13	13	STW	STW
	IV		~0.38	~0.1	~25	—	—	Incomplete cycle						~29	—	STW	STW
C5-No 2	I	?	0.22	0.12	57	—	—	0	18	1.8	3.4	1.8	1.8	0	0	ST/HL	ST
			0.24	0.13	53	—	—	9	9	2.6	2.6	1.9	1.9	7	7	ST/HL	ST/HL
	III		0.22	0.13	57	—	—	10	0	2.4	2.4	2.4	1.8	0	7	ST	ST/HL
	IV		0.22	0.15	71	—	—	11	11	1.8	1.8	1.3	1.3	7	7	ST/HL	ST/HL
C6-No 1	I	?	0.21	0.11	54	—	—	6	—5	2.2	2.2	2.7	1.9	4	11	STW	STW
C6-No 2	I	?	0.24	0.12	50	—	—	18	13	2.6	3.3	1.9	1.5	0	3	ST/HL	ST/HL
	II		0.28	0.06	25	—	—	19	10	8.3	6.0	3.7	2.5	6	3	ST/HL	ST/HL
C7-No 1 (69)	I	?	0.21	0.13	65	—	—	16	13	2.7	1.6	1.2	1.6	4	8	ST/HL	ST/HL
	II		0.21	0.1	50	—	—	16	15	2.7	3.1	1.9	1.2	—4	8	ST/HL	ST/HL
	III		0.21	0.13	59	—	—	17	20	2.0	2.8	2.5	1.2	4	0	ST/HL	ST/HL
	IV		~0.33	—	—	~10	—	Incomplete cycle						~52	—	VSW	—
C7-No 2 (70)	I	?	0.23	0.1	45	—	—	23	0	3.1	4.0	4.0	1.4	0	3	ST	ST/HL
	II		~0.53	—	—	~21	—	Incomplete cycle						0	~50	ST/HL	VSW

(*Contd.*)

1	2	3	4	5	6	7	8	9	10	11	12	13	14	15	16	17	18
C8-No 1		?	0.21	0.16	74	—	—	18	0	1.6	1.6	1.6	1.1	0	4	ST/HL	ST/HL
C9-No 1	I	?	0.19	0.09	50	—	—	22	17	2.9	2.9	1.7	1.6	—4	8	ST/HL	STW
	II		0 24	0.11	47	—	—	0	18	2.8	2 8	1.5	2.8	0	13	ST/HL	STW
	III	?	0.25	0.13	50	—	—	0	17	2.3	3.0	1.7	2.3	0	6	ST/HL	ST/HL
	IV		~0.31	~0 09	~30	—	—			Incomplete cycle				~15	—	STW	STW
C10-No 1	I	?	0.18	0.09	55	—	—	18	18	2 8	2.8	1.6	1.6	4	4	ST/HL	ST/HL
	II		0 24	0.14	62	—	—	0	21	1.9	1.9	1.1	1.9	0	14	ST/HL	STW
C11-No 1	I	?	0.19	0.12	63	—	—	12	8	2.4	1.7	1.4	1.4	4	13	ST/HL	STW
	II		0.24	0.13	53	—	—	5	9	2.3	2.8	2.0	2.0	10	7	STW	STW
C11-No 2	I	?	0.17	0.11	64	—	—	29	13	1.8	2,7	1.8	0.8	9	0	ST/HL	ST/HL
	II		0.16	0.11	70	—	—	17	29	1.5	2.3	1.0	1.0	0	—10	S-FT/HL	S-FT/HL
	III		0.16	0.13	80	—	—	34	0	1.5	1.5	1.5	0.7	0	0	S-FT/HL	S-FT/HL
	IV		0.16	0.11	70	—	—	34	14	1.5	2 3	1.5	0 7	10	0	S-FT/HL	S-FT/HL
	V		0.21	0.14	69	—	—	13	22	1.6	2.2	1.2	1.2	0	—8	S-FT/HL	S-FT/HL
	VI		~0.28	~0 14	~50	—	—			Incomplete cycle				~3	—	ST/HL	ST/HL
C12-No 1	I	?	0.14	0.09	67	—	—	—17	17	1.2	2.0	1.2	2.0	11	—11	STW	ST/HL
	II		0.17	0.15	86	—	—	0	7	0.8	2.1	1.8	0.8	0	—5	ST	ST/HL
	III		0.16	0.13	80	—	—	33	0	1.2	1.2	1.2	0.7	0	0	S-FT/HL	S-FT/HL
	IV		0.16	0 13	90	—	—	0	29	1.0	2.3	1.0	1.0	0	0	S-FT/HL	S-FT/HL
	V		0 14	0.13	89	—	—	0	0	0.8	2.0	2.0	0.8	0	0	S-FT/HL	S-FT/HL
C13-No 1 (71)	I	?	0.25	0.11	44	—	—	17	18	3	2.2	1.7	1.7	25	10	STW	STW
	II		0.35	0.13	36	—	—	11	0	4.5	3.4	3.4	3.7	0	0	ST/HL	STW
C15-No 1	I	?	0.17	0.17	100	—	—	0	0	1.2	1.2	0.8	0.8	0	0	SFT	S-FT
	II		0.19	0.16	83	—	—	15	15	1.4	1.4	1.0	1.0	—8	8	S-FT/HL	S-FT/HL
	III		0 17	0.16	91	—	—	17	0	1.2	1.2	1.2	0.8	—9	0	S-FT/HL	S-FT/HL
	IV		0.21	0.17	85	—	8	0	0	0.9	1.2	1.2	1.2	0	0	S-FT/HL	S-FT/HL
	V		0.21	0.16	77	—	—	25	25	1.6	1.6	0.9	0.9	0	0	ST/HL	ST/HL
	VI		0.22	0.16	72	—	—	11	10	1.3	2.5	1.8	1.0	7	—7	ST/HL	ST/HL

C17-No 1	I	?	0.24	0.11	45	—	—	13	13	3.0	2.0	2.0	2.0	13	19	STW	STW
C22-No 1	I	?	0.18	0.12	65	—	—	12	21	1.9	1.9	0.9	1.9	0	9	ST/HL	ST/HL
(65)	II		0.15	0.1	68	—	—	0	0	1.7	1.4	1.4	1.7	11	11	STW	ST/HL
C23-No 1	I	?	0.19	0.14	75	—	—	14	—14	1.4	1.4	2.0	1.0	8	8	ST/FL	ST/HL
	II		0.16	0.13	80	—	—	17	17	1.5	1.5	1.0	1.0	10	10	S-FT/HL	S-FT/HL
	III		0.16	0.13	80	—	—	17	0	1.5	1.5	1.5	1.0	0	10	S-FT/HL	S-FT/HL
	IV		0.14	0.09	67	—	—	33	17	2.0	2.0	1.3	0.8	11	0	S-FT/HL	S-FT/HL
	V		0.14	0.1	72	—	—	25	18	2.0	1.6	1.0	1.0	0	17	S-FT/HL	STW
	VI		0.21	0.13	62	—	—	33	11	2.3	2.3	1.6	0.9	—8		S-FT/HL	S-FT/HL
	VII		0.21	0.13	62	—	—	22	22	2.3	2.3	1.2	1.2	0	0	S-FT/HL	S-FT/HL
	VIII		0.22	0.09	43	—	—	27	18	3.7	3.7	1.1	1.3	0	7	ST/HL	ST/HL
	IX		0.19	0.13	71	—	—	13	7	2.0	1.7	1.4	1.4	4	8	ST/HL	ST/HL
	X		0.25	0,16	63	—	—	18	18	2.2	2.2	1.3	1.3	13	13	STW	STW
C25-No 1	I	?	0.17	0.14	90	—	—	25	0	2.7	0.8	0.8	1.2	0	10	S-FT/HL	S-FT/HL
(74)	II		0.14	0.11	78	—	—	17	19	2.0	1.2	0.8	1.2	—11	11	S-FT/HL	S-FT/HL
	III		0.16	0.13	80	—	—	23	0	1.8	1.2	1.2	1.0	0	—5	S-FT/HL	S-FT/HL
	IV		0.14	0.09	67	—	—	33	19	2.0	1.2	0.8	0.8	11	0	S-FT/ML	S-FT/HL
	V		0.14	0.12	83	—	—	19	10	1.6	1.2	1.0	1.0	—6	—11	S-FT/HL	S-FT/HL
	VI		0.16	0.13	80	—	—	33	17	1.5	1.5	1.0	0.7	—10	0	S-FT/HL	S-FT/HL
	VII		0.14	0.11	78	—	—	19	33	1.2	2.0	0.8	0.8	—22	11	S-FT/HL	S-FT/HL
	VIII		0.16	0.13	80	—	—	17	0	1.5	1.5	1.5	1.0	0	10	S-FT/HL	S-FT/HL
	IX		0.17	0.13	73	—	—	29	29	1.8	1.8	0.8	0.8	0	0	S-FT/HL	S-FT/HL
	X		0.16	0.11	70	—	—	29	17	1.3	1.5	1.0	1.0	—10	0	S-FT/HL	S-FT/HL
	XI		0.17	0.13	73	—	—	29	0	1.8	1.8	1.8	0.8	0	0	S-FT/HL	S-FT/HL
	XII		0.16	0.13	80	—	—	17	17	1.5	1.5	1.0	1.0	10	10	S-FT/HL	S-FT/HL
	XIII		0.19	0.13	67	—	—	25	12	2.0	2.0	1.4	1.0	—8	0	S-FT/HL	S-FT/HL
	XIV		0.17	0.13	73	—	—	15	15	1.8	1.5	1.2	1.2	—9	9	S-FT/HL	S-FT/HL
C27-No 1	I	?	0.14	0.11	78	—	—	19	17	1.2	2.0	1.2	0.8	11	11	?	?
	II		0.16	.11	70	—	—	—17	0	1.0	1.5	1.5	1.5	20	10	STW	STW
	III		0.16	.12	75	—	—	17	7	1.5	1.9	1.5	1.0	5	10	?	?
	IV		0.13	.12	94	—	—	0	—11	1.3	0.8	1.0	1.3	6	0	STW	S-FT

(*Contd.*)

1	2	3	4	5	6	7	8	9	10	11	12	13	14	15	16	17	18
	V		0.15	0.13	94	—	—	0	19	1.1	1.4	0.9	1.1	11	0	ST/HL	S-FT
	VI		0.17	0.13	77	—	—	31	0	1.6	1.3	1.3	0.9	0	−10	ST	ST/HL
	VII		0.16	0.12	75	—	—	28	0	1.2	1.5	1.5	0.7	20	5	STW	ST/HL
	VIII		0.19	0.13	71	—	—	−20	12	1.0	2.0	1.4	1.7	8	4	STW	ST/HL
C28-No 2	I	0.5	0.16	0 09	59	—	—	18	22	1.7	3.0	1.7	1.0	1	4	ST/HL	ST/HL
	II	0.27	0.23	0.13	56	—	—	28	10	1.7	4.1	1.7	1.3	6	0	ST/HL	ST/HL
	III	0.11	0.44	0.15	37	—	—	4	−10	1.6	3.4	4.5	2.1	23	10	STW	STW
C28-No 3	I	0.51	0.19	0.1	54	—	—	17	16	2.8	2.2	1.4	1.7	18	4	STW	ST/HL
	II	0.50	0.16	0.11	68	—	—	8	13	2.2	1.5	1.3	1.5	4	0	STW	ST/HL
	III	0.51	0.18	0.11	57	—	—	16	22	2.0	2.6	1.6	1.1	4	0	ST/HL	ST/HL
	IV	?	0.35	0.23	65	—	—	6	−17	0.6	4.8	3.4	0.9	−1	17	ST/HL	STW
C28-No 4	I	0.87	0.09	0.04	50	—	—	22	22	3.5	3.5	1.3	1.3	0	0	ST/HL	ST/HL
	II	0.87	0.12	0.07	56	—	—	22	42	1.3	2.7	0.8	0.8	−16	0	S-FT/HL	S-FT/HL
	III	0.87	0.12	0.08	64	—	—	17	18	2.4	2.0	1.1	1.4	0	0	ST/HL	ST/HL
	IV	0.64	0.14	0.09	64	—	—	25	14	1.9	2.9	1.9	0.9	0	5	ST/HL	ST/HL
	V	0.6	0.15	0.11	68	—	—	15	14	1.7	2.0	1.3	1.1	0	0	ST/HL	ST/HL
	VI	0.45	0.16	0.1	63	—	—	21	19	1.8	2.9	1 4	1.1	5	5	ST/HL	ST/HL
	VII	0.36	0.21	0.1	46	—	—	33	18	4.2	2.8	1.6	1.1	0	13	ST/HL	ST/HL
	VIII	0 17	0.36	0.17	46	—	—	31	8	3.0	2.6	2.6	1.1	2	12	ST/HL	STW
C28-No 5	I	0.53	0.14	0.06	48	—	—	0	27	2.4	2.4	1.1	2.4	19	0	STW	ST/HL
	II	0.55	0.14	0.1	72	—	—	0	17	1.8	1.5	1.0	1.8	9	0	STW	ST/HL
	III	0.7	0.14	0.1	72	—	—	0	20	1.3	1.8	1.0	1.3	9	−5	STW	ST/HL
	IV	0.67	0.12	0.09	74	—	—	20	36	1.2	1.4	0.6	0.7	0	−10	S-FT/HL	S-FT/HL
	V	0.76	0.13	0.08	65	—	5	20	55	1.0	1.2	0.5	0.6	0	−5	S-FT/HL	S-FT/HL
	VI	0.86	0.13	0.09	70	—	—	36	31	1.2	1.9	0.9	0.5	0	0	S-FT/HL	S-FT/HL
	VII	0.84	0.12	0.08	68	—	—	33	31	1.7	2.0	0.8	0.7	0	0	S-FT/HL	S-FT/HL
	VIII	0.76	0.13	0.09	70	—	—	15	15	1.9	1.9	1.1	1.1	0	0	ST/HL	ST/HL
	IX	0.55	9.17	0.11	62	—	—	17	0	2.1	1.8	1.8	1.3	−4	15	ST/HL	STW
C28-No 6 (60)	II	]~1.1	0.12	0.06	53	—	12	30	25	2.2	0.5	0.1	0.8	−6	−6	FT/HL	ST/HL
	III		0.1	0.06	63	—	31	0	33	0.9	0.3	0.2	0.9	0	−8	FT/HL	ST/HL

C28-No 7 (66)	I	0.54	0.16	0.09	55	—	—	0	6	2.2	1.7	1.5	2.2	16	12	STW	STW
	II	0.46	0.19	0.10	53	—	—	0	5	1.9	2.5	1.9	1.9	13	10	STW	STW
	III	0.52	0.18	0.11	59	—	—	6	0	1.9	1.9	1.9	1.7	11	14	STW	STW
	IV	0.57	0.16	0.11	66	—	—	6	—6	1.7	1.7	1.9	1.5	12	12	STW	STW
	V	0.59	0.16	0.11	70	—	—	0	—6	1.5	1.5	1.7	1.5	8	12	STW	STW
	VI	0.62	0.15	0.11	70	—	—	7	0	1.5	1.7	1.7	1.1	13	4	STW	FT/HL
	VII	0.61	0.16	0.13	84	—	—	23	15	1.0	1.0	0.8	0.6	12	—8	ST/HL	FT/HL
	VIII	0.51	0.18	0.14	78	—	—	31	13	1.3	1.3	1.1	0.8	4	0	ST/HL	STW
	IX	0.38	0.24	0 14	60	—	—	9	11	1.5	2.4	1.7	1.2	13	13	STW	STW
C28-No 8 (67)	I	0.36	0.16	0.11	69	—	—	7	0	2.2	1.3	1.3	1.7	14	9	STW	STW
	II	0.31	0.24	0.16	70	—	—	0	0	1.6	1.5	1.5	1.6	13	6	STW	STW
	III	0.34	0.21	0.15	72	—	—	0	0	1.3	1.6	1.6	1.3	14	7	STW	STW
	IV	0.41	0.20	0.15	73	—	—	8	0	1.2	1.7	1.7	1.1	11	7	STW	STW
	V	0.42	0.24	0.18	75	—	—	0	—10	1.1	1.5	2.1	1.1	6	—3	STW	ST/FL
	VI	0.38	0.19	0.15	77	—	—	13	0	1.4	1.5	1.5	1.0	0	4	ST/HL	STW
	VII	0.43	0.20	0.16	77	—	—	0	0	1.2	1.5	1.5	1.2	4	4	STW	STW
	VIII	0.50	0.18	0.11	63	—	—	6	19	1.9	1.9	1.2	1.7	13	—4	STW	ST/HL
	IX	0.38	0.19	0,12	62	—	—	6	17	1.9	1.4	2.2	1.5	12	—4	STW	ST/FL
	X	0.14	~0.53	~0.21	~39	—	—	Incomplete step						~20	—	STW	—
C28-No 9 (68)	I	~0.20	0.33	0.11	35	—	—	0	—11	2.3	1.5	3.7	2.3	34	9	STWL	ST/FL
	II		0.35	0.13	37	—	—	21	10	4.0	2.5	1.4	1.7	25	29	STWL	STW
	III		0.32	0.13	40	—	—	17	8	4.7	2.1	1.7	2.1	5	23	ST/HL	STW
	IV		0.35	0.10	29	—	—	19	—22	6.7	1.5	3.0	2.4	8	33	ST/HL	STW
	(V)	Stop															
	VI	~0.70	0.14	0.09	63	—	—	50	9	2.0	1.5	1.1	0.4	5	—5	S-FT/HL	S-FT/HL
	VII		0.12	0.115	95	—	—	0	44	1.4	0.7	0.5	1.4	0	0	S-FT/HL	S-FT/HL
C28-No 10 (63)	I	0.30	0.24	0.11	47	—	—	11	15	2.7	3.8	1.4	1.4	0	0	ST/HL	ST/HL
	II	0.37	0.21	0.12	60	—	—	13	10	2.2	2.2	1.3	1.7	0	0	ST/HL	ST/HL
	III	0.41	0.18	0.14	76	—	—	15	0	1.8	1.4	1.4	1.4	0	7	ST/HL	ST/HL
	IV	0.49	0.16	0.13	81	—	—	8	6	1.5	1.5	1.1	1.3	—4	4	ST/HL	ST/HL

(*Contd.*)

1	2	3	4	5	6	7	8	9	10	11	12	13	14	15	16	17	18
	V	0 58	0.15	0.12	83	—	—	0	0	1.3	1.3	1.3	1.3	0	0	ST	ST
	VI	0.67	0.145	0.11	74	—	—	8	14	1.6	1.9	1.1	1.1	−4	0	ST/HL	ST/HL
	VII	0.86	0.145	0.12	82	—	—	0	15	1.2	1.6	1.6	0.9	0	4	ST	ST/HL
C28-No 11	I	0.35	0.19	0.07	36	—	—	10	5	2.7	5.2	3.6	1.8	10	21	STW	STW
C28-No 13	I	?	0.41	0.17	41	—	—	9	22	3.7	3.7	1.6	2.2	12	6	ST/HL	ST/HL
	II		0.34	0.14	42	—	—	19	17	2.9	4.7	2.1	1.5	7	7	ST/HL	ST/HL
	III		0.33	0.13	41	—	—	14	10	3.6	3.3	2.4	2.0	15	4	STW	ST/HL
	IV		0.26	0.14	58	—	—	0	—7	2.0	1.7	2.0	2.0	24	0	STW	ST
	V		~0.51	0.15	19	—	—	19	—8	Cycle not completed				~3	~29	STW	STW

LEGEND, HERE AND FURTHER : FT/HL=Fast trot with predominance of hind limbs; S-FT=movement on border of slow and fast trots; S-FT/HL=same with predominance of hind limbs; ST=Slow trot; ST/HL or FL=slow trot with predaminance of hind limbs or front limbs; STW=slow trot-like walk; VSW=very slow walk. The remaining designations are the same as in Table 2.

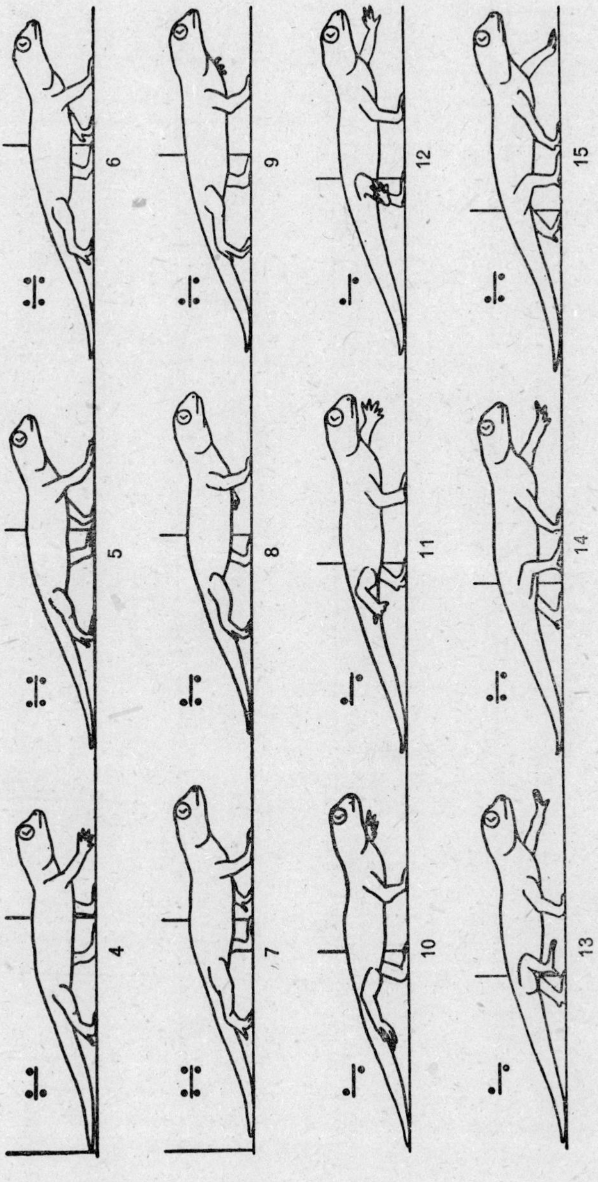
4
5
6
7
8
9
10
11
12
13
14
15

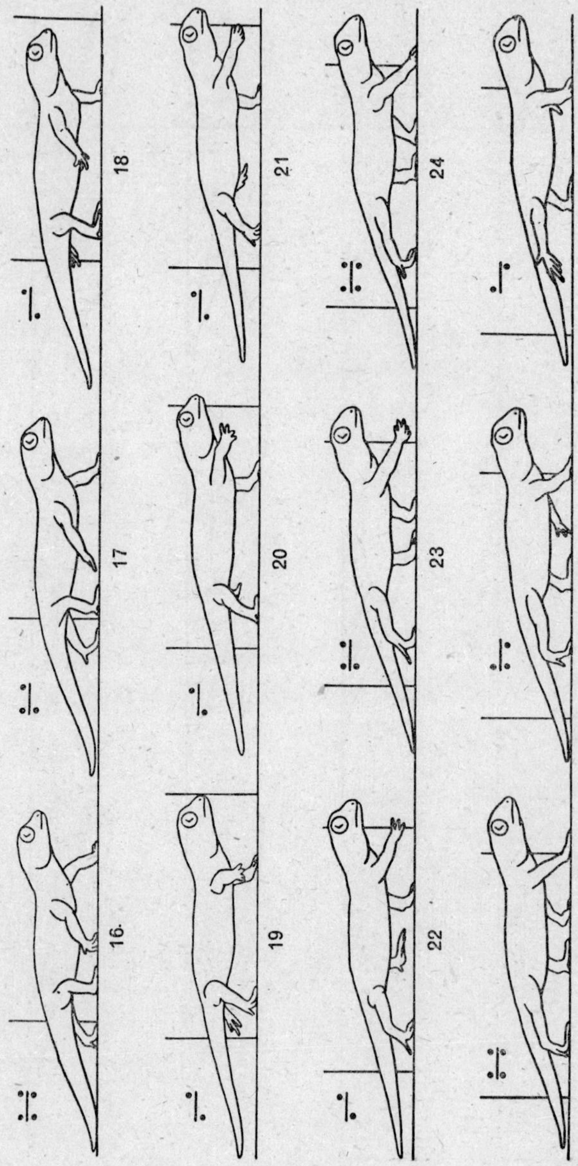

Figure 61. Slow trot with predominance of hind limbs during movement of plate-tailed gecko at a speed of 0.3 to 0.4m per second.

Series C28-No. 10; frames 4 to 27. Legend same as in Figure 59.

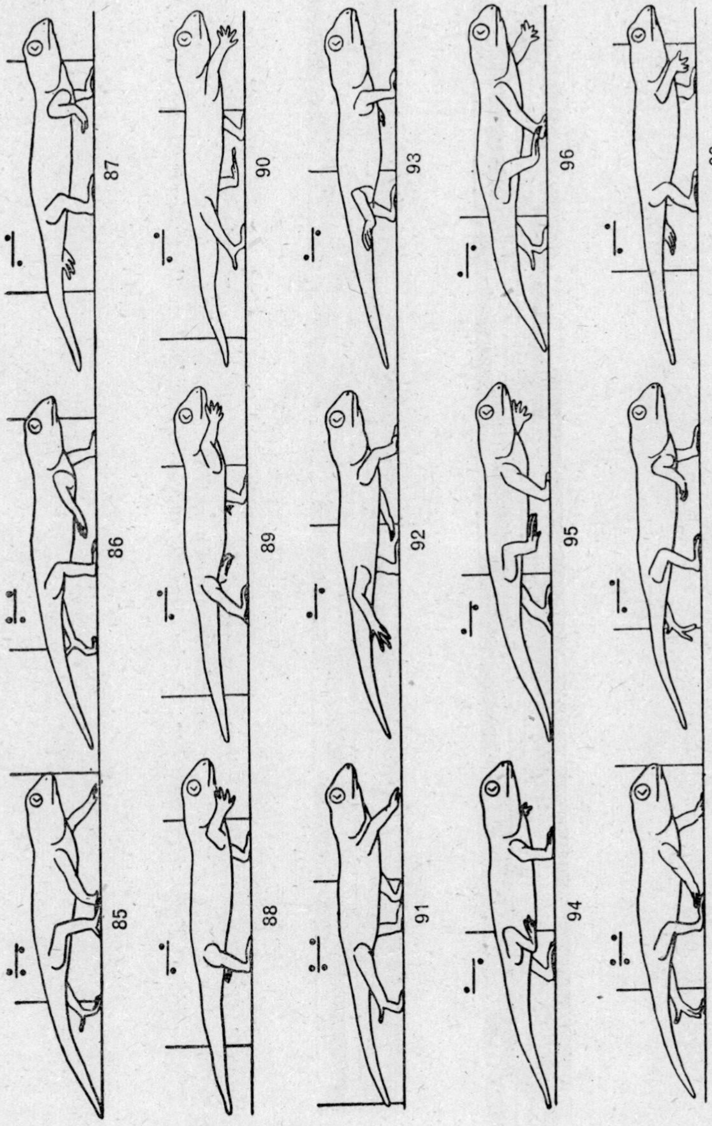

Figure 62. Slow trot with predominance of hind limbs during movement of plate-tailed gecko at a speed of about 0.7 to 0.8m per second.

Series C28-No. 10; frames 85 to 99. Legend same as in Figure 59.

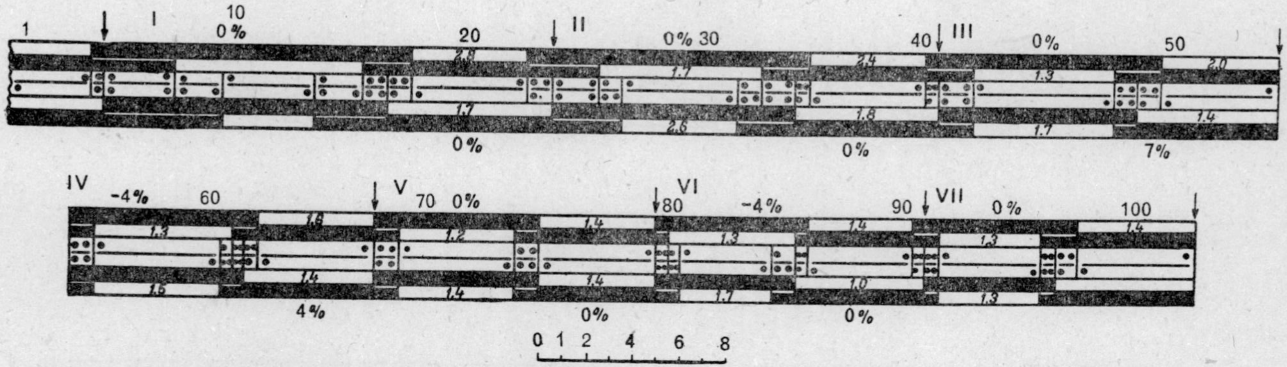

Figure 63. Diagram of uniform increase of movement for plate-tailed gecko passing in the form of a slow trot with predominance of hind limbs.

Series C28-No. 10: frames 1 to 102; film speed 80 frames per second. Legend same as in Figure 40.

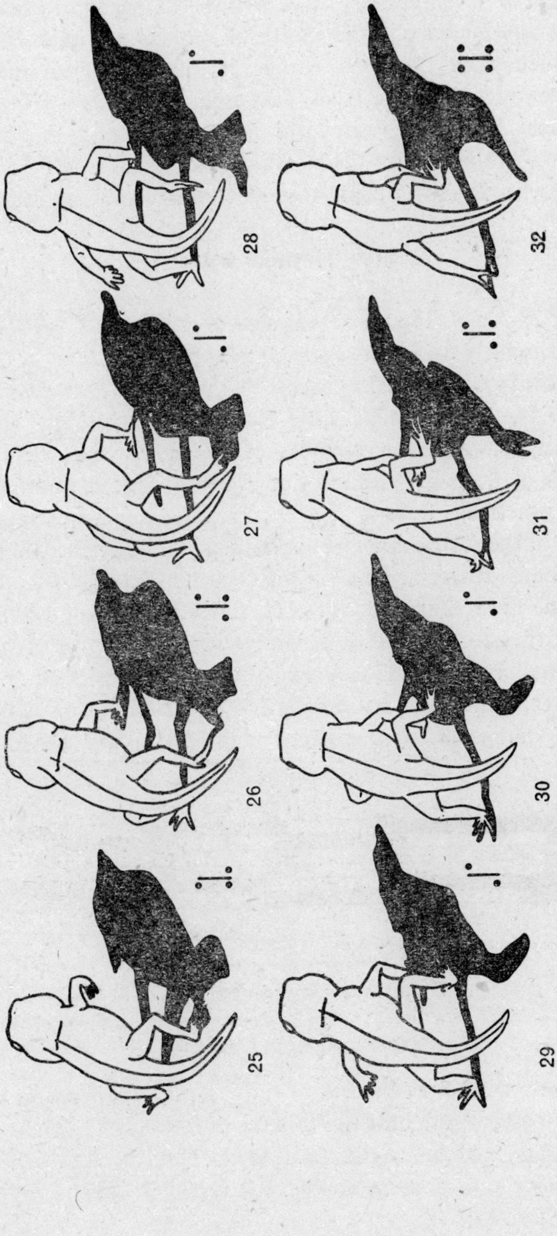

Figure 64. Slow trot with predominance of hind limbs in plate-tailed gecko in field conditions. *Series C22-No. 1; frames 25 to 32. Legend same as in Figue 59.*

(Table 5). The rhythm of limb action is significantly reduced with an increase of speed, but in all cases it is more than 1. Altogether, the speed at the beginning of the series on the level corresponds to the norm of the slow trot. With a three-fold increase of speed toward the end of the series, the duration of the cycle is reduced by 1.7 times. In other words, the speed increase is equally responsible for the increase in the length of walk and a quickening of limb movement which was observed earlier in other material (Chapter VI). Calculations conducted on the basis of other series (C28-No. 4) in that portion where movement took place similarly in the form of the slow trot with predominance of the hind limbs (Table 5), give identical results. In Figures 64 and 65, the gecko is shown using this gait under field conditions.

Slow Trot-like Walk

In series C28-No. 7 (Figure 66) the slow trot-like walk is observed in the first five and similarly in ninth cycle. It passes approximately at the same speed as the slow trot with predominance of hind limbs in series C28-No. 10 (Table 5). On the level, speed is close to the norm of the slow trot or slightly below it. However, the resemblance ends here. Rhythm of locomotion varies in limits of 8 to 16% and is not equal to zero. Predominance of the hind limbs is practically absent, or is even replaced by a not very noticeable predominance of the forelimbs. The support plans for primary and secondary tripodal stages are different. The forelimb in the diagonal, as before, lifts earlier than the hind limb but this occurs not because of its lesser length but because it transfers sooner. The limbs work in turn in a typical symmetrical-diagonal sequence. Lifting earlier from the ground, the forefoot passes behind the hind one in touching the substratum. As a result, there seems to be a change of support plan for the secondary tripodal stage.

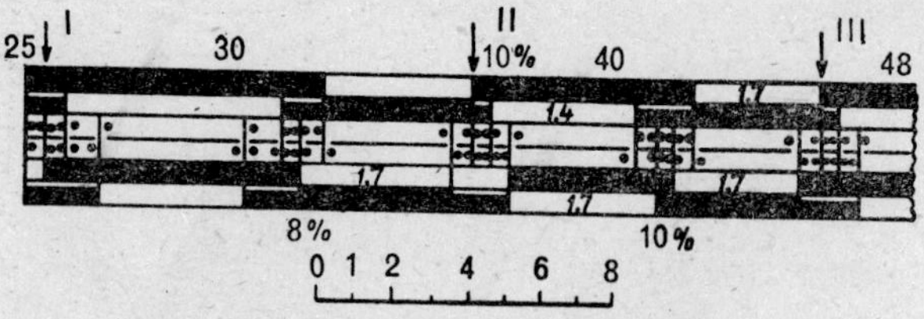

Figure 65. Diagram of movement of plate-tailed gecko.
Series C22-No. 1; frames 25 to 48; film speed 64 frames per second. Legend same as in Figure 40.

Slower movements with the use of those gaits were fixed in series C17-No. 1 (Table 5)where speed, judging from the duration of the cycle, is close to 0.3m per second (some what higher than the norm of the slow trot-like walk). The rhythm of locomotion in the series is still further from the rhythm of trot than in series C28-No. 7.

Slow Trot with Predominance of Forelimbs and Very Slow Walk

These gaits were met extremely rarely in our material and that too in the form of incomplete cycles. The slow trot with predominance of forelimbs was fixed in series C28-No. 8 (Table 5; Figure 67), C28-No. 9 (Table 5; Figure 68), C23-No. 1 (Table 5), C27-No. 1 (Table 5). Almost everywhere it is connected with a slow trot-like walk as this is put in it but never observed during

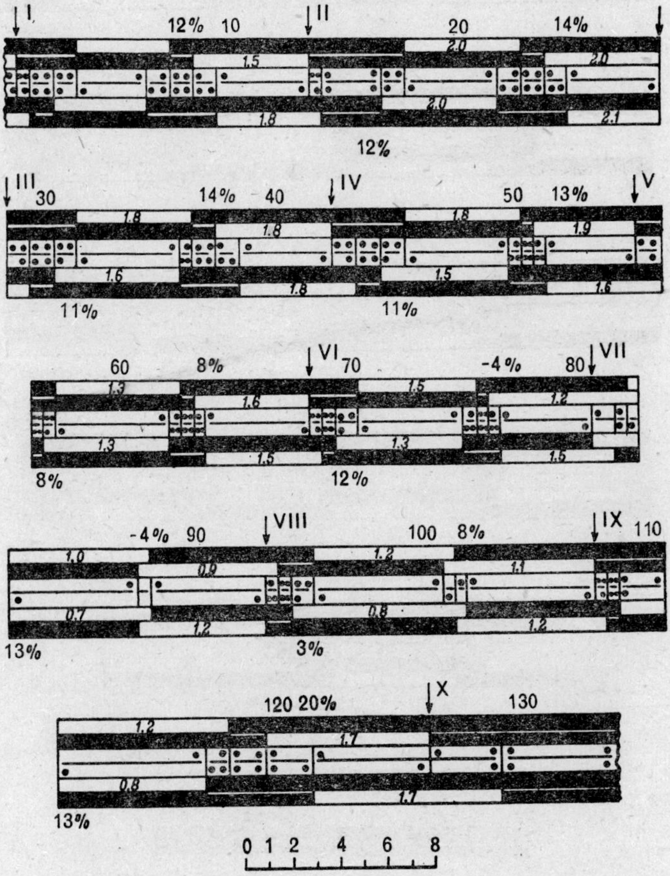

Figure 66. Diagram of movement of plate-tailed gecko.
Series C28-No. 7; frames 1 to 134; film speed 80 frames per second. Legend same as in Figure 40.

slowing prior to a stop. On the other hand, only during the latter circumstances in geckos is a very slow walk observed, for example in series C6-No. 2,

C7-No. 1 (Table 5; Figure 67), C7-No. 2 (Table 5; Figure 70), C13-No. 1 (Table 5; Figure 71).

From our material (Table 5; Figures 68 to 74), it is considered that geckos often move using several forms of locomotion in a complicated and not

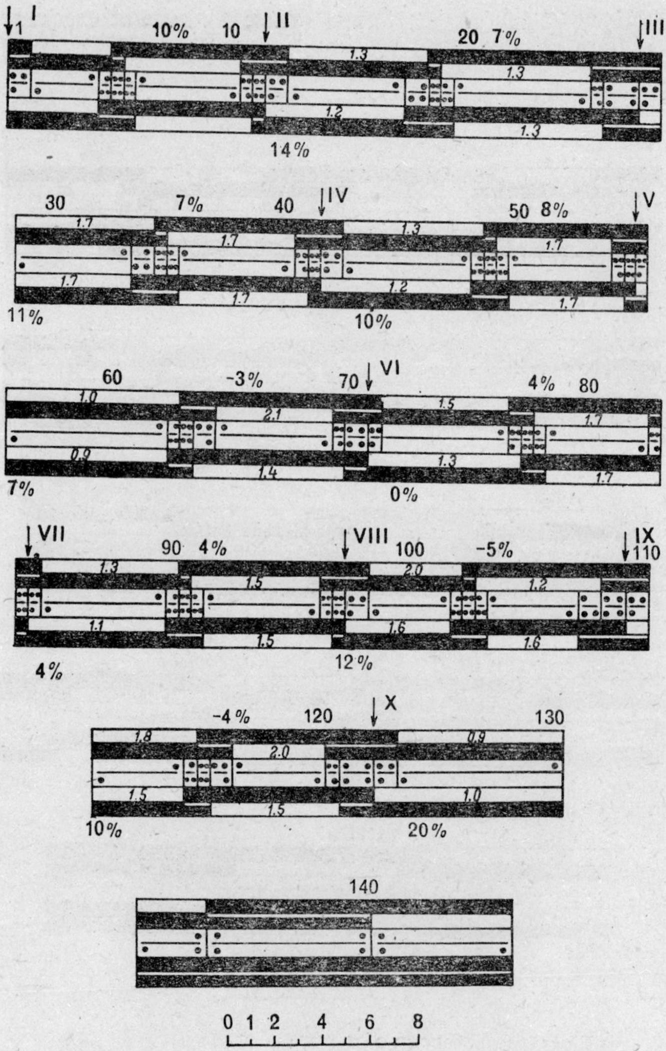

Figure 67. Diagram of movement of plate-tailed gecko.

Series C28-No. 8 ; frames 1 to 146; film speed 68 frames per second. Legend same as in Figure 40.

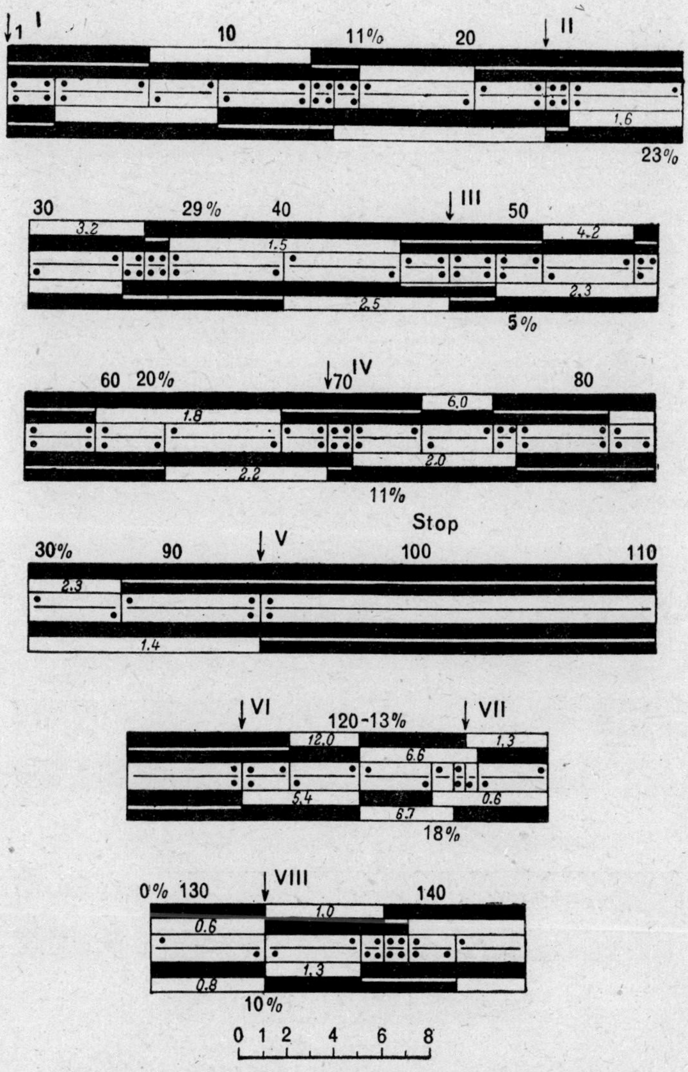

Figure 68. Diagram of movement of plated-tailed gecko.
Series C-28-No. 9; frames 1 to 144; film speed about 70 frames per second. Legend same as in Figure 40.

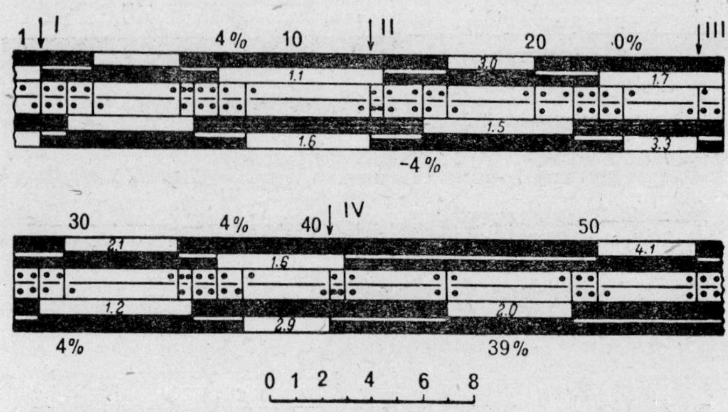

Figure 69. Diagram of movement of plate-tailed gecko.
Series C7-No. 1; frames 1 to 55; film speed 64 frames per second.
Legend same as in Figure 40.

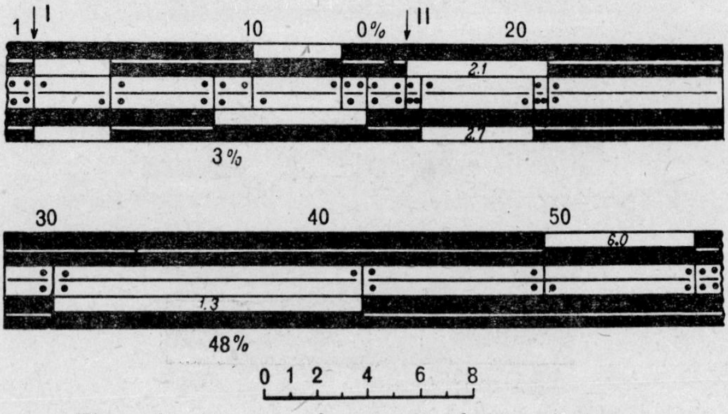

Figure 70. Diagram of movement of plate-tailed gecko.
Series C7-No. 2; frames 1 to 56; film speed 64 frames per second.
Legend same as in Figure 40.

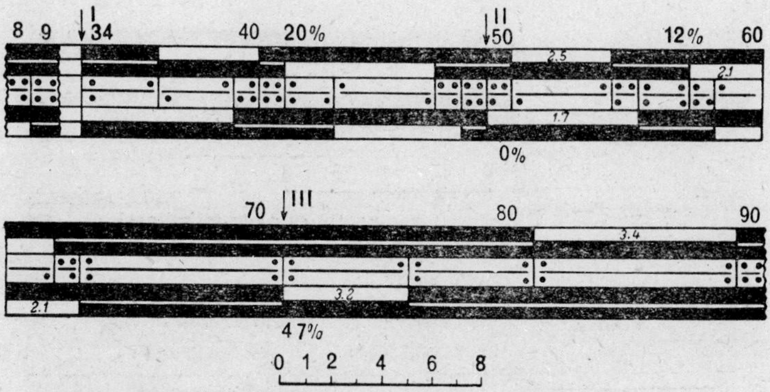

Figure 71. Diagram of movement of plate-tailed gecko.
Series C13-No. 1; frames 8 to 90; film speed 64 frames per second.
Legend same as in figure 40.

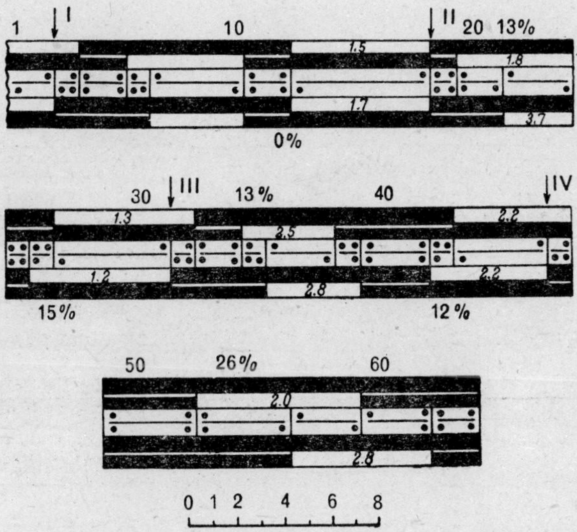

Figure 72. Diagram of movement of plate-tailed gecko.
Series C5-No. 1; frames 1 to 64; film speed 64 frames per second.
Legend same as in Figure 40.

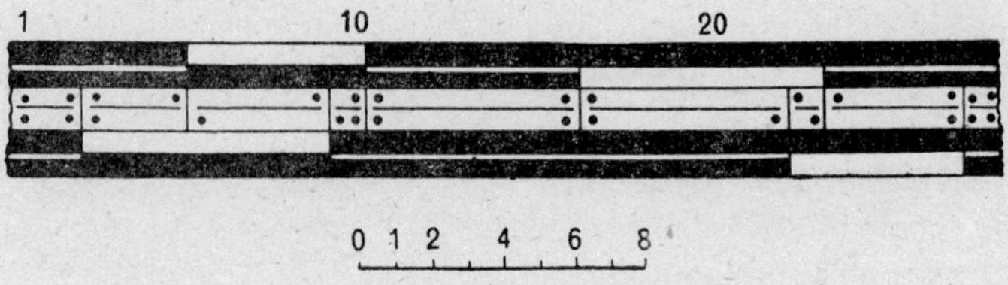

Figure 73. Diagram of movement of plate-tailed gecko.
Series C8-No. 1; frames 1 to 28; film speed 64 frames per second.
Legend same as in Figure 40.

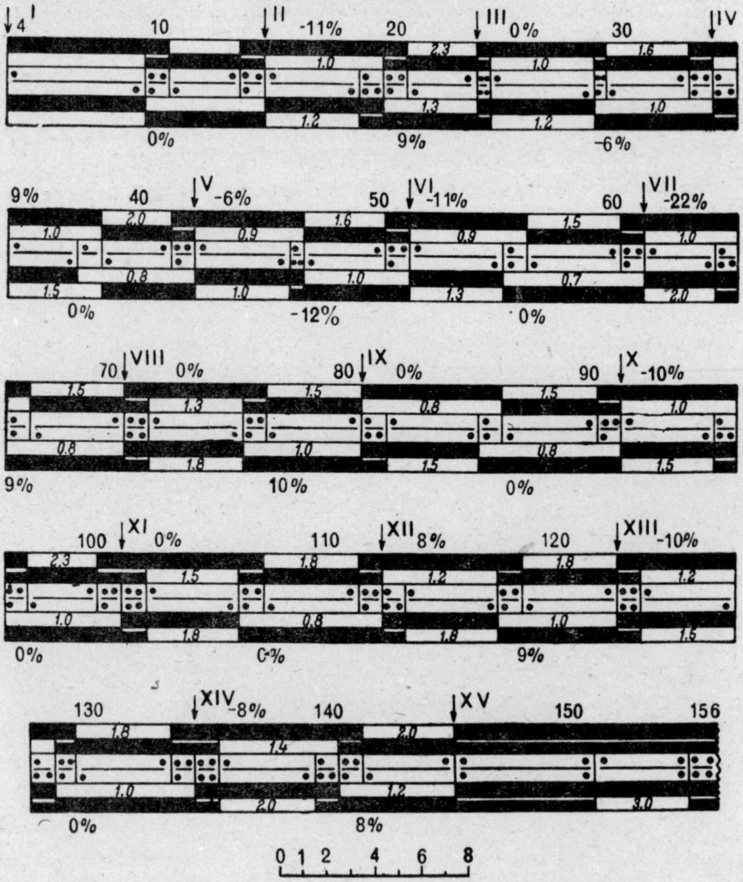

Figure 74. Diagram of movement of plate-tailed gecko.
Series C25-No. 1; frames 4 to 156; film speed 64 frames per second.
Legend same as in Figure 40.

always understandable combination. So in series C28-No. 3 (Table 5) the first half of the I to II cycles represent the slow trot-like walk, but the second, a slow trot with predominance of hind limbs. A still more complicated picture of gait alternation is observed in series C28-No. 8 (Table 5; Figure 67) where after the first four cycles of a slow trot-like walk, a half-cycle of a slow trot continues with predominance of forelimbs and a half-cycle with predominance of hind limbs, two cycles of a slow-trot-like walk, a half-cycle of a slow trot with predominance of hind limbs, a half-cycle of a slow trot-like walk, a half-cycle of a slow trot with predominance of forelimbs, and prior to the stop, an incomplete cycle of a slow trot-like walk. An analysis of such mixed series does not permit a judgment about any regularities in the change of duration of stages, rhythms of locomotion, and so on. This increases the value of the not so numerous and often too short series where movement is completed primarily in one form, but the speed is changed in one direction. Among such series may be named the already described C28-No. 6 (Figure 68), C-28-No. 10 (Figures 69). Among the remaining materials, the slow trot-like walk is observed in the following series: C5-No. 1 (Figure 72), C6-No. 2 (Table 5), C8-No. 1 (Figure 73), C11-No. 1 (Table 5), C13-No. 1 (Figure 71), C22-No. 1 (Figures 64, 65), C28-No. 7 (Figure 66), C28-No. 8 (Figure 67), C28-No. 11 (Table 5); the slow trot with predominance of hind limbs in series C5-No. 2, C6-No. 2 (Table 5), C7-No. 1 (Figure 69), C7-No. 2 (Figure 70), C8-No. 2, C10-No. 1, C28-No. 2, C28-No. 4, C28-No. 5, C28-No. 13 (Table 5). In several series an increase of movement is observed bordering on the slow and fast trot: C11-No. 2, C12-No. 1, C15-No. 1, C23-No. 1 (Table 5), C25-No. 1 (Figure 74). Such ratios of recorded slow and fast movement confirm the conclusion drawn earlier (Chapter VI) that geckos form a relatively slow- walking group of lizards rarely running to fast locomotion.

Eremias velox and Eumeces schneideri

Material on the movement of these lizards is very limited as it can only be analyzed from motion pictures photographed from above. Lacertids and scincids, when moving slowly, do not raise the body much above the substratum, their limbs are short in relation to their body compared for example, to the limbs of geckos or toad-headed lizards; because of this, they often do not straighten completely. So scincomorphs are not photogenic: if photographed from the side, the movement of limbs of the opposite side do not register. At the same time, even to read the shots photographed from above is not easy. The moment of establishing contact with the substrate can only be determined by the degree of focusing the image of the hands or feet. However, it often happens that if the hand in relation to the substrate has already stopped to be replaced, its image becomes sharp, but the real contact, judging from the shadow, has still to be established. Shooting was conducted only in the laboratory. Fast barbs were used only in connection with their availability. This selection happened to be unsuccessful because once on the platform, the lizard immediately ran with great speed, and to catch this movement was difficult. So it was possible to fix only some short series of two to three cycles of fast run. In one of these we actually observed some similarity of slow, disconnected stops of movement changing afterwards into fast run. This series B1-No. 1 (Figure 75, A) serves for our detailed analysis.

The first four frames of the series represent support stages for the limbs of the left diagonal. The forefoot loses contact with the substrate earlier than the hind one. It can be well seen (still 5) that the right forefoot has already started coming out in front, but the left hind one still rests on its distal phalanges (secondary unipodal stage). At the same time, the left forefoot, judging from the shadow, still does not touch. Contact is established in the sixth frame. It is interesting that diagonally from it, the hind limb is still in the air as its outline is blurred. Usually, the forefoot of the diagonal touches first only in the trot-like walk or in the trot with predominance of forelimbs, but this should not be in a fast trot with predominance of hind limbs. The apparent explanation of such a disturbance during the course of movement comes from two facts: first, the tail of the barb is strongly turned on the side which influences the animal toward the left in a sudden turn; secondly, movement at this moment is retarded. All this together, apparently, results in a brief disturbance for forms of locomotion. The origin of a predominance of forelimbs likewise promotes the fact that the right hind limb at the end of protraction was not bent at the knee to the degree characteristic for the real fast run, as for example in Figure 76 (frames 3, 6, 10, 19 and 23).

Support stages of the right diagonal limbs continue until the tenth frame (Figure 75, A). The next primary tripodal stage is already fixed. The change between them is not completely clear. However, judging from the character of movement, it should correspond to the diagram. It is appropriate to mention that the left hind limb at the end of protraction and in the beginning of retraction continues to be bent at the knee (frames 10 and 11). Respectively, the step which it completed before this was reduced in length. Successive frames up to the stop in frame 19, pass in the form of a slow trot with predominance of hind limbs but the primary tripodal stage is very short (on the diagram of half frame), while the secondary encompasses almost three frames. During this, the right hind foot also makes an incomplete step but now it is not only not bent at the start of the propulsive period, but is still bent at lift off, not having completed its retraction. Factually, although the left forelimb is still in the air, progressive movement has already stopped. The stop is continued for 32 frames; only the right hind foot moved slightly on frame 51 in comparison with 19.

With the 52nd frame, the forward right forelimb starts coming out. Thus, even the long stop does not disturb the diagonal sequence of movement

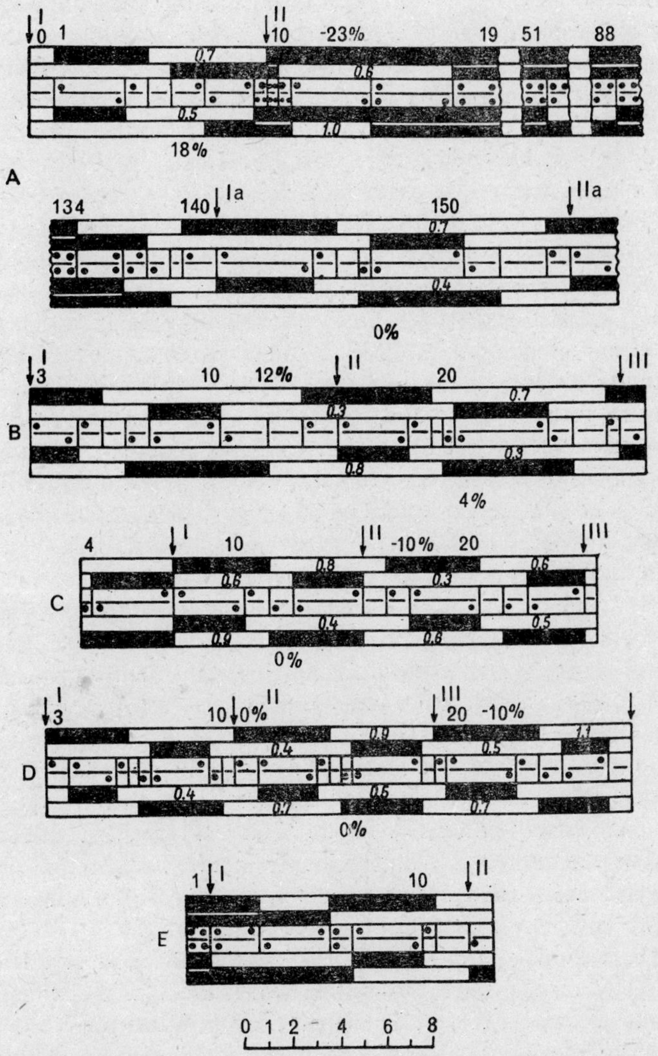

Figure 75. Diagram of locomotion of fast barbs *(Eremias velox)*. *A—Series Bl-No. 1, frames 0 to 157; B—Series Bl-No. 2, frames 3 to 28; C—Series Bl-No. 3, frames 4 to 25; D—Series Bl-No. 4, frames 3 to 27; E—Series Bl-No. 6, frames 1 to 13. Film speed : A and B—88 frames per second; C, D, and E—on an average, 70 frames per second. Legend same as in Figure 40.*

of limbs.[3] Transport of this foot is of a long duration, and apparently stopped somewhere in the region of frames 75 to 80. The hand is apparently arrested by the preaxial border. Afterwards, a new stop follows with support on four feet until the 134th frame where the movement in front is started by the left hind limb. Formally, the portion of the diagram between frames 14 and 134 may be determined as very slow walk. In the following frames (135 and 136) the change from rest to fast movement is observed almost in the form of a jump. Increase is caused by the retraction of the limbs on the right diagonal but after the lift off of the forelimb (frame 137), then the right hind foot. During this, the ipsilateral forelimb is passively retracted dragging on the substrate. Its protraction starts (frame 137) only shortly before the landing of the left hind limb (frame 138). This leads to an increase in the primary unipodal stage. The change to the latter from the secondary unipodal stage is not fixed. On the diagram a very short stage of free flight is conditionally shown.

Further frames in the series correspond to fast trot with predominance of hind limbs, one cycle of which is shown in Table 6. Movement continues with a significant increase, e.g., contains a stage of free flight. However, in comparison to other series, for example B1-No. 4, the duration of the cycle is quite long. The speed is close to 0.6 to 0.7 m per second.

Fast trot with predominance of hind limbs is clearly shown in series B1-No. 4 (Figure 75, D, Figure 76). Diagrams of frames (Figure 76) are clearly convincing in this. Though not all stages are traced during the entire series, their reconstruction does not call for any doubts, since the principal stages characterising this gait have all the same been recorded. The primary single-support (frames 3, 7, 11, 15, and 24 in Figure 76). secondary single-support (frames 6, 10, 14 and 23) and stages of free flight (frames 19 and 27). Since the average speed in the series hardly exceeds 1 m per second, the stages of free flight are usually eliminated. Figure 76 also shows that the bending of the body in barbs in the course of movement takes place in the form of standing waves which are particularly noticeable in the tail region. This is in full agreement with the movement by a trot (Chapter V).

In the remaining series—B1-No. 2 (Figure 75, B), B1-No. 3 (Figure 75, C), and B1-No. 6 (Figure 75, E)—fast barbs also use a fast trot with predominance of hind limbs (Table 6). The latter, from the same series, is interesting in that on the duration of one cycle, the barb goes directly from a state of rest to a fast trot with predominance of hind limbs. At the end of a very long cycle, a long stage of flight has appeared. In the beginning of the cycle, its place is still occupied by a support stage on the two hind limbs which was also observed in plate-tailed geckos.

Thus, the material on the fast barb confirms the conclusion made in

[3]In its time this was mentioned for salamander (Chapter V). Many such examples may be discovered in plate-tailed geckos, for examples in series C28-No. 9 (Figure 68) and C9-No. 1 (Figure 71).

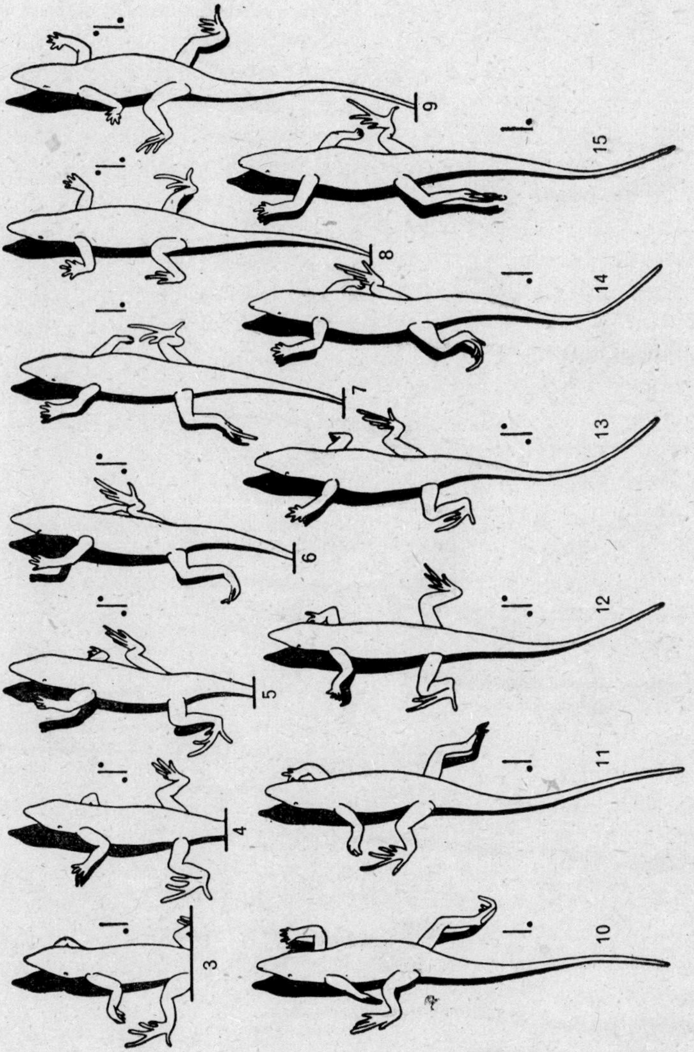
3
4
5
6
7
8
9
10
11
12
13
14
15

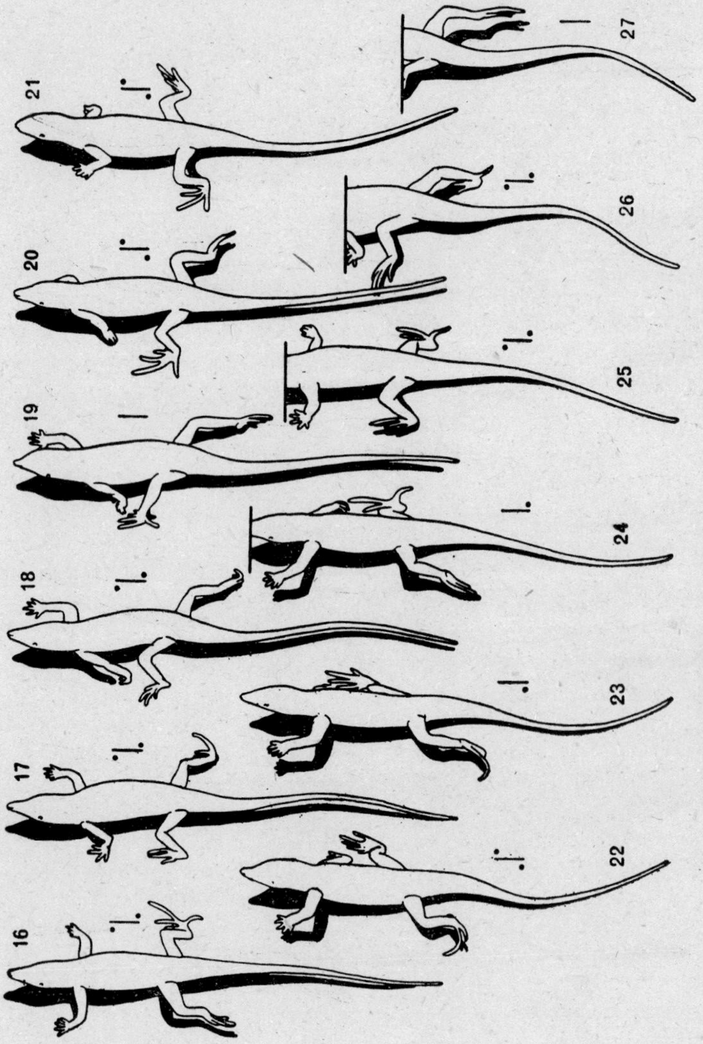

Figure 76. Fast trot with predominance of hind limbs in fast barbs. *Series B1-No. 4; stills 3 to 27. Legend same as in Figure 59.*

Table 6. Characteristics of locomotion for fast barb and long-legged scink (in cycles)

Series (shot number)	Cycle number	Speed (in m per sec)	Duration of: Cycle (in sec)	Duration of: Diagonal support (in sec)	Duration of: Diagonal support (in %)	Duration of: Secondary four-support stages (in %)	Duration of: Free flight (in %)	Degree of predominance (in %): LH-RF	Degree of predominance (in %): RH-LF	Rhythm of limb work (in conditional units): LH	RH	LF	RF	Rhythm of locomotion in half-cycles (in %): I	II	Form of location in half-cycles: I	II
B1-No 1 (75,A)	Ia	∞0.65	0.17	0.09	53	—	20	33	33	0.7	0.7	0.4	0.4	7	0	FT/HL	FT/HL
B1-No 2 (75,B)	I	∞1.26	0.15	0.06	39	—	19	56	50	0.5	0.9	0.3	0.2	4	—4	FT/HL	FT/HL
	II		0.14	0.08	58	—	17	33	33	0.6	0.8	0.5	0.3	4	4	FT/HL	FT/HL
B1-No 3 (75,C)	I	∞1.2	0.1	0.07	67	—	?	18	26	0.8	0.9	0.5	0.6	—12	12	FT/HL	FT/HL
	II		0.16	0.09	63	—	21	13	24	0.6	0.8	0.5	0.5	—11	—6	FT/HL	FT/HL
B1 No 4 (75,D)	I	∞1.0	0.1	0.06	57	—	10	44	29	0.8	0.7	0.4	0.3	0	—6	FT/HL	FT/HL
	II		0.1	0.07	66	—	10	36	17	1.0	0.7	0.5	0.5	—5	—5	FT/HL	FT/HL
	III		0.16	0.09	56	—	13	34	30	0.7	0.7	0.4	0.4	—12	6	FT/HL	FT/HL
B1-No 6 (75,E)	I	?	0.18	0.09	50	—	—	—	—	1.4	1.2	0.8	0.4	—	—	—	FT/HL
E1-No 2 (77,B)	I	∞0.15	0.42	0.21	50	8	—	9	—4	1.6	2.3	2.6	1.3	14	28	STW	STW
	II		0.52	0.28	55	9	—	13	6	1.9	2.1	1.8	1.3	14	23	STW	STW
	III		0.64	0.29	46	6	—	10	6	1.9	2.2	1.9	1.5	22	27	STW	STW

Chapter VI that fast movement in these animals is by a fast trot with predominance of hind limbs which is valued at 30 to 50%. Among the remaining peculiarities of locomotions in fast barbs which is strikingly more significant than in plate-tailed geckos, is the deviation of the rhythm of locomotion into the negative zone (Table 6). Free flight consists of the usual 10 to 20% of the cycle. Change from slow movement to fast, judging from the series B1-No. 1, is completed during a speed of about 0.6 to 0.7 m per second. Similar figures were shown for the retinal barb of more or less equal size to the fast barb based on the study of tracks.

Two film series of the long-legged scink do not yield, of course, all the possible forms of its movment; moreover, they correspond to only slow movement with a speed not exceeding 0.15 m per second; however, a speed of about 1.3 m per second was observed in the field. Nevertheless, they register some sequences which deserve attention.

Slow movement in series E1-No. 1 (Figure 77, a) is followed by an unusual behavior for lizards: making one step, the animal lies on its abdomen. Thus, conditions of equilibrium are suddenly changed. Photographed are the

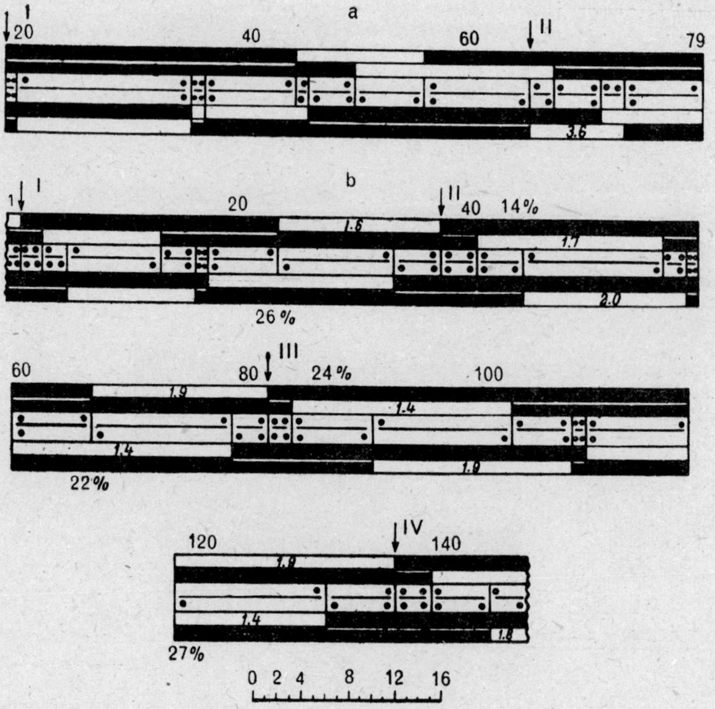

Figure 77. Diagram of slow movement of long-legged scink
(Eumeces schneideri).
a—Series E-1 No. 1, frames 20 to 79. b—Series E1-No. 2, frames 1 to 143.
Film speed 85 frames per second. Legend same as in Figure 40.

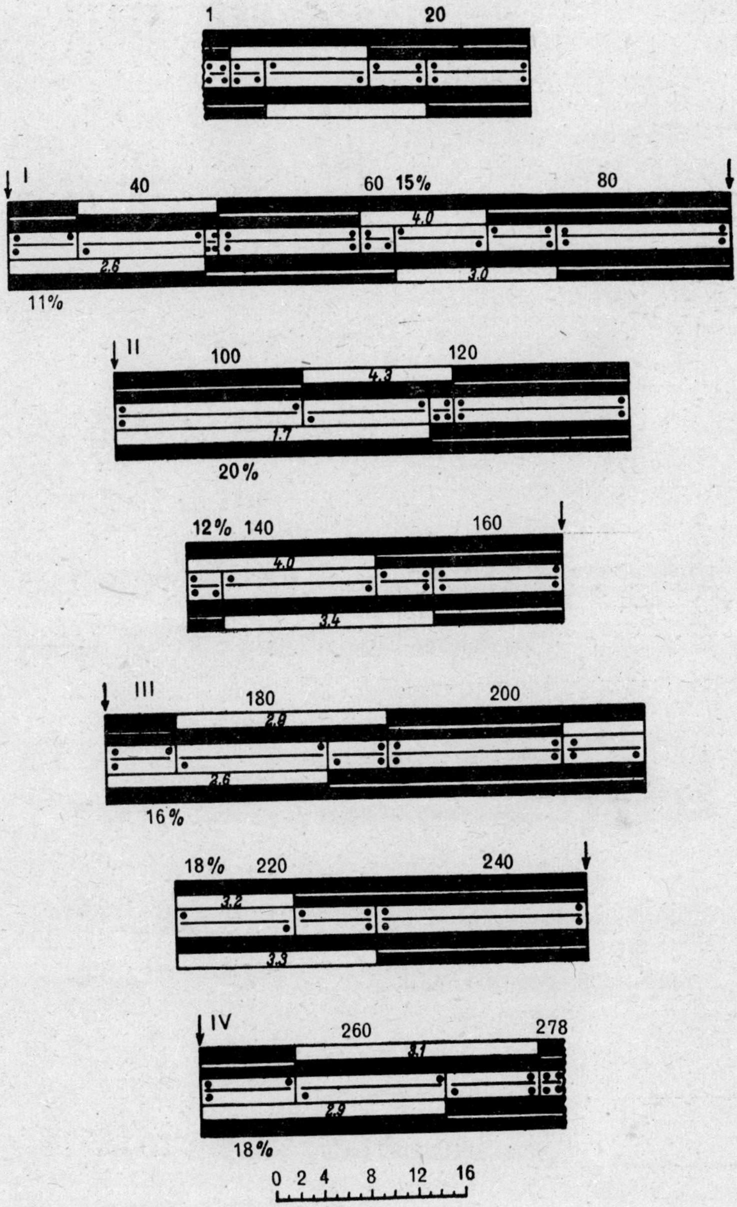

Figure 78. Diargam of movement of Kumodo monitor (Varanus komodoensis). *Series K1-No. 1; frames 1 to 278; film speed 24 frames per sceond. Legend same as in Figure 40.*

Table 7. Characteristics of locomotion for komodomonitor (in cycles)

Series (still number)	Cycle number	Duration of: Cycle (in sec)	Duration of: Diagonal support (in sec)	Duration of: Diagonal support (in %)	Degree of predominance (in %): LH-RF	Degree of predominance (in %): RH-LF	Rhythm of limb work: LH	Rhythm of limb work: RH	Rhythm of limb work: LF	Rhythm of limb work: RF	Rhythm of locomotion in half-cycles (in %): I	Rhythm of locomotion in half-cycles (in %): II	Form of locomotion in half-cycles: I	Form of locomotion in half-cycles: I I
1	2	3	4	5	6	7	8	9	10	11	12	13	14	15
K1-No 1(78)	I	2.6	0.8	31	10	— 6	4.2	3.5	4.6	2.6	11	15	STW	STW
	II	3.2	1.0	32	21	— 3	4.5	3.2	3.7	1.8	24	11	STW	STW
	III	3.4	0.96	28	2	0	3.5	3.8	3.8	3.3	14	17	STW	STW
K1-No ?(79)	I	1.6	0.27	33	16	4	4.6	2.9	2.6	2.9	23	13	STW	STW
	II	1.6	0.66	41	— 4	7	2.5	2.5	2.0	3.0	13	15	STW	STW
	III	1.6	0.66	36	7	0	3.0	3.4	3.4	2.2	10	13	STW	STW
K1-No 4(80)	I	1.3	0.71	57	—13	12	2.4	1.3	1.0	4.0	?	13	STW	STW
	II	1.4	0.79	56	0	8	1.4	2.8	2.1	1.4	9	18	STW	STW
	III	1.2	0.62	52	0	0	2.2	1.9	1.9	2.2	14	14	STW	STW
	IV	1.1	0.54	48	5	11	2.9	2.4	1.7	2.4	11	15	STW	STW
	V	1.1	0.62	58	0	6	1.9	2.3	1.9	1.9	12	12	STW	STW

1	2	3	4	5	6	7	8	9	10	11	12	13	14	15
K2-No 1(81)	I	1.1	0.53	47	7	8	3.5	2.0	1.6	2.6	13	13	STW	STW
	II	1.1	0.47	44	— 4	12	2.4	2.8	1.8	2.8	15	15	STW	STW
	III	1.1	0.50	46	0	6	2.8	2.3	1.9	2.8	14	10	STW	STW
K2-No 2(82)	I	0.8	0.31	41	— 6	22	3.0	3.0	1.4	2.4	8	29	ST/HL	STW
	II	0.6	0.28	45	7	26	2.6	3.4	1.4	2.1	5	15	ST/HL	STW
K2-No 3(84)	I	0.5	0.27	57	0	20	1.9	2.2	1.2	1.9	14	0	STW	ST/HL
	II	0.5	0.28	58	5	18	2.1	2.4	1.4	1.8	10	0	STW	ST/HL
	III	0.6	0.28	52	0	15	1.9	2.9	1.7	1.9	17	0	STW	ST/HL
	IV	0.6	0.28	49	0	14	1.8	3.6	2.1	1.8	16	0	STW	ST/HL
	V	0.5	0.27	52	4	17	2.3	2.7	1.5	2.0	15	0	STW	ST/HL
	VI	0.6	0.30	51	4	14	2.1	3.1	1.8	1.8	14	3	STW	ST/HL
	VII	0.8	0.48	62	0	16	1.8	1.8	1.2	1.8	13	10	STW	STW

important limitations in the movement of lower tetrapods which have evolved their gaits toward a trot, i.e., the impossibility of supporting the body in equilibrium resting on only the two one-sided limbs. As a result of increased movement during the beginning of cycle I in the form of a very slow walk, the scink still lifts the left forefoot from the substrate before landing on the ipsilateral hind leg. Primary quadrupodal stages change into a stage of lateral support, which does not have anything in common with the same-named stage of normal walk because, at this moment, the lizard lies on its abdomen. Actually, as also in the quadrupodal stage, progressive movement was stopped here.

The second series E1-No. 2 (Figure 77, b) reflects a faster movement by the same specimen. During this, a trot-like walk is used with a rhythm close to the norm. In this series, predominance of hind limbs was not observed much (Table 6).

Varanus komodoensis

The name Komodo monitor is associated in literature with many popular fanciful ideas. It is usually compared to the dinosaur. Gigantic in terms of lizards and sufficiently large even among reptiles, the Komodo monitor becomes an extraordinarily interesting object for the study of locomotion as its locomotion makes it possible to explain the limitations of its ability for movement in this or that pattern. A study of this monitor should remove frequent doubts about reptiles as a whole in that it is judged as a modern lizard.

Unfortunately, photographs of the Komodo monitor are, as a rule, done primarily for entertainment. Only three series of frames (K1-No. 1, No. 2, No. 3) from the French film permit an interpretation, but even here it is necessary to reconstruct allowing that the limbs of both diagonals in the duration of one cycle work similarly. Materials obtained from I. S. Darevskii similarly include three series of frames (K2-No. 1, No. 2, No. 3). These were taken however from a more professional viewpoint of the zoologist.

The slowest movement of the monitor is fixed in the series K1-No. 1 (Figure 78) where the speed is somewhat less than the level of norm of a slow trot-like walk in the form of which movement flows. Rhythm of locomotion varies from 11 to 20%, i.e., it is somewhat closer to the norm of the given gait than to the rhythm of the trot. The degree of predominance is greatest in the limbs of the left diagonal, the dominant role is played by the hind limbs but also the right forefoot. Degree of predominance of the latter is less however (Table 7). In the series K1-No. 2 (Figure 79) and K1-No. 3 (Figure 80) the varanus moves faster. The duration of the cycles in these series is reduced comparatively speaking two and three times respectively with the longest cycles of the receding series.

However, the form of movement is not changed by the rhythm of locomotion; judging from its real importance shown on the diagram of series, it is somewhat closer to the rhythm of a trot. This does not exclude the retention of a trot-like walk during an increase of speed of movement which is related to the larger sizes of the animals, so in the photographs of Darevskii where the animal was smaller (about 1.5 to 2 m), even then a change of gait is observed. In fact the speed here of movement is also more. In the series K2-No. 1 (Figure 81) it more or less corresponds to the series K1-No. 3. However, the same speed level determined by the rhythm of limb action corresponds in small monitors to a somewhat shorter cycle than in the larger specimens. The speed is 1.5 times higher in one series (K2-No. 2, Figure 82) and two times higher in the other (K2-No. 3, Figures 83 and 84).

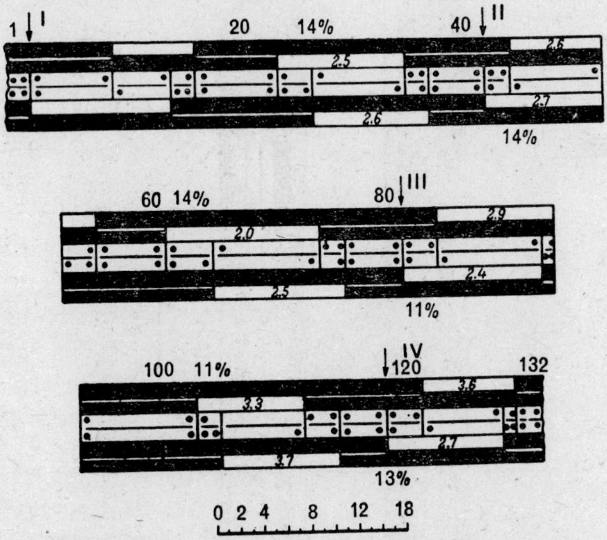

Figure 79. Diagram of movement of Komodo monitor.
Series K1-No. 2, frames 1 to 132; film speed 24 frames per second. Legend same as in Figure 40.

In these two series, a slow trot-like walk of one half-cycle starts alternating with a slow trot with predominance of hind limbs in the other where the limb of the right diagonal is carried forward. Predominance of the hind foot is increased in this diagonal (Table 7). Rhythm of locomotion starts suddenly changing in the course of the cycle from zero in a trot halfway up to 10 to 17% in a walk. However, at the end of series K2-No. 3 (Figure 84) the order is changed. In the second half of cycle VII, a trot-like walk appears together with the trot, i.e., in this form the whole cycle passes, but in the beginning of the next where the limbs of the left diagonal are already carried in front, the trot-like walk is replaced by a slow trot. The monitor, as if tired of trotting on one pair of limbs decides to change to the other pair. Interestingly, both

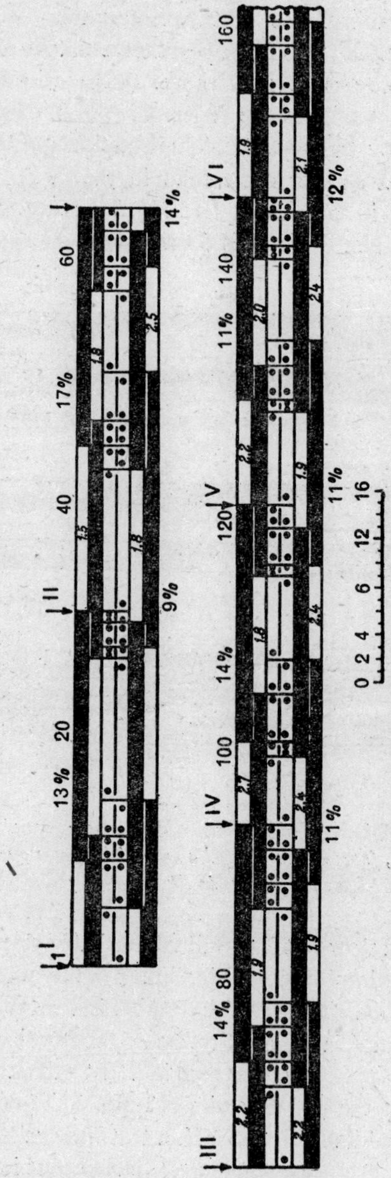

Figure 80. Diagram of movement of Komodo monitor.
Series KI-No. 3, frames 1 to 162; film speed 24 frames per second. Legend same as in Figure 40.

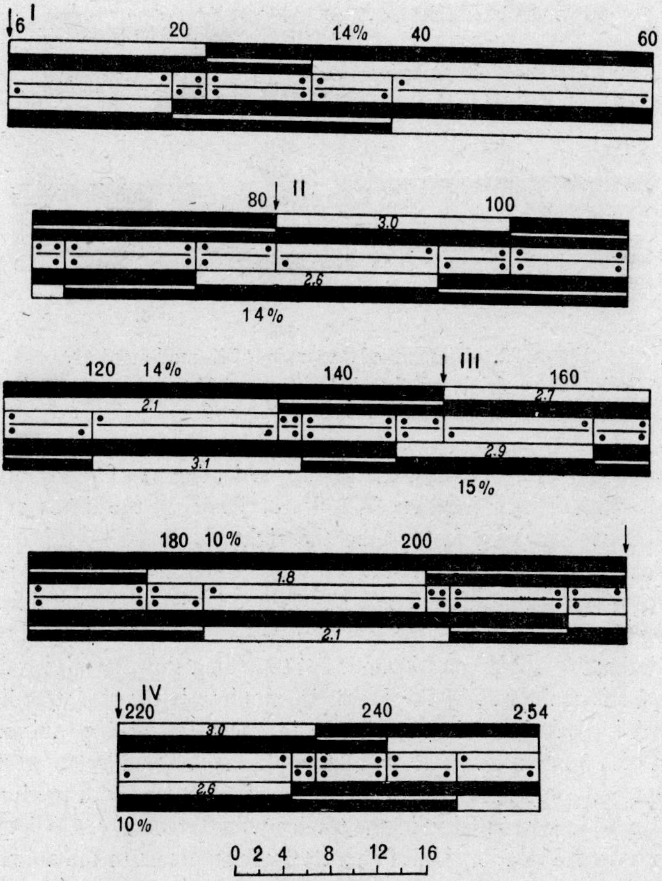

Figure 81. Diagram of movement of Komodo monitor

Series K2-No. 1, frames 6 to 154; film speed 64 frames per second. Legend same as in Figure 40.

pair of limbs of this animals work differently; the first series (K2-No. 1, Table 7), was wholly occupied by a slow trot-like walk. In the left diagonal, movement takes place slower than in the right (the rhythm of limb action is higher here), but in the latter there is a greater predominance of the hind limb. When the speed increased (K2-No. 2, Table 7), the rhythm of action of both pairs of

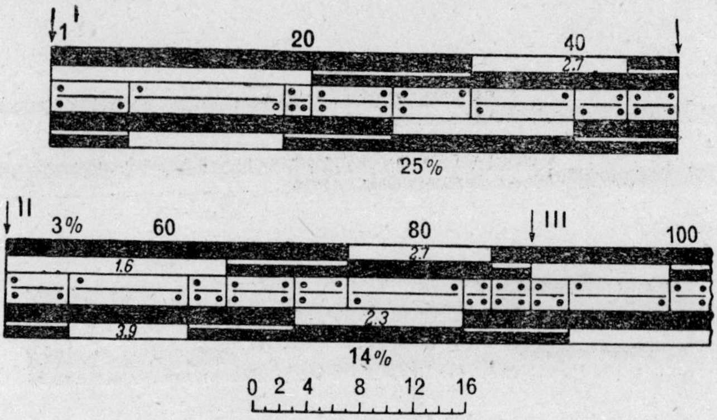

Figure 82. Diagram of movement of Komod monitor.
Series K2-No. 2, frames 1 to 102; film speed 64 frames per second. Legend same as in Figure 40.

limbs was compared, but only the difference in degree of predominance is increased. With further increase (K2-No. 3, Table 7), the limbs of the left diagonal began working faster than the right.

A clear presentation about the locomotion of Komodo monitor is given in Figure 83 where frame after frame shows one cycle of locomotion. In the beginning (frames 159 to 173) the monitor used a slow trot with predominance of hind limbs; toward the end (frames 174 to 188), a slow trot-like walk.

Thus, the main gait of the Komodo monitor is the slow trot-like walk which with increased speed may change in the not-so-large animals to a slow trot with predominance of hind limbs. In the still smaller desert monitor, movement may even take place in the form of a fast trot with predominance of hind limbs, as overlapping in the track was never observed (Chapter VI). Consequently, the relationship of character of movement to the animal size is indisputable.

Phrynocephalus mystaceus

Photographs of movement of toad-headed lizard were obtained only in the field. Attempts to photograph them in the laboratory were unsuccessful; in only two cases was it possible to determine the speed of movement and the duration of the cycle (1.2 m per second, cycle about 0.09 seconds; 1.8 m per second, cycle 0.1 second), which may serve as standard. The latter give only an estimate, however, as the speed of locomotion during photography in the

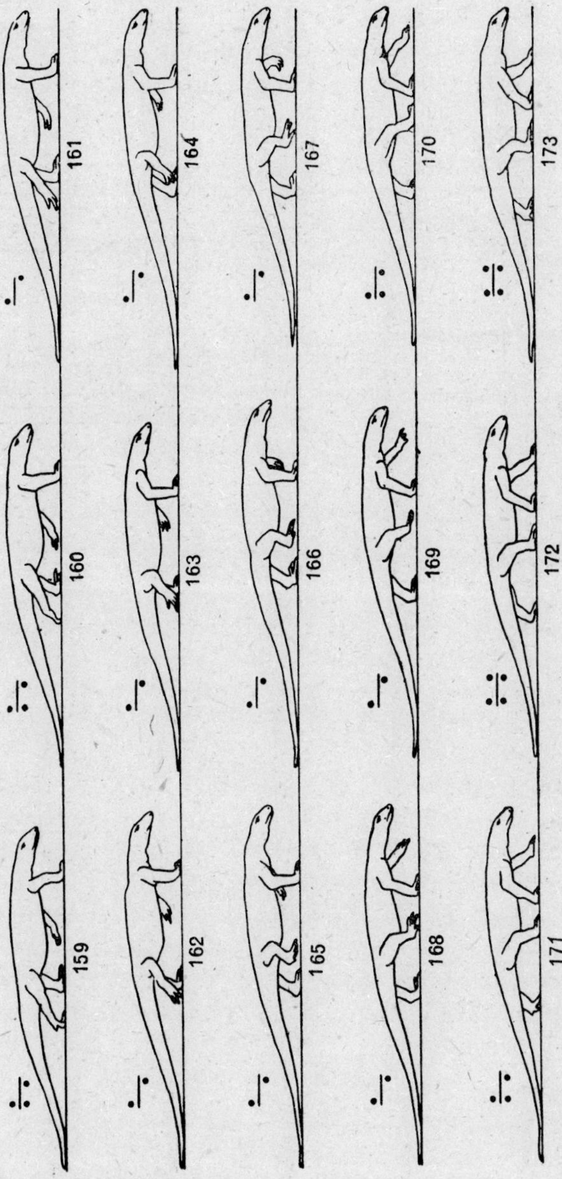
159
160
161
162
163
164
165
166
167
168
169
170
171
172
173

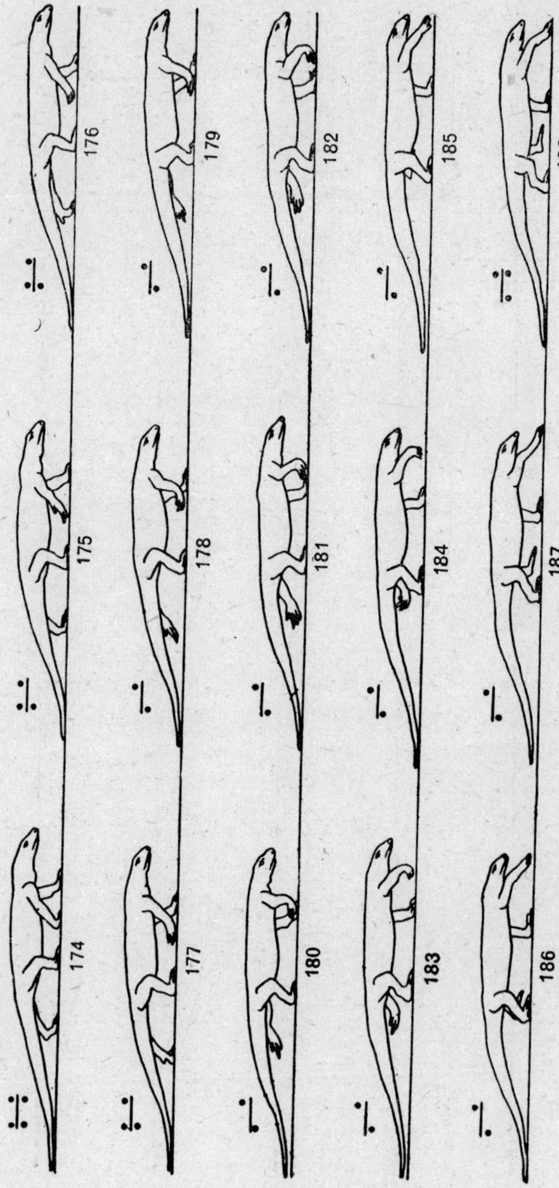

Figure 83. Slow trot with predominance of hind limbs and slow trot-like walk of Komodo monitor. *Series K2-No. 3, frames 159 to 188. Legend same as in Figure 59.*

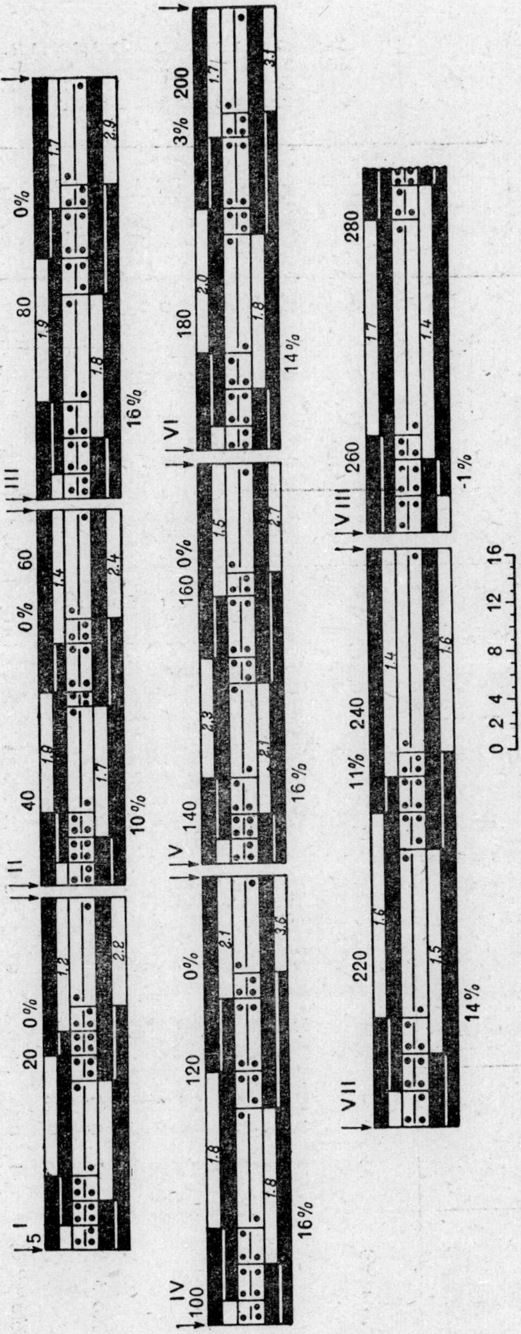

Figure 84. Diagram of movement of Komodo monitor.
Series K2-No. 3, frames 5 to 284; film speed 64 frames per second. Legend same as in Figure 40.

Table 8. Characteristics of locomotion for big-eared round-headed (in cycles)

Series (still number)	Cycle number	Duration of: Cycle (in sec)	Duration of: Diagonal support (in sec)	Duration of: Diagonal support (in %)	Duration of: Free flight (in %)	Degree of predominance (in %): LH-RF	Degree of predominance (in %): RH-LF	Rhythm of limb action (in conditional units): LH	RH	LF	RF	Rhythm of locomotion in half-cycles (in %): I	II	Form of locomotion in half-cycles: I	II
Y8-No 1(86)	I	0.14	0.08	56	11	25	50	0.8	0.8	0.7	0.5	0	0	FT/HL	FT/HL
	II	16	0.1	65	11	25	30	0.7	1.0	0.5	0.4	0	—5	FT/HL	FT/HL
	—						Stop							—	—
	I	0.15	0.07	47	21	33	45	0.5	0.9	0.4	0.3	0	0	FT/HL	FT/HL
Y10-No 1(88)	I	0.185	0.14	75	4	17	27	1.0	0.9	0.5	0.7	0	—8	FT/HL	FT/HL
	II	0.18	0.1	57	—	33	22	1.9	3.6	1.6	0.8	4	4	ST/HL	ST/HL
Y10 No 2(89)	I	0.15	0.09	58	11	29	40	0.6	1.1	0.5	0.4	0	0	FT/HL	FT/HL
	II	0.17	0.09	55	14	40	33	0.8	0.7	0.4	0.4	5	0	FT/HL	FT/HL
	III	0.16	0.09	55	15	29	40	0.6	1.0	0.4	0.3	0	0	FT/HL	FT/HL
	IV	0.16	0.09	60	5	33	46	0.8	1.2	0.4	0.4	5	—5	FT/HL	FT/HL
															FT/HL
Y10-No 3(90)	I	0.17	0.09	57	19	30	29	0.9	0.5	0.3	0.5	0	—5	FT/HL	FT/HL
	II	0.17	0.11	67	10	22	30	0.8	0.8	0.5	0.5	—5	0	FT/HL	FT/HL
	III	0.18	0.12	65	9	30	27	0.8	0.9	0.5	0.4	4	4	FT/HL	FT/HL
															FT/HL
Y11-No 1(91)	I	0.1	0.06	62	8	33	33	0.9	0.9	0.4	1.0	15	—15	FT/HL	FT/HL
	II	0.12	0.07	60	13	17	43	0.9	0.9	0.4	0.5	—7	—7	FT/HL	FT/HL
	III	0.13	0.08	63	13	33	25	0.6	1.0	0.6	0.3	0	0	FT/HL	FT/HL
	IV	0.14	0.09	61	11	29	33	0.6	1.0	0.5	0.4	—6	0	FT/HL	FT/HL

Y12-No 1(93)	I	0.16	0.07	45	20	50	38	0.7	0.7	0.3	0.4	—5	0	FT/HL	FT/HL
	II	0.14	0.07	50	17	43	38	0.6	0.8	0.4	0.3	—6	—6	FT/HL	FT/HL
	III	0.16	0.07	45	20	38	50	0.7	0.7	0.4	0.3	0	—5	FT/HL	FT/HL
	IV	0.14	0.08	65	12	33	33	0.6	1.1	0.6	0.4	—6	0	FT/HL	FT/HL
	V	0.15	0.08	53	21	38	29	0.7	0.6	0·4	0.4	—5	—5	FT/HL	FT/HL
	VI	0.14	0.08	56	17	43	29	0.6	0.6	0.4	0.3	—6	—6	FT/HL	FT/HL
	VII	0.14	0.08	56	11	43	33	0.6	1.0	0.5	0.3	—6	—6	FT/HL	FT/HL
	VIII	0.14	0.08	56	11	43	33	0.6	1.0	0.5	0.3	—6	—6	FT/HL	FT/HL
	IX	0.14	0.08	56	17	43	29	0.6	0.6	0.4	0.3	—6	—6	FT/HL	FT/HL
														FT/HL	
Y13-No 1(92)	I	0.13	0.05	41	25	33	50	0.6	0.6	0.2	0.3	0	—6	FT/HL	FT/HL
	II	0.16	0.09	55	15	37	33	0.7	0.8	0.4	0.3	—5	—5	FT/HL	FT/HL
	III	0.16	0.06	40	20	50	50	0.7	0.7	0.3	0.3	—5	0	FT/HL	FT/HL
	IV	0.14	0.08	56	11	33	43	1.0	0·6	0.3	0.5	—6	—6	FT/HL	FT/HL
	V	0.16	0.09	55	15	37	33	0.7	0.8	0.4	0.3	—5	—5	FT/HL	FT/HL
														FT/HL	
Y16-No 1(95)	I	0.13	0.08	63	13	29	29	0.8	0.8	0.5	0.5	—0	0	FT/HL	FT/HL
	II	0.16	0.09	55	15	38	33	0.7	0.8	0.4	0.3	—5	—5	FT/HL	FT/HL
	III	0.15	0.06	42	19	43	50	0.6	0.7	0.3	0.3	—5	0	FT/HL	FT/HL
	IV	0.13	0.07	56	13	29	43	0.8	0.8	0.3	0.5	0	—6	FT/HL	FT/HL

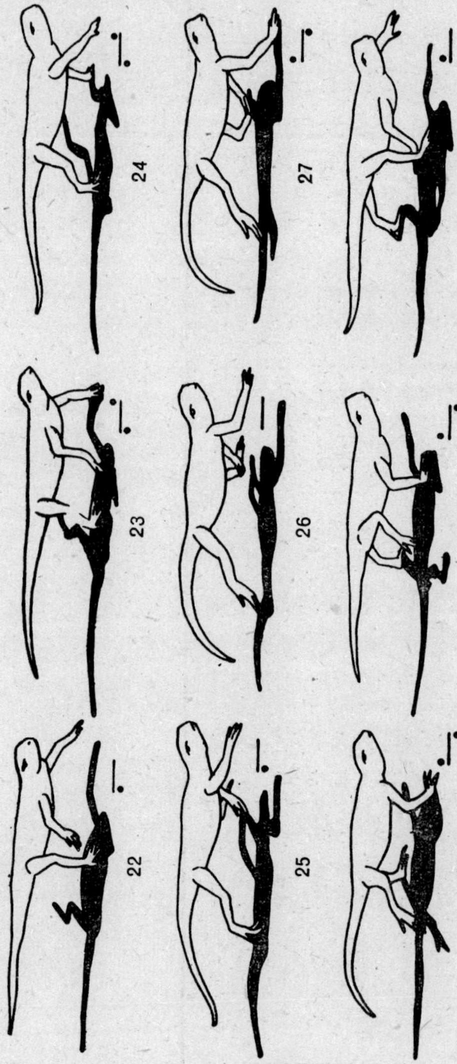

Figure 85. Fast trot with predominance of hind limbs in toad-headed lizard.
Series Y8-No. 1, frames 22 to 30. Legend same as in Figure 59.

field was not fixed. Among our lizards, the toad-headed seems to be the best object for the study of fast movement with the help of motion pictures because their habitat is frequently in open landscapes. Though the speed of photography (64 frames per second) was extremely low for registering all stages of the cycle (6 to 10 frames on 8 stages, from which 4 are extraordinarily short), yet several series (Table 8: Y8-No. 1; Y10-No. 1, No. 2, No. 3; Y11-No. 1; Y12-No. 1; Y13-No. 1; Y16-No. 1), presented by diagrams (Figures 86, 88 to 95) and by frames (Figures 85 and 87) give a complete presentation of a fast trot with predominance of hind limbs, the main and almost the only form of locomotion for toad-headed lizards. This gait is observed in all the series mentioned and only one of them (Y10-No. 1; Figures 87 and 88) shows a fixed change from it to the slow trot with predominance of hind limbs.

Figure 85 (Y8-No. 1) shows how fast the running toad-headed moves. The series starts with a primary unipodal stage (frame 22). Only the right hind limb makes contact with the substrate. The shadow on the sand shows that the

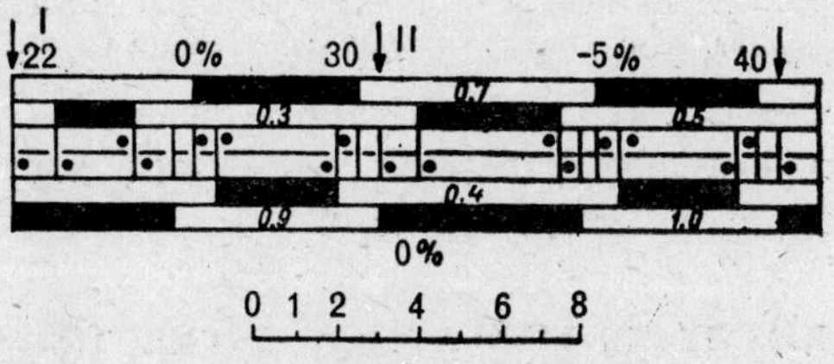

Figure 86. Diagram of movement of toad-headed lizard.
Series Y8-No. 1, frames 22 to 41; film speed 64 frames per second. Legend same as in Figure 40.

remaining feet are suspended in the air. The body and tail at this time are kept nearly horizontal. Contact with the substrate by the left forefoot is established when the right hind one is already retracted to a considerable degree. It is this, as mentioned in Chapter VI, which leads to some increase of the constant walk during the change from slow movement to fast. The other result of this seems to be the bend of the body in front at the time of diagonal support (Figure 108, c). Stages of diagonal support are continued in all for two frames (23 and 24). The forefoot is shorter than the hind one. Therefore, it has to be lifted from the substrate (still 25) until the end of hind limb retraction (secondary unipodal stage). After the free flight, landing takes place on the hind foot of the opposite side. This stage was not caught by the cine camera even though it is, as a rule, observed in all series.

Series Y10-No. 1 is of special interest (Figures 87 and 88). The toad-headed lizard, which had run with a fast trot, slowed down and stopped. The entire transfer occurs in only two cycles. In the beginning of the series (Figure 88, frames 1 to 10), all the characteristic stages of a fast trot with predominance of hind limbs were observed: primary and secondary unipodal, and stages of free flight, but by the 13th frame, the character of the movement has changed. The left hind foot takes a short step (Figure 87). It is seen that it is ready to lift from the ground though the second hind foot has not yet touched the soil, but on the 14th frame, support is formed by the two limbs of the left diagonal. It appears that the transfer is associated with a single disconnection of one hind limb and landing by the other, as shown on the diagram (Figure 88). Somewhat later (frame 19) when the speed has been greatly reduced, an analogous situation appears with a support stage on only two hind limbs, i.e., one of them remained in contact while the second had touched. The bipodal stage is changed to a tripodal one (frame 20). Starting from this moment, movement becomes a slow trot with predominance of hind limbs, but it continued for only one cycle. As a whole, movement in the series corresponds to the track represented in Figure 55.

Other forms of locomotion in toad-headed lizard are not observed. This completely confirms the suggestion in Chapter VI that agamids represent a highly specialized fast-running group which, in view of their many representatives, lost the capability for slow locomotion. Specifically, toad-headed do not run with a slow trot-like walk (rhythm of locomotion varies in narrow limits ± 6) and are restricted to the use of a slow trot with predominance of hind limbs (1 to 2 cycles before the stop).

2. RHYTHM OF LIMB ACTION AND RHYTHM OF LOCOMOTION IN RELATION TO SPEED

Rhythm of limb action is reduced during the increasing speed. This is easily observed in salamanders (Table 2) as well as in lizards (Tables 5 to 8). Locomotion of plate-tailed geckos in series C28-No. 10 may serve as an example where speed is increased more or less uniformly (Figure 96). The size of the index of the rhythm of action for both hind limbs is suddenly reduced from the beginning of the speed increase of 0.3 to 0.5 m per second and afterwards is left almost unchanged (in the given case, it even increases somewhat). As will be seen later, it is related to the fact that the duration of the cycle has a lower limit. In the forelimbs, the rhythm of action is changed considerably in magnitude and because of this, it is even less in the initial state than in the hind limb due to the predominance of the latter.

As the rhythm of limb action is determined by the ratio of support time to transport time, it may be predicted that a decrease of rhythm with a growth of speed is responsible for the difference in the rates of reduction of the latter. This is shown in a diagram (Figure 97). The support time is reduced two times in the same speed interval and the rhythm of limb action also stops changing and attains constant level. During an increase in transport time, there is practically no change. The given diagrams (Figures 96 and 97) reflect one more peculiarity in the movement of lizards—a consi-

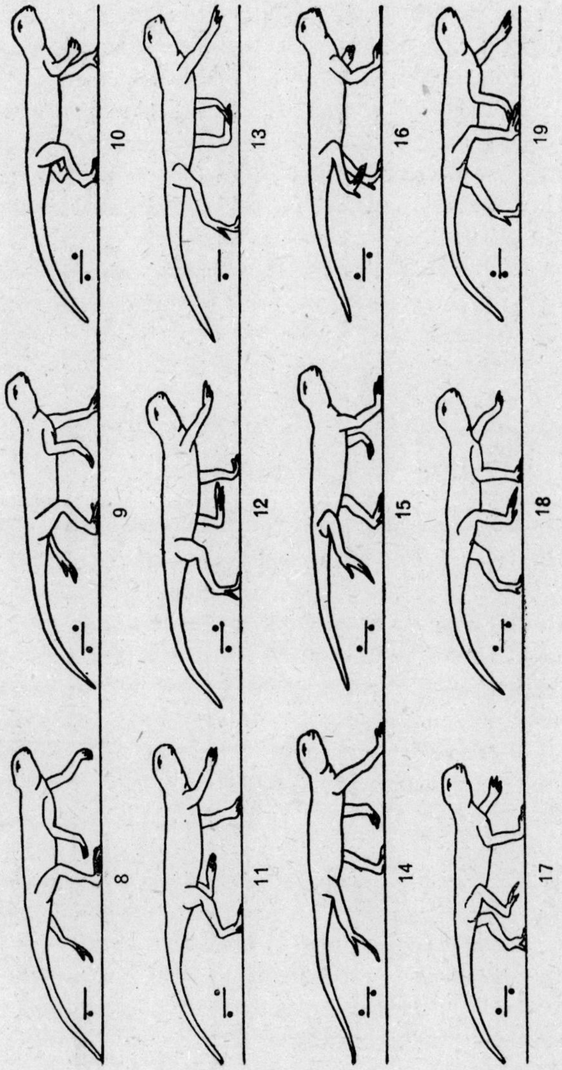
8
9
10
11
12
13
14
15
16
17
18
19

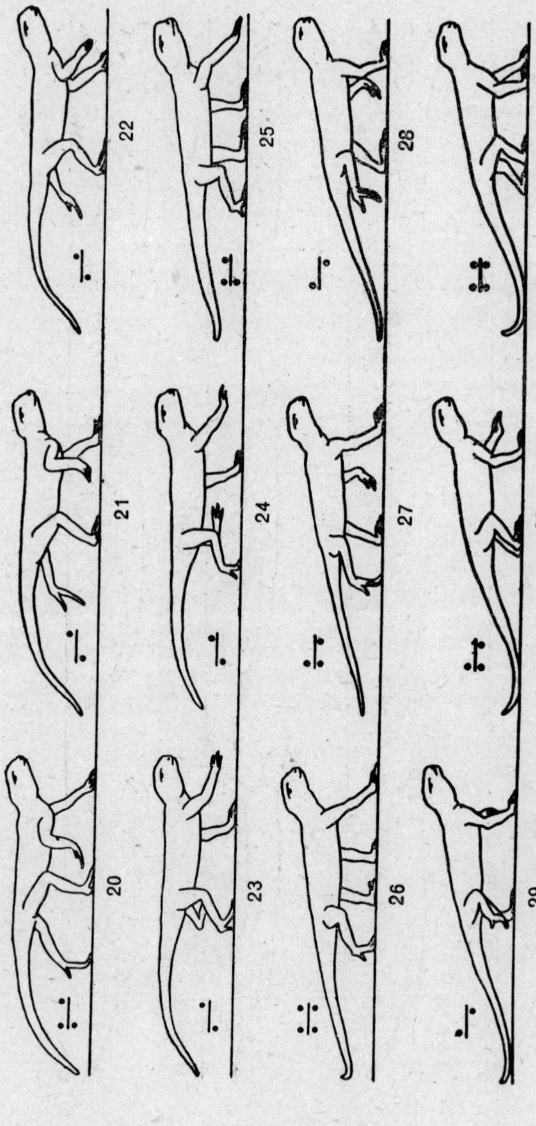

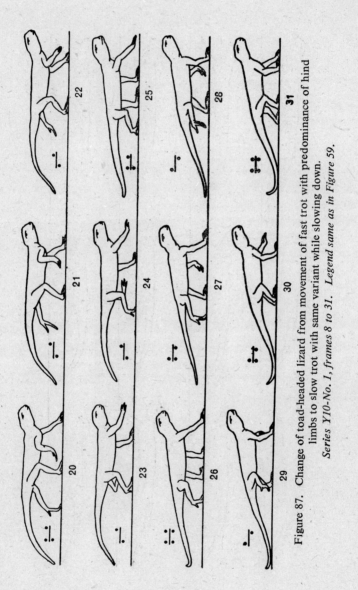

Figure 87. Change of toad-headed lizard from movement of fast trot with predominance of hind limbs to slow trot with same variant while slowing down.
Series Y10-No. 1, frames 8 to 31. Legend same as in Figure 59.

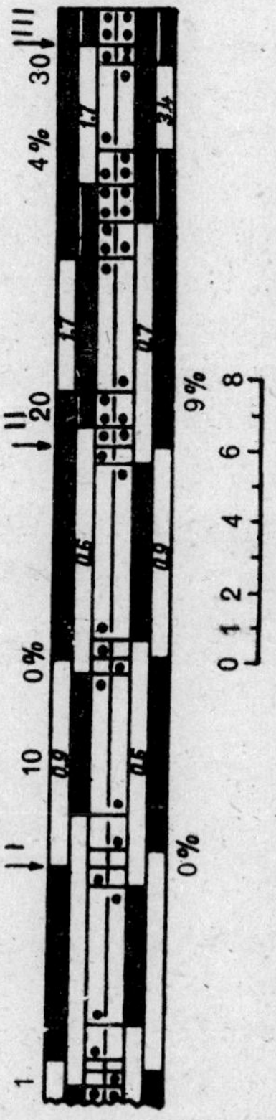

Figure 88. Diagram of movement of toad-headed lizard shown in Figure 87.
Film speed 64 frames per second. Legend same as in Figure 40.

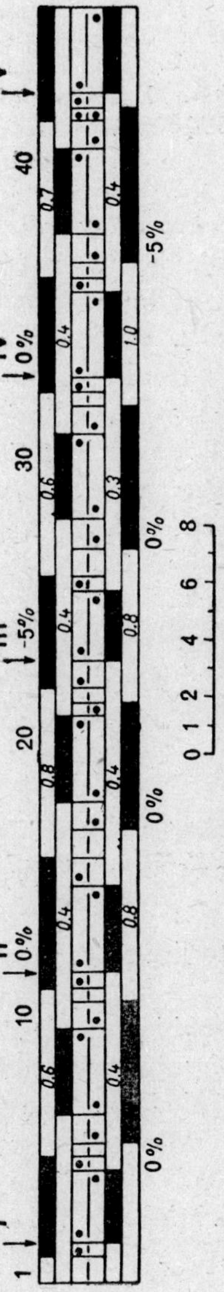

Figure 89. Diagram of movement of toad-headed lizard.
Series Y10-No. 2, frames 1 to 45; film speed 64 frames per second. Legend same as in Figure 40.

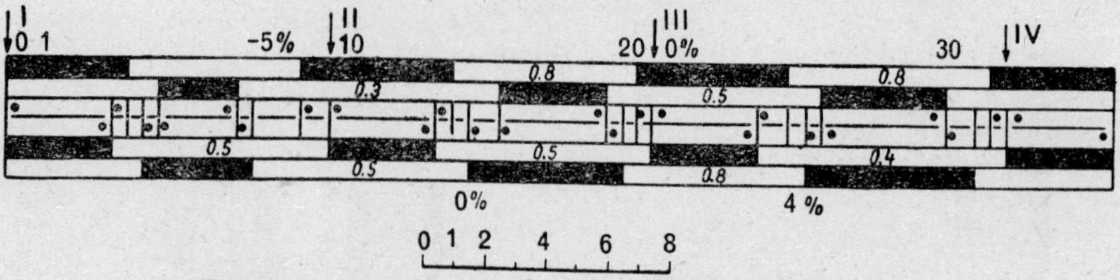

Figure 90. Diagram of movement of toad-headed lizard.
Series Y10-No. 3. frames 0 to 35; film speed 64 frames per second. Legend same as in Figure 40.

derably high degree of coordination in the limb action of one diagonal compared, for example, to the limbs of contralateral pair (either fore or hind).

The rhythm of locomotion varies in different forms of lizards within rather wide limits. Maximum range is observed in plate-tailed geckos (Table 5), usually from 50 to —11%. The range is considerably narrower in Komodo monitor (Table 7), from 24 to 0% and very much less in toad-headed lizards (Table 8), from 5 to —8%. Such differences are explained by the fact that plate-tailed geckos, though they may not develop a speed commensurate with that of the toad-headed lizards, nonetheless use all

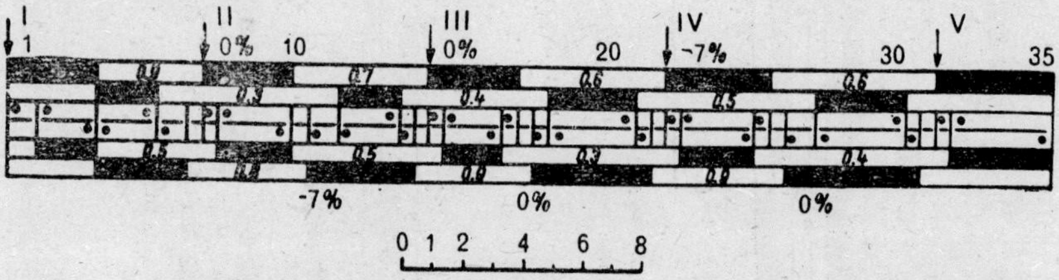

Figure 91. Diagram of movement of toad-headed lizard.
Series Y11-No. 1, frames 1 to 35; film speed 64 frames per second. Legend same as in Figure 40.

gaits available to lizards in general. Actually, toad-headed move only with fast trot.

During a speed increase leading to a change in form of locomotion (see below) from a very slow walk through a slow trot-like walk to slow trot with predominance of hind limbs, the rhythm of locomotion approaches the rhythm of a trot. So the rhythm of locomotion for the plate-tailed gecko in the beginning of series C28-No. 9 (Figure 68) was near to the norm of a slow trot-like walk, but after a brief stop and a sudden increase, it fell to zero. The corresponding rhythm for a very slow walk in geckos attains 50% (Table 5, C7-No. 1, No. 2). During a slow trot-like walk, rhythm varies from 6 to 34% although it was often equal to 9 to 15%. As has been mentioned, a fast trot is rarely seen in geckos (C28-No. 6), but among our data there are records of movement approaching the slow and fast trots. This suggests the limits of change of the rhythm of locomotion for all trots (from 12 to —11; in two cases, to —16

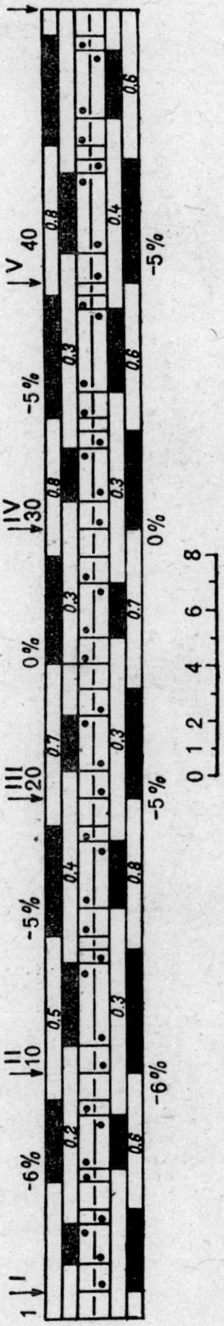

Figure 92. Diagram of movement of toad-headed lizard.
Series Y13-No 1, frames 1 to 48; film speed 64 frames per second. Legend same as in Figure 40.

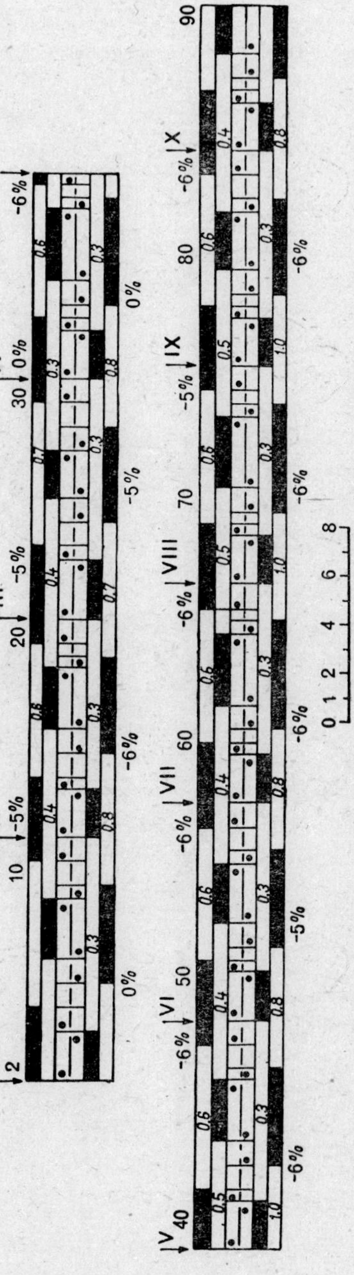

Figure 93. Diagrams of movement of toad-headed lizard.
Series Y12-No. 1, frames 20 to 90; film speed 64 frames per second. Legend same as in Figure 40.

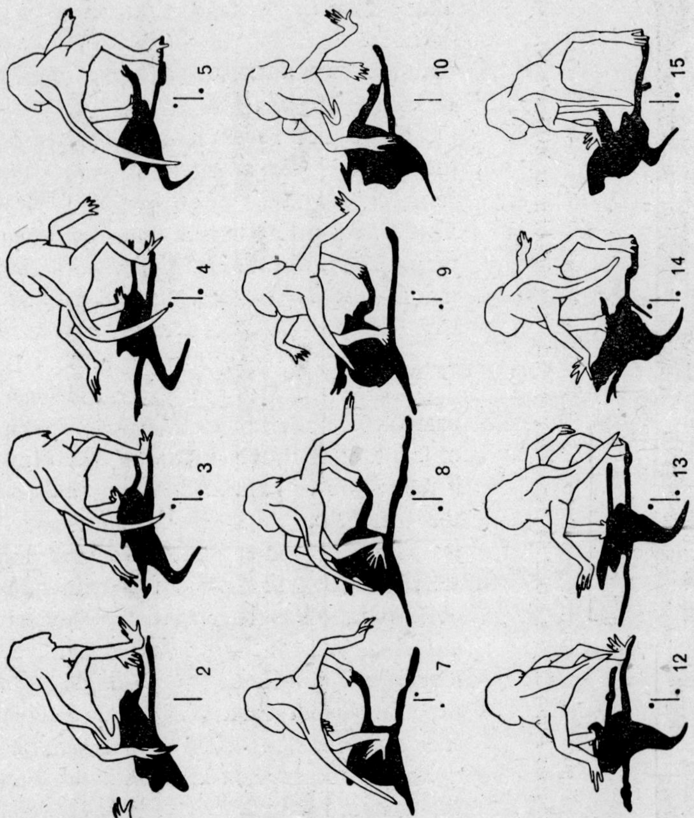

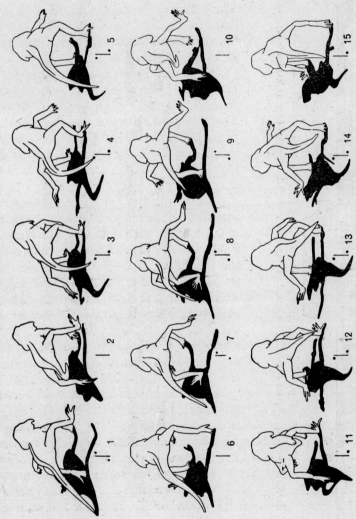

Figure 94. Fast trot with predominance of hind limbs in toad-headed lizard. *Series Y16-No. 1, frames 1 to 15. Legend same as in Figure 59.*

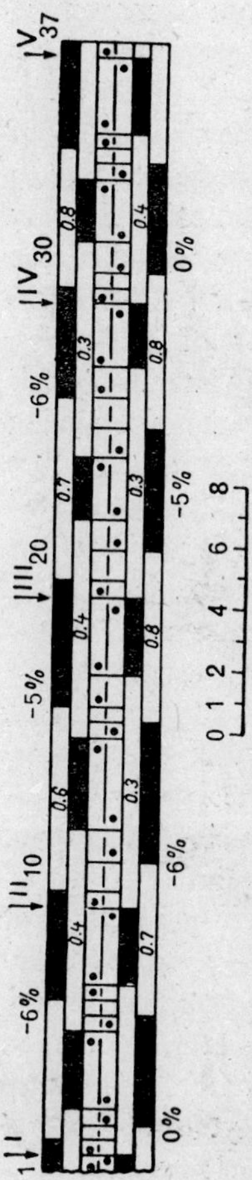

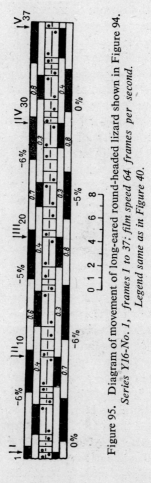

Figure 95. Diagram of movement of long-eared round-headed lizard shown in Figure 94. *Series Y16-No. 1, frames 1 to 37; film speed 64 frames per second. Legend same as in Figure 40.*

and —22), and from this to determine that the size of the corresponding rhythm for a slow trot which in this zone often falls from 10 to 0 (in 50 cases, the rhythm is equal to 0, in 54 cases, above 0, and only in 14 cases, below 0), but of increased and fast trot—from 0 to —10 (in 37 cases, the rhythm is equal to 0, in 9 cases, above 0, and in 20 cases, below 0).

Together with speed, the rhythm of locomotion is changed in Komodo monitor (p. 210) moving by a slow trot-like walk. This becomes still more apparent when the monitor starts alternating between a slow trot-like walk (rhythm 10 to 16%) and slow trot with predominance of hind limbs (0 to 3%) during a single cycle. Thus, as in salamanders, an increase of four-paced movements in lizards is followed by a closeness of the rhythm of locomotion to the rhythm of trot. However, if this is quite natural for amphibians since they move only with a very slow and slow trot-like walks, then lizards are freer in their selection; they may use a trot with a rhythm of locomotion close to zero for slow as well as fast motion. At the same time, the rhythm of locomotion in the gaits may be changed, independence of a speed change, but only during slow motion. If the speed is increased, then the rhythm of locomotion will by all means remain the rhythm of trot.

Rhythm of locomotion during movement by trot deserves special consideration. In this case, it has a tendency to fluctuate about to zero. Deviation is observed during any speed but as a rule, it does not exceed ±10% limit, which can be conveniently taken as the border between the trot and trot-like walk. Of course, the rhythm of locomotion during a trot sometimes also exceeds this limit. Similarly, the range of the slow trot-like walk may partially overlap the trot, i.e., a 10% limit is quite conditional. However, it can almost be determined that both walks are the center around which are grouped separate specific rhythms of locomotion for this or that cycle of its half.

According to identification marks during the index of rhythm of locomotion (Chapter II), one can see the use during a symmetrical sequence. Thus, if the rhythm of locomotion varies in limits of ±10%, then it should serve as an indicator of the disturbance of habitual diagonal sequence of movement of limbs for lower tetrapods, and also, as an indicator of disturbance of the lateral sequence replacing the diagonal sequence in the course of the cycle. So in plate-tailed geckos in series C28-No. 6 (Figure 60), the sequence with which limbs act may be identified on the middle portions corresponding to support time (as locomotion takes place in a trot, discussion concerns only the insignificant passing ahead or, on the other hand, leaving behind of one limb from the other). The pattern is the same: *RF-LH-RH-LF-LH-RF-RH-LF-RF-LH.* Consequently, the sequence in continuity of half-cycles, starting with carrying forward the right hind limb is typically lateral. To this corresponds also a negative rhythm of locomotion. However, at the beginning and end of the series, the left hind limb follows normally after the right fore one. The change itself from a diagonal sequence to a lateral is completed through the consequent movements of both hind limbs (in the beginning of the series) or of both forelimbs (in the end). Logically, it may be imagined that if a strict sequence of change of diagonal sequence is fixed in one-half of the cycle, of lateral in the other half, then it leads to a locomotion in asymmetrical-diagonal sequence. However, there is no current basis for confirming that asymmetrical locomotion occurs in such a manner. It is advisable to also mention that the combination of different sequences in the movement of geckos (C28-No. 6) occurs so that each limb never starts carrying out in front for the second time until this has been done by the other two limbs.

It is difficult to say what should be called a deviation of the rhythm of locomotion during a trot on both sides of zero. Will this appear as the reflection of a weakening of strict control of limb action imposed on them by the necessity to maintain equilibrium or is this more or less a regular phenomenon independent of the speed of locomotion? In support of the latter, one proposes the above-mentioned ratio of frequency of deviations of rhythm of locomotion of plate-tailed geckos on the positive and negative side of zero in connection with the speed of movement. In toad-headed lizards during fast trot with predominance of hind limbs, the number of negative rhythms suddenly increased: in 25 cases, rhythm of locomotion was equal to 0; in 35, below 0; and in 4 only, above. A theory is suggested that the faster the movement the more suitable to have a maximum unstable stages related to the use of a lateral sequence in the cycle. It is interesting that in horses during a fast amble, variations of the rhythm of locomotion from 100% are observed on the positive as well as the negative side. Sometimes the deviation is so great, that it may be remarked in the fast amble-like walk in the diagonal (Figure 14) or lateral (Figure 15) sequence. All this indicates how lateral locomotion could develop during fast movement for some mammals and at the same time serves as an indirect proof in favor of the proposition about the transient nature of the trot and amble developed in the first part of this work linking diagonal locomotion with lateral.

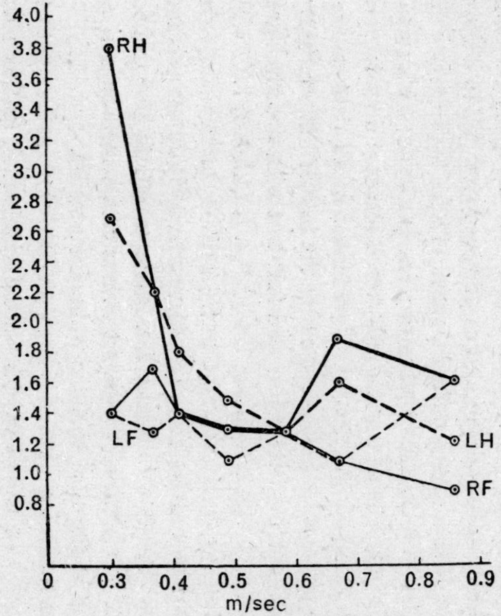

Figure 96. Ratio of speed of movement and rhythm of limb action in locomotion of plate-tailed gecko

Abscissa—*speed (in m per second).* Ordinate—*rhythm of action of limbs (in conditional units); curves characterizing change of rhythm of action of each limb, shown by usual indices for the right and left fore and hind limbs (LH, LF, RH, RF). Series C28-No. 10.*

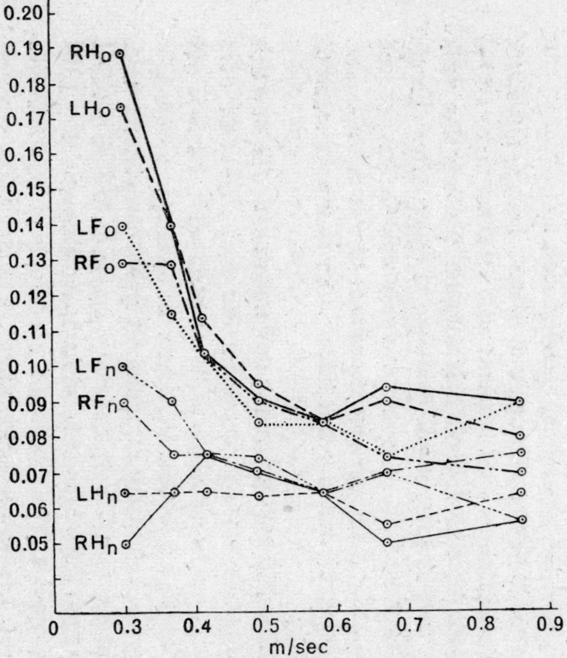

Figure 97. Ratio of speed of movement to duration of support time and transport time of each limb in locomotion of plate-tailed gecko.

Abscissa—*speed (in m per second).* Ordinate—*time (in seconds); curves charactrizing change of support time in left and right hind limbs, designated* LH_o *and* RH_o *; transport time—*LH_n *and* RH_n*. Front limbs are similarly designated :* LF_o *and* RF_o*,* LF_n *and* RF_n*.*

3. CORRELATIONS OF GAITS FOR DIFFERENT LIZARDS

It has been shown that there are five gaits in lizards. During movement with increased speed, the lizard uses a fast trot with predominance of hind limbs. As the movement becomes slower, it may shift later to a very slow walk before the cycle (or even its half) stops. However, stopping often occurs during a slow trot-like walk. Thus, the role of a very slow walk is reduced to the minimum in lizards; a change from movement to rest or vice versa. It is appropriate to remember that in salamanders a very slow walk seems to be their major gait.

The three remaining gaits are used during slow movement. The slow trot with predominance of forelimbs was rarely seen in our research, but this does not reflect its position in nature, as its use as slow movement by barbs is not known and needs to be studied further. As a rule, this gait corresponds to a very low speed of motion but at the same time it is not associated with a subsequent stop, as in the very slow walk. For example, in the plate-tailed gecko in series C28-No. 8 (Table 5) movement starts and ends as a slow trot-like walk, but two unconnected half-cycles of a slow trot with predominance of forelimbs occur in it. Characteristically, when the animal takes recourse to this variant of the trot, the rhythm of action of the forelimbs shows a sudden increase, thereby testifying to the slowing of movement. It is important to stress that the presence of predominance of forelimbs in a given cycle still does not speak about the movement by the same-named variant of slow trot. It may also be observed during a very slow and slow trot-like walk.

Slow trot-like walk and slow trot with predominance of hind limbs seem to be the main forms of slow locomotion for lizards. However, the first form occurs during less speed. So, geckos in the beginning and end (cycles I and XI) of series C28-No. 5 (Table 5) where the speed was lower than in the middle used the slow trot-like walk and with increased speed changed to a slow trot with predominance of hind limbs during a speed of about 0.85 m per second with a fast trot. Likewise, Komodo monitor usually moving by a slow trot-like walk (Table 7) only during a maximum speed increase does it alternate with a slow trot with predominance of hind limbs. In all cases when the locomotion of the plate-tailed gecko occurs on the border between slow and fast, as a rule, this combined into slow and fast trot with predominance of hind limbs (Table 5: C11-No. 2, C12-No. 1, C15-No. 1, C23-No. 1, C25-No. 1) but not a slow trot-like walk and fast trot. Toad-headed lizards during retardation of a fast trot also changed to a slow trot with predominance of hind limbs (Table 8, Y10-No. 1; Figure 88). It is appropriate here to mention that the position of the norm of the slow trot was established on a speedier level than the norm of the slow trot-like walk (Chapter II).

In this way the following outline is formed. The slow movement of the lizard usually occurs as a slow trot-like walk during which further retardation may change it to a very slow walk; a stop follows this, or a slow trot with predominance of forelimbs, if for any reason the animal prefers to use trot. Increased speed, on the other hand, causes a change to a slow trot with predominance of hind limbs which in its turn changes to a corresponding variant of the fast trot. Consequently, a change in form of locomotion during increase of speed if it coincides with that, should have occurred in the evolution of lower tetrapods while mastering dryness and adaptation to faster movement. Salamanders were stopped in the first phase of this development as very slow walk in them only changes to a slow trot-like one.[4] Reptiles moved much further possessing slow as well as fast trot. Development of the slow trot with predominance of forelimbs present, perhaps, a secondary phenomenon related in scincogeckonomorphs with the development of an ability to decrease the functional length of the hind limbs, i.e., this is again a special adaptation to a particular slow movement in the form of the trot.

4. PREDOMINANCE OF CERTAIN LIMBS AND SPEED

In all the lizards studied, one limb of a diagonal pair usually touched the substrate for more time than the other one. In other words, excluding the dependence to the forms of locomotion, the latter continues with predominance of any limbs, the degree of which varies strongly (Tables 5 to 8). As a rule, the hind limbs play a predominant role more often; calculations of the degree of predominance were done more than 400 times, but only in 23 cases was a predominance of the forelimbs observed.

In about 70 cases, the degree of predominance was equal to zero. However, this figure is considered an overestimation for the slow-speed film used for fast movement, several stages of the cycle are not recorded.

The maximum predominance of hind limbs (up to 56%) is observed in the fast barb. Toad-headed lizards come close behind (50%), which corresponds to the big difference in the length of their forelimbs and hind legs (Chapter VI). However, studies concerned with the direct relationship of degree of predominance to different lengths of limbs do not accurately reflect the total aspects of the problem. In special cases of the fast run of plate-tailed geckos with a minimum inequality of limbs, the degree of predominance sometimes attained 50% and even 55%, though often it did not exceed 35%. Thus, the degree of predominance is to a considerable extent dependent upon the speed of locomotion, directly proportional. As toad-headed almost always run at high speed, predominance of posterior limbs in them is valued in all between 25 to 50% in which the degree of predominance in 40 to 50% is observed frequently (in 21 cases out of 47). This is probably due to the fact

[4]It is interesting that the slow trot-like walk of salamanders usually passes in the rhythm (10 to 15%) closer to the rhythm of walk than in lizards (10 to 15%).

that in filming in the field, toad-headed may develop speed close to their maximum. On the other hand, fast barb being filmed in the laboratory, though it moved by a fast trot with predominance of hind limbs could not develop as much speed (Table 6). The respective degrees of predominance varied within wide limits—from 13 to 56%, but more often it equaled 25 to 35%.

Of course, from the frequency of different degrees of predominance, only an estimate of its optimal size can be given for different gaits. However, the vast material on the plate-tailed gecko (Table 5) shows a clear tendency to increase the degree of predominance with increased speed. Individually considered, the greatest frequency of different degrees of predominance occurred in these three types of gaits: 1) the slow trot-like walk and the trot with predominance of the forelimbs; 2) the slow trot with predominance of hind limbs; 3) locomotion bordering on the slow and fast, and fast trot with predominance of hind limbs. In the first group, predominance varied from —22 to +21%. The degree which occurred most often (31 cases) was valued at 0; 39 times it was higher than zero, with its peak in the region of 6 to 13%; and 17 times, below zero. In the second group, the range of variation extended from 6 to 33% with the peak in the region of 15 to 22%. The greatest scattering of points (8 to 55%) corresponded to fast locomotion, but their maximum number (40 out of 60) concentrated in the region of 17 to 33%. In 13 cases, the degree of predominance is also valued here as 0. But, as already mentioned, this is an artificial phenomenon (in the second group, there were 15 points). In support of this is their absence in the region of 0 to 5% and a closer grouping in the position of the remaining points.

A similar picture was observed in the movement of the same gecko (C28-No. 5, No. 10); during a speed of 0.3 to 0.6 m per second, the degree of predominance was valued at 0 to 15%; during a speed of 0.8 to 0.9 m per second, from 15 to 40%. Additionally, slow motion in long-legged scink is associated with a predominance from —2 to 13%. In Komodo monitor, the latter varies from—13 to 26. The maximum is in the region of zero, but in the positive porion of the scale, there is a peak in limits of 4 to 16%.

Why is the very slow movement of the trot occasionally associated with predominance of forelimbs but increased speed is always associated with a predominance of hind limbs? In regard to the center of gravity, the fore and hind limbs occupy different positions respectively. The longitudinal component of strength developed by the latter on the substrate is considerably more in the forelimbs (Figure 33), but the vertical component is less (Barclay, 1946, Fig. 4). Consequently, progressive locomotion in the front results more from the activity of the hind limbs than the forelimbs, whose purpose is to provide support to regulate the direction of movement, etc. At the same time, the forelimbs during support exert considerable stopping force which would hinder fast movement. Thus, the predominance of the hind limbs during speedy locomotion brings an appreciable advantage: the load is reduced on the forefeet which sometimes touch the substrate starting to retract while still in the air. Thereby, the retardation effect of the latter is reduced. In fact, the main of specialization in lizards is fast locomotion—bipedal run may be considered as the development of an extreme degree of predominance of hind limbs (100%). It is natural that during slow locomotion the opposite should take place; consequently, a propulsive activity of the hind limbs is somewhat softened by the presence of predominance in the forelimbs. However, this is only one aspect of the problem.

It is important to stress that a special slow trot may become effective only with the appearance of tripodal stages in the cycle, the introduction of quadrupodal stages (cf. Figure 11, C and Figure 18, B). During slowing the latter increase so much that they threaten to stop motion. In Chapter V, this was shown in salamander. The problem of reduction of quadrupodal stages in the cycle is of special significance only during the movement by a trot, as during the theoretically equal level of speed, the correct duration of the cycle, quadrupodal stages of the slow trot-like walk are much shorter than during the trot. The appearance of predominance of any limb solves the problem allowing a reduction of quadrupodal stages and not increasing the speed. From this, it can be concluded that during four-paced movement there are no special reasons for an increase in length of hind limbs in relation to the forelimbs (this does not concern the biomechanical aspect of the problem). It is not accidental that predominance in salamander is not high (from —5 to 19). At the same time the appearance of the trot in reptiles became the prerequisite for the selection of animals on the increase of difference in length of fore and hind limbs, since during fast as well as the slow trot, movement in the form of their external variants greatly increases locomotory possibilities. During a fast trot, this provides the maximum biomechanical effect of action in the hind limbs in combination with a reduction of the stopping activity of the forelimbs; during slow, it permits a lowering of speed to the minimum while retaining all the advantages of a trot before the four-paced forms of movement.

5. LOCOMOTORY CYCLE AND ITS DEPENDENCE ON SPEED AND FORM OF MOVEMENT

As mentioned in the preceding sections, gaits of lizards depend on different speed levels. Therefore it is natural that each specific form of locomotion corresponds to the duration of the cycle and does not change within particular limits (Table 9). Figures given in the Table show that in large animals, e.g., monitors, the duration of the cycle is much greater than in small animals moving by the same gait. On the other hand, within the limits of one gait, the frequency of limb motions in the smallest lizards (sandy and takyr toad-headed) is more than in forms of the same genus whose sizes exceed their own (toad-headed). Some exceptions consist of young steppe agamids but possibly this was caused by long confinement against their will. The largest duration of cycle is registered in salamander whose locomotion apparently is characteristically different from such lizards as, in the latter even the very slow walk passes with a higher frequency of limb action than the slow trot-like walk of salamander.

The ratio of the duration of the cycle to the speed of locomotion in different lizards is shown in Figure 98. It submits to the standard formulas of reverse dependence of two sizes:

$$t = a + m/v,$$

where t=duration of the cycle (in seconds), v=speed of locomotion (in m per second) a and m=coefficients related to the size of the animal and the specialities of its locomotion. The asymptote a shows the lower limit of cycle

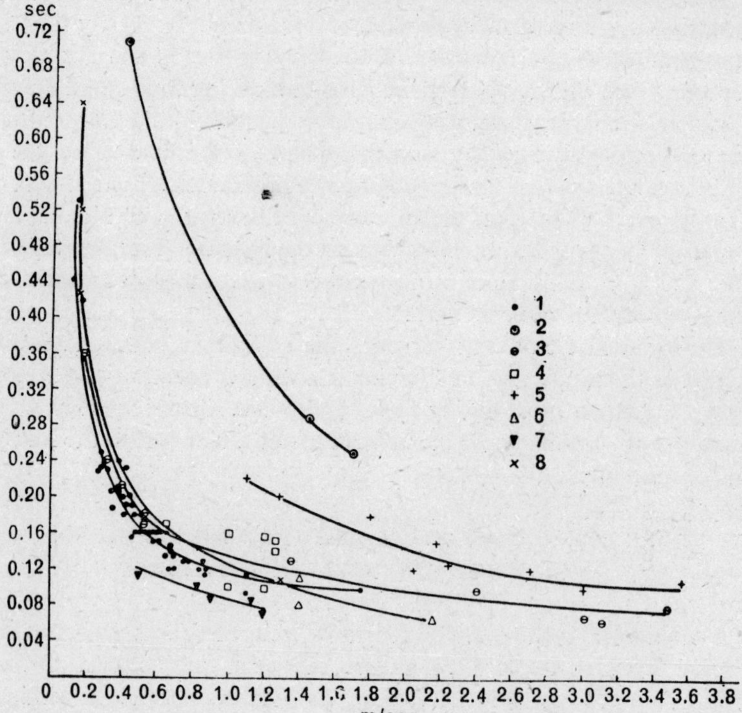

Figure 98. Dependence between the speed of locomotion and the duration of the locomotory cycle in some lizards.

Abscissa—*speed (in m per second)*; Ordinate—*time (in seconds). 1—plate-tailed gocks; 2—desert monitor; 3—retinal barb; 4—fast barb; 5—toad-headed, 6—desert toad-headed; 7—takyr toad-headed; 8—long-legged scink.*

Table 9. Duration of cycle and speed of locomotion for different gaits (from the data of motion pictures and study of tracks)

Species	Nature of recording	Duration of cycle (in sec) and speed of locomotion (in m per sec)			
		Very slow walk	Slow trot-like walk	Slow trot with predominance of hind limbs	Fast trot with predominance of hind limbs
Salamandra salamandra	Film	1.3—1.6(0.03—0.04)	0.6—1.2(0.05—0.1)	—	—
Eumeces schneideri	Film	?	0.42—0.66(∼0.15)	?	?
	Track	?	?	?	0 11(1.3)
Teratoscincus scincus	Film	0.3—0.6	0.15—0.44(0.11—0.6)	0.12—0.23(0.3—0.9)	0.09—0.12(∼0.9—1.1)
	Track	?	0.14—0.42(0.15—0.7)		0.07—0.14(0.7—1.75)
Eremias velox	Film	?	?	?	0.10—0.18(0.7—1.3)
E. grammica	Track	?	0.17—0.42(0.2—0.7)		0.07—0 13(1.3—3.5)
Phrynocephalus mystaceus	Film	—	—	0.18	0 10—0.17
	Track	—	—	?	0.10—0.22(1.1—3.7)
Ph. mystaceus (juv.)	Track	—	—	?	0.08—0.14(1.2—2.4)
Ph. interscapularis	Track	—	—	?	0.065—0.08(1.4—2.5)
Ph. helioscopus	Film	—	—	?	0.07—0.12(0.5—1.2)
Agama sanguinolenta	Track	—	—	?	0.11(2.7)
A. sanguinolenta (juv.)	Film	—	—	0.15—0.24(0.5—0.8)	
Varanus griseus (juv.)	Track	?	0.7—0.4	0.25—0.29(1.45—1.70)	
V. komodoensis	Film	?	1.08—3.40	0.45—0.75	—

NOTE : Speed of locomotion is shown in brackets; dash means that the animal may not move by the given gait.

duration (in seconds). *A priori*, it may be confirmed that it is different in small and large forms. This can be supported by the fact that the minimum known cycle duration decreases in several forms with a decrease in size of trunk: Komodo monitor; desert monitor; toad-headed; retinal barb; desert toad-headed (Table 9). In more or less the same sized scincogeckonomorphs, this limit is possibly close to 0.07 to 0.08 seconds; in small desert monitors (length of body 0.39 m, gleno-acetabular distance 0.2 m) to 0.15 to 0.18 seconds; in desert and takyr toad-headed, to 0.06 to 0.07 seconds. The existence of such a limit is perhaps related to the speed of action of physiological processes by the biomechanical specialities of the animal, etc.

The second coefficient, *m*, is directly determined by the sizes of lizards. For greater accuracy, this expression was used in the special diagram (Figure 98) for plate-tailed geckos, retinal barbs, and long-legged scinks, forms of practically the same size; curved changes of duration of cycle almost coincide within the limits of the same speed. For all practical purposes, it may be said that there is one general curve for similar-sized scincogeckonomorphs in wide limits of speed change. It was empirically calculated that such a curve fits the aforementioned formula when the coefficient *m* is the size of gleno-acetabular distance in meters (in the given case, it is equal to 0.04 to 0.05m). It is important to mention that by putting into the formula the size of the gleno-acetabular distance of the desert monitor and the corresponding value of the coefficient *a*, with known speed of locomotion (0.4, 0.45 and 1.7 m per second), one may calculate the duration of the cycle. In so doing, the calculated size almost coincides with the real. Data on monitors are less but nevertheless it may be confirmed that curved changes of cycle duration should be more gentle than in scincogeckonomorphs in connection with an increase in the coefficient *m*.

The curve formed for toad-headed lizards differs somewhat from that of the scincogeckonomorph. In all three species of toad-headed lizards, curves lie in the region of increased speeds which, for small forms, is below the corresponding curve of scincogeckonomorphs, but in the toad-headed lizard it is higher. Attention must be given to the fact that in the latter, the lower limit of the duration of the cycle is attained during considerable speed of locomotion: the lower portion of curves almost parallels the abscissa during speed beginning from 2.6 m or about there. In scincogeckonomorphs, the same takes place during a speed of 1.2 to 1.4 m per second. In other words, an increase of speed in fast locomotion for the toad-headed lizard is, to a considerably larger extent, due to the reduction cycle, and consequently, the increase of the stride to a lesser extent than in retinal barb, where the ratio of changes of step and cycle duration is inverse. This is related to the fact that toad-headed lizards may not change the functional length of the hind limbs (during a change to slow trot with predominance of hind limbs, the step is reduced mainly at the cost of reducing the angle of hip swing). At the same time, the initial size of the step in them is, by far, more than in barbs. In fact, in the beginning of movement, a maximum swing of limbs is used. They are forced to increase the frequency of limb movements in order to develop a higher speed.

One more speciality of locomotion in lizards is reflected in the diagram (Figure 98). The existence of lower limits of reduction in the duration cycle, attained in scincogeckonomorphs quite rapidly, which almost parallels the abscissa in passing by the curve during increased speed of movement (i.e., continued increase), shows that in these lizards, the speed of fast locomotion is to a larger extent dependent upon an increase of the stride, mainly at the cost of free flight, than upon an increase in frequency of limb action. During slow motion, the role of both factors is equal, but during very slow motion, as in salamander, the frequency of motion (Chapter V) is of greater importance. Consequently, the differences between barbs and geckos mentioned above (Chapter VI) as to how far their speed is determined by size of step and duration of cycle, are merely explained by the level of adaptation to speedy movement, and not by the difference in the direction of specialization. On the other hand, scincogeckonomorphs and iguanomorphs represent different branches in the evolution of lizard locomotion.

In the locomotory cycle of lizards, the stages of diagonal support (Table 10) occupy an important place. Only during the very slow walk are they absent, but their place is taken by secondary quadrupodal stages. With an increase in speed of locomotion, the specific weight of stages of diagonal support in the cycle is increased up to the change to the fast trot, but afterwards is somewhat reduced in connection with the appearance and further development of stages of free flight which replace primary quadrupodal stages. The latter, naturally, are longer during the very slow walk. Thus, changes in the relative duration of separate stages of the cycle, related to an increase of speed and change from one gait to another, are similar to that of salamanders (Chapter V, Figure 45). The only differences are in the speed of locomotion for salamanders on the one side and lizards on the other. At the time of four-paced movement in lizards, primary and secondary tripodal stages occupy an important place in the cycle. During a change to the trot, these are reduced, determined now only by the degree of predominance of any limb. It is difficult to identify the relative duration of unipodal stages in the cycle of the fast trot with predominance of hind limbs as the cycle is very short. However, based on the frequency with which small stages are captured in frames the following assumption may be made: Primary unipodal stages are almost always fixed by the movie camera. Secondary are rarely met. Usually they are observed as stages of free flight which occur frequently. Hence, it might be thought that secondary unipodal stages are definitely twice as short as primary. If speed increases, stages of free flight occur with greater frequency. This is especially observed in toad-headed lizards. But

Table 10. Relative duration of individual stages of cycle for different gaits (in%) of barbs

Species	Very slow walk		Slow trot-like walk		Slow trot with predominance of hind limbs		On the border of slow and fast trot with predominance of hind limbs			Fast trot with predominance of hind limbs	
	Primary quadrupodal stage	Secondary quadrupodal stage	Primary quadrupodal stage	Diagonal support stage	Primary quadrupodal stage	Diagonal support stage	Primary quadrupodal stage	Diagonal support stage	Stage of free flight	Diagonal support stage	Stage of free flight
Salamandra salamandra	40—65	2—18	12—35	8—48	—	—	—	—	—	—	—
Teratoscincus scincus	?40—44	11—15	7—35	19—77	4—29	41—86	0—12	62—94	5—8	53—63	12—31
Eumeces schneideri	?	?	5—9	45—55	?	?	?	?	?	?	?
Eremias velox	?	?	?	?	?	?	?	?	?	38—67	10—20
Varanus komodoensis	?	?	9—44	25—58	13—24	49—62	—	—	—	—	—
Phrynocephalus mystaceus	—	—	—	—	?18	?57	0—13	75	4	40—67	5—25

NOTE: Dash means that the animal may not move with the given gait.

it happens often enough that when the cycle becomes too small, stages of free flight in general are not captured on film though their presence in the cycle and even in relatively great length, may be guaranteed.

Absolute duration of stages, as a rule, is reduced by the increase of speed. But this is completely justified only during movement by the trot, e.g., in the plate-tailed gecko in series C28-No. 4 (Table 5) and toad-headed lizard in series Y10-No. 3 (Table 8). In an increase of four-paced movement in connection with a change of the rhythm of locomotion, the duration of diagonal support may even increase somewhat as was mentioned in salamander (Chapter V).

As the movement of lizards is usually followed by a predominance of hind limbs, at the moment of change from the slow trot to the fast some atypical stages may appear in the cycle, as mentioned, in the plate-tailed geckos and toad-headed lizards with support only on the hind limbs. The appearance of similar stages is explained by Figure 99. Diagrammatic representations of five cycles of a trot with predominance of hind limbs are given,

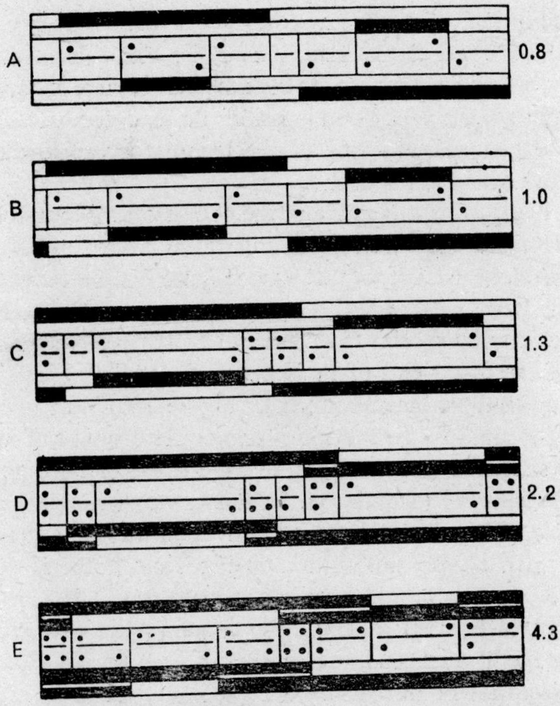

Figure 99. Change from fast trot (A) to slow (E) during movement with predominance of hind limbs with formation of several intermediate stages (B, C, D).

The rhythm of limb action is to the right of the diagram.

differing in the rhythm of limb action and, consequently, in the speed of movement. The relative duration of a stage in the extreme cycles representing a fast (Figure 99, A) and a slow (Figure 99, E) trot with predominance of hind limbs is close to that which really exists in nature. It is assumed that slowing from A to E equally influences support time of fore and hind limbs. During this in the first step of slowing in the cycle stages of free flight fall out (Figure 99, B), but in their place appear bipodal stages (Figure 99, C and D). Unipodol stages are reduced (Figure 99, C), but afterwards are replaced by tripodal (Figure 99, D). In the final phase, bipodal stages are excluded by quadrupodal (Figure 99, E). All these intermediate stages are also sometimes observed in natural conditions, e.g., in toad-headed lizard in series Y10-No. 1 (Figures 87 and 88), in plate-tailed geckos in series C28-No. 5 (Figure 75) and C25-No. 1 (Figure 74); in fast barb in series B1-No. 1 (Figure 75, A) and B1-No. 6 (Figure 75, E).

6. ANALYSIS OF LIMB ACTION IN LIZARD LOCOMOTION

This description of limb movements in lizards during locomotion is not presented as a real biomechanical analysis. This is merely introductory and limited by the original data. For the time being, there is no way in which the force acting on the limbs can possibly be analyzed. Actually, there is even now no functional anatomy of the locomotory apparatus of lizards. All this must be tackled in the future.

How the limbs of lizards move in the course of a locomotory cycle may be understood from the motion pictures given above of the plate-tailed geckos (Figure 59, 61, 62, 64), of fast barb (Figure 76), of Komodo monitor (Figure 83), and of toad-headed lizard (Figures 85 and 87). However, it is shown more clearly by special diagrams of two types. One characterizes the movements of the distal end of main segments of limbs (knee, intertarsal, and IVth metatarsal-phalangeal joints in Figure 100) with reference to the acetabulum or glenoid fossa. Another reflects the position of any limb with regard to the substrate (for example, in Figure 101 of the right hind limb) at different moments of locomotion. In this case, we have to deal with the real trajectories of the replacement of individual joints, segments of limbs, and so on, which is very important during biomechanical constructions. This method of analysis of limb action goes back to the first photographs by Marey and is widely used during cyclodiagrammatic researches. On the other hand, in the first method, locomotion of each limb is characterized by minimum trajectories of displacement of separate joints in relation to the acetabulum which is considered to be immobile. The advantage of this method is that it permits an accurate evaluation of the degree of movement in the hip joint, the degeee of abduction and adduction of the thigh, etc. Snyder (1952, 1962) used the latter method in his study on the locomotion

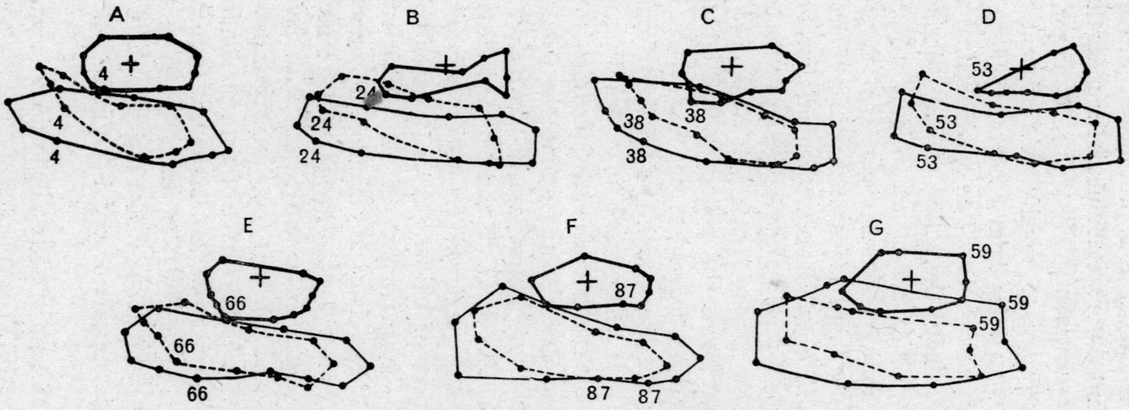

Figure 100. Displacement in relation to acetabulum of distal ends of separate segments of the right hind limb of the plate-tailed gecko during locomotion.

Trajectory construction for six consecutive cycle (A—F) of slow trot with predominance of hind limbs (series C28- No. 10) and of one cycle (G) of fast trot with predominance of hind limbs (series C28- No. 6); trajectory displacement of knee joint is designated with thick line; *of intertarsal with* broken line; *of metatarsal-phalangeal joint by a* thin line. *Position of acetabulum is marked by a* cross. *Position of respective portions of limbs is shown by* dots: *A—for 4th, 8th, 10th to 15th, and 17th frames; B—for 24th, 26th to 32nd, 34th and 38th frames; C—for 38th, 40th, 41st, 43rd to 48th, 50th and 51st frames; D—for 53rd, 55th, 56th, 58th to 61st, 63rd and 65th frames; E—for 66th to 76th frames F—for 87th, 89th, 91st to 97th frames; G—for 59th to 67th frames. In each figure,* numbers *mark the position of limbs only for that frame in which the given cycle begins.*

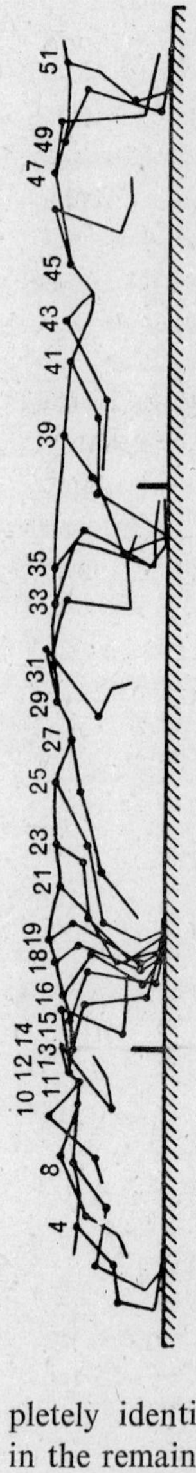

Figure 101. Displacement in relation to the substrate of right hind limb of plate-tailed gecko in the course of three consecutive cycles of slow movement. *Series C28-No. 10; Numbers in the diagram denote frame numbers.*

of lizards. In principle, both methods are advisable and should be used together, but unfortunately, a large portion of filmed material is not suitable, though to construct, by individual dots, the trajectory of replacement in relation to the acetabulum is far easier than in relation to the substrate.

It is necessary to specify that adjacent cycles may very strongly differ from each other depending on how the limbs work. Based on one individual cycle, it is difficult to judge the action of limbs during the course of the entire movement. This is shown in Figure 100. During several cycles the degree of abduction of the thigh varies at the time of protraction. In cycles I, III and V, the acetabulum almost occupies the center of the ellipse corresponding to the trajectory of the knee joints (Figure 100, A, C and F). In other words, the degree of abduction and adduction of the thigh is almost equal but the thigh is suddenly raised during the disconnection of the limb from the substrate. On the other hand, in cycles II and IV (Figure 100, B and D), the distal end of the thigh is raised higher than the cavity at the head of the femur, but only at the end of protraction. In the majority of cycles (Figure 100, B, C, E and F), and the acetabulum is equally removed from the anterior and posterior borders of ellipse, but in I and IV (Figure 100, A and D), the movement of the thigh posterior to the normal plane is visibly limited. The angle of thigh swing is almost equal throughout the complete series; nevertheless, movement passes with increase (Table 5, C28-No. 10). It is not increased, however, during the change to the fast trot with predominance of hind limbs (Figure 100, G). However, the corresponding ellipse in cycle II (Figure 100, B) is completely identified as stretched in the anterior-posterior direction more than in the remaining cases. Similar variations are observed also in toad -headed lizards (Figure 107, A and B).

The movement of the right hind limb of plate-tailed geckos in relation to the substrate is reflected in Figure 101. The presence of a linear scale permits speed calculation of foot replacement in each of the three cycles. Step size increase together with speed; in cycle I, it is equal to 5.8 cm; in II, 7.4 cm; and III, 8.1 cm. Transport time is similarly increased from 4 to 5 and 6 frames (Figure 63). Thus, with the known speed of photography (80 frames per second), the speed in cycle I is determined as 1.16 m per second; in II, as 1.18 m per second; in III, as 1.08 m per second. Consequently, with increased speed in progressive movement, transport speed is almost unchanged. However, if in cycle I the latter is 3.9 times in excess of the speed of locomotion, then in III their ratio is equal to 2.6. A similar calculation for faster movement in series C28-No. 6 (1.4 m per second) shows that the difference becomes still less (ratio equal to 1.3). On the other hand, in salamander, where the speed does not exceed 0.1 m per second, steps are displaced 4 to 6 times faster than the animal itself.

On the whole, the right hind limb in plate-tailed geckos works in the following manner. The limb is stretched to the maximum immediately following lift off (Figure 101, frame 10, 27 and 41). The knees are unbent, the foot curved ventrally to the maximum, and the distal ends of the fingers are also often curved (frame 10). However, the thigh starts protracting even

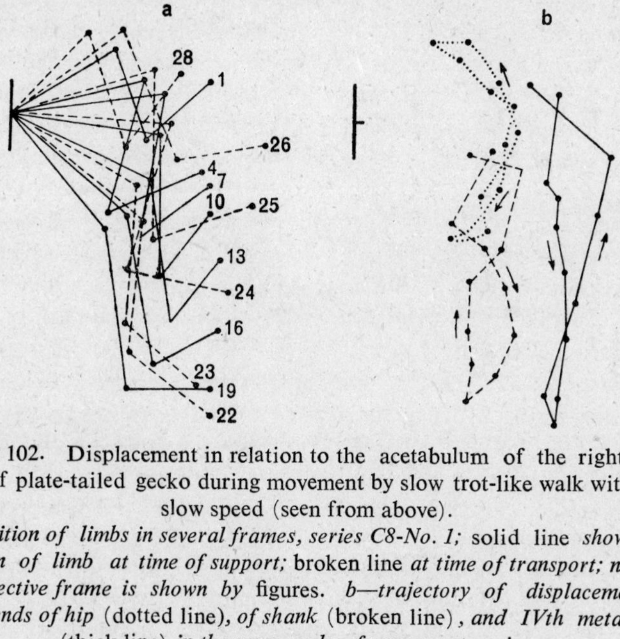

Figure 102. Displacement in relation to the acetabulum of the right hind limb of plate-tailed gecko during movement by slow trot-like walk with very slow speed (seen from above).
a—position of limbs in several frames, series C8-No. 1; solid line *shows the position of limb at time of support;* broken line *at time of transport; number of respective frame is shown by* figures. *b—trajectory of displacement of distal ends of hip* (dotted line), *of shank* (broken line), *and IVth metatarsal* (thick line) *in the same cycle of movement as in a.*

before ligft off of the foot (Figure 102, a) of position of limb in 19th and 22nd frame; foot contact with the ground is lost only in the 23rd frame, Figure 73. A bend at the knee precedes the extension (dorsal extensor) of the foot. The knee is bent to a maximum in the middle of the restoration period (Figure 101, frames 13, 29 and 45). The higher the speed of movement, the greater is the straightening of the limb before landing. So the gecko regulates the functional length of its hind limbs. In Figure 103, c and d, are photographs of a gecko at the first movement of landing on one of the hind limbs. Movement is quite fast, and the limb straightens at the knee considerably more than at a similar moment in a slow-moving animal (Figure 103, b). The fixation of the bent knee during protraction in very slow movement (C8-No. 1, Figure 73) is shown in Figure 102, a. The distal end of the shank during the maximum anterior position of the thigh (frames 1 to 28) remains posterior to the normal plane which only the ends of the fingers follow. During faster (C28-No. 10) and fast (C 28-No. 6) movement, the entire shank is carried behind the plane of the norm (Figure 100, A to G). Thus, even if the angle of thigh swing is almost unchanged, the size of the step may either strongly increase, or decrease.

The hind limb of the gecko comes into contact with the substrate in a foot-gaiting position (Figure 101, frames 14, 15, 33 to 35; Figure 103, c and d). The long axis of the foot (toe IV) during fast locomotion is almost parallel to the direction of movement; deviation does not exceed 20°. During slower movement, as in Figure 102, a, it is inclined laterally under 40 to 50°. Throughout the propulsive period, the thigh is retracted and the knee opens (Figure 101). The foot actively takes part in propulsion, bending ventrally. At the end of the period, support is formed specifically on the distal phalanges of the toes. This leads to an increase of distance from the acetabulum to the substrate at the moment when the functional axis of the limbs assumes a vertical position (Figure 101). The thigh of the gecko works more or less in the horizontal plane, though the amplitude of adductive-abductive movement is quite high (Figure 100). No trace of an increase of adduction during increase is observed: the distal end of the thigh describes the same ellipse as occurs during slow movement (cf. Figure 100, A and G). The adduction of the thigh starts, as a rule, after attaining an extremely protracted position. A similar phenomenon, but to a greater degree, is observed in the forelimbs of salamander, where lifting the feet from the substrate occurs, apparently, after the start of upper arm retraction. This is known from the fact that the following hand of the salamander remains immobile with regard to the substrate for quite a long time (sometimes up to 7 frames when the photographic speed is about 70 frames per second) though its contact with the substrate was not yet established, which is seen usually by the formation of a shadow on the film. Since the progressive movement of the animal continues, we have to assume that the foot is lifted from the soil having started to move back still in the air.

A considerable portion of the ellipse, corresponding to the trajectory of the intertarsal joint, lies after the plane of the norm (Figure 100). The long axis of ellipse is not horizontal as in the thigh, but clearly inclined forward. The highest position of the intertarsal joint comes in the beginning of the restoration period. Afterwards, the shank together with the thigh is carried forward, but its distal end gradually comes closer to the substrate. During the course of the cycle of slow movement, the shank practically does not deviate from the parasagital plane. This is indicated by the partial combination of the trajectory of the knee and the intertarsal joint during observation from above (Figure 102, b). With increased speed, the entire limb may protract in a somewhat unbent position so that the distal end of the shank is placed in front much more laterally to the proximal. The latter is particularly observed in barbs (Figure 76, frames 11 to 13) and toad-headed lizards (Figure 94, frames 7 to 10, 12 to 14).

The foot bends throughout the entire propulsive period and, perhaps, in the first moment after the limb disconnects from the substrate. In any case, the metatarsal-phalangeal joint describes an ellipse, a portion of which lies posterior to the ellipse, corresponding to the movement of the intertarsal joint. All this makes it possible to confirm that lifting of the limb from the substrate is not a result of the animal stroking up and forward, but is caused by a protraction of the thigh, a bending of the limb at the knee, and the extreme bending of the foot, which leads to the conclusion that for sometime its plantar surface approaches medially and somewhat dorsally. The animal waddles as it were on the end of its fingers (Figure 62, frame 86).

During the course of propulsion, the foot of the gecko turns laterally (Figure 102, a). This is seen also in Figure 103, b (cf. both hind limbs). Thus, the intertarsal joint not only rises over the substrate during the bending of the foot, but also makes an arc situated medially of the center of support. This results in the preaxial border of the distal phalanges causing greater pressure on the soil than the postaxial. The lateral turn of foot not only is the result of complicated turning movements of thigh, shank, and foot in the propulsive period, but also provides conditions for the normal transport of the limb in front after its disconnection. During the active bending of the foot, an absence of turn could have led at the moment of disconnection to its plantar surface being located dorsally. As the distal end of the shank only comes closer to the substrate, then to extend the foot without touching the ground, would have been impossible. As a result of the turn the plantar surface of the foot seems to be turned medially. Now extension takes place not in the vertical plane, but almost in the horizontal as can be seen in Figure 102, a and b. At the time of protraction, consequently, the foot is carried forward quite high over the substrate so that the metatarsal-phalangeal joint makes an ellipse during the course of the cycle, which is not lesser in width to the similar ellipse of the distal end of the shank. The extension of the foot may result, even at separate moments of the cycle, in the metatarsal-phalangeal joint being situated higher than the intertarsal (Figure 100, E and G). In other words, the distal end of the right foot moves clockwise in the course of the locomotory cycle (Figure 62, frame 90 to 97). Another problem concerns salamanders where the foot at the time of propulsion does not turn laterally (partially because of the flexibility of the autopode). In order to compensate the outcome of this inconvenience, salamanders and newts during protraction need to raise the hind feet very high (Figure 20, A); hence sometimes, during observation from the side, the hind limb of the opposite side can be seen.

The hind limbs of the monitors work very similarly to those of the gecko. The foot rests on the substrate by all its plantar surface (Figure 83, frames 168 to 170; Figure 104, a). Massiveness and small length of foot consequently lead to track on the sand representing a single imprint (see the photograph of track of Komodo monitor: Hoogerwerf, 1958). Then, as in other lizards, e.g., toad-headed, imprints of distal phalanges often are not connected with the imprint's heel. The foot of the monitor lands so that finger III is directed forward, i.e., its long axis is almost parallel to the direction of movement (Figure 104, c). The turn of the foot during propulsion is shown well (Hoogerwerf, 1958, p. 138, photo; Figure 104, a to d of the present work), but as the foot actively bends and assumes the digitigrade position (Figure 83, frames 159 to 160),[5] the track on the substrate does not reflect this turn. Therefore, it is advisable to consider that although all tracks of primitive lower tetrapods of the Carboniferous and Permian periods are arranged in the direction of movement, this is still not proof for the absence of a lateral turn of the foot in the propulsive period, but only shows that the hind limbs before landing are more or less extended in the knee. Only the development of the ability to fix the knee in a bent position, as in some lizards, led to the appearance of transversely arranged tracks for the hind feet (Figure 51).

In the beginning of the restoration period, the foot of the monitor, as in geckos, is left in a bent position (Figure 83, frames 178 to 183); extension starts in the middle of the period. During forward transport, the limb is raised less than in geckos. The foot is almost dragged on the substrate, often leaving characteristic scratches on the sand (Figure 57, A; Figure 104, a and d).

The hind limbs of toad-headed lizards work in principle similarly to those of other lizards. A limb soon after lift off extends to the maximum (Figure 85, frame 26; Figure 94, frames 2 and 6): the knee at this moment is extended, the foot is strongly bent ventrally. Unlike geckos, the transport of the whole limb forward, at least in the beginning of the restoration period, is achieved almost in a straightened position. Actually, the whole hind foot moves in one plane (Figure 94; frames 7 to 10). For some time the foot still continues to be bent (Figure 85, frames 26 to 28; Figure 87, frames 14 and 15; Figure 106, B, frames 27 to 37). The knee starts curving closer to the joint in the middle of the restoration period (Figure 85, frames 28 and 29), but the flexion never attains the degree observed in geckos or barbs. Before release from the ground, the leg extends again. Contact with the substrate takes

[5]Limbs of monitors may take up a digitigrade position not only in the course of movement, but also while standing on alert, for example, in an agressive posture (Figure 105).

Figure 103. Plate-tailed gecko in different postures of movement and rest.
a—posture at rest; b—posture corresponding to quadrupodal stage of cycle; c—tripodal; d—stage of diagonal support (possibly, unipodal stage on left hind limb).

Figure 104. Desert monitor in different postures of movement.
a—end of quadrupodal stage; b—beginning stage of diagonal support; c—middle stage of diagonal support; d—secondary tripodal stage.

Figure 105. Aggressive posture of desert monitor.

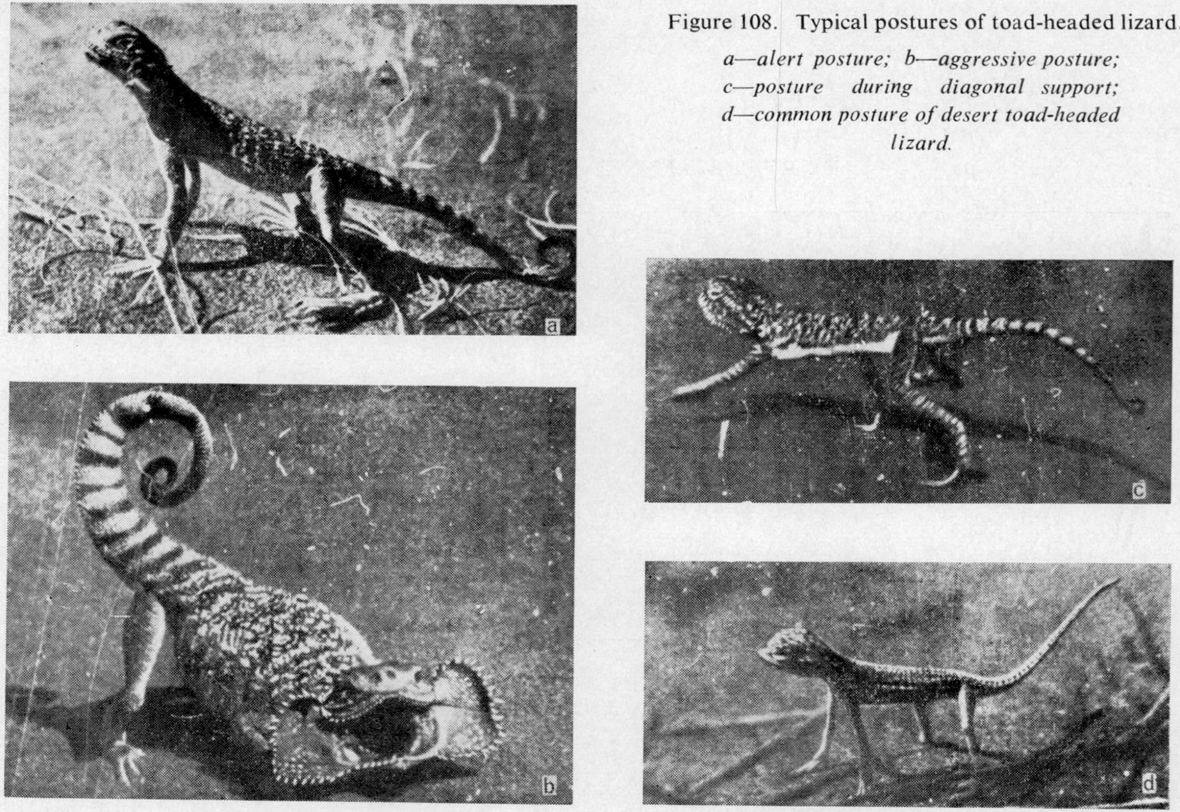

Figure 108. Typical postures of toad-headed lizard.

a—alert posture; b—aggressive posture; c—posture during diagonal support; d—common posture of desert toad-headed lizard.

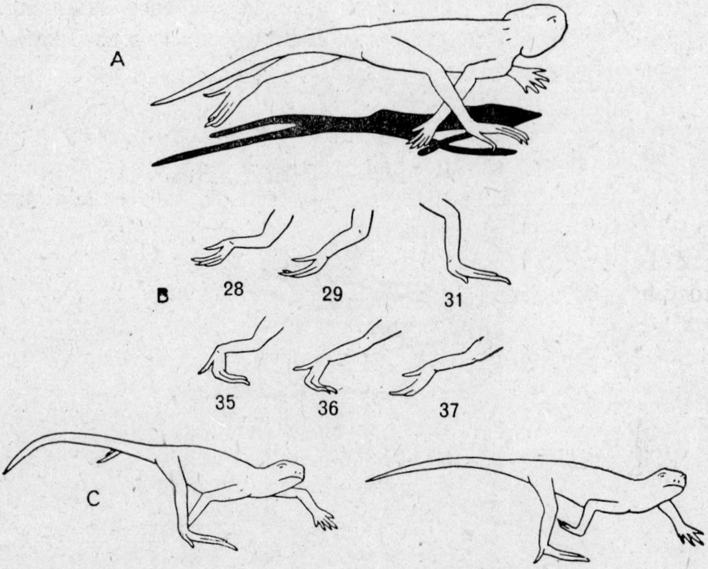

Figure 106. Toad-headed lizard and its limbs in seperate moments of locomotory cycle (from motion pictures).
A—position of the body and limbs at the time of free flight, series Y14-No. 1, frame 30. B—foot in the course of locomotion cycle, series Y18-No. 1, frames 28, 29, 31, and 35 to 37. C—position of body and limbs at the beginning and end of primary unipodal stage, series Y18-No. 1, frames 21 and 22.

place in the plantigrade position (Figure 94, frames 11 and 12; Figure 106, B, frame 31), but almost instantly, the foot starts bending and raising the intertarsal joint above the substrate. It is necessary to mention that in geckos, the foot usually assumes the digitigrade position behind the normal plane (trajectory of intertarsal joint starts rising upwards behind the perpendicular, released from the acetabulum, especially in the cycles shown in Figure 100, D and F). This takes place in toad-headed lizards when the entire limb is still in front of the indicated plane (Figure 107, A and B). At the end of the support period, the limb rests only on the ends of the toes (Figure 87, frames 12, 19 and 20; Figure 94, frames 14 and 15; Figure 106, B, frame 36; Figure 108, c). The hind limb is carried forward lateral of the ipsilateral which is back at its maximum (Figure 94, frame 10). Thus, at the time of free flight, the two ipsilateral limbs cross (Figure 106, A). This is possibly related to the necessity of transporting the whole foot forward in an almost straightened condition so that its distal end makes a wide arc, far-removed from the center but the plane in which the trajectory of displacement of the metatarsal-phalangeal joint lies, is inclined below and inside to a larger degree than in geckos (cf. Figure 102, b). The result of this is the raising of the foot high over the substrate during the protraction of the limb (Figure 94, frame 8).

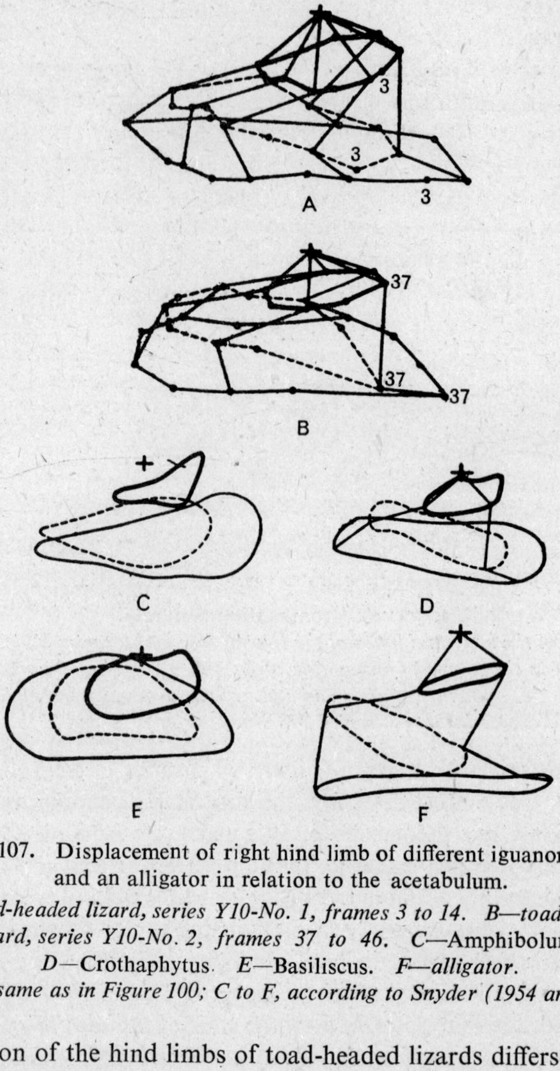

Figure 107. Displacement of right hind limb of different iguanomorphs and an alligator in relation to the acetabulum.
*A—toad-headed lizard, series Y10-No. 1, frames 3 to 14. B—toad-headed lizard, series Y10-No. 2, frames 37 to 46. C—*Amphibolurus. *D—*Crothaphytus. *E—*Basiliscus. *F—alligator.*
Legend same as in Figure 100; C to F, according to Snyder (1954 and 1962).

The action of the hind limbs of toad-headed lizards differs from geckos mainly in that the thigh moves in a more vertical plane. In Figure 107, A and B, it can be seen that the distal end of the thigh, even during protraction, does not rise to the level of the acetabulum. Perhaps this character is typical to this extent in all iguanomorphs, as the same is observed in *Amphibolurus* (Figure 107, C), *Crotaphytus* (Figure 107, D), and *Basiliscus* (Figure 107, E) which should be considered as the result of specialization for fast running. Strong adduction of the thigh in toad-headed lizards is not only observed during movement (an alligator's limb works in a still more vertical plane; cf. Figure 107, F), but also in aggressive poses similar to that given in Figure

108 b, or of rest (Figure 108, a and d) which seems to be quite rare for modern reptiles.

The forelimbs of all lizards act similarly. The movement of the forelimb of the Komodo monitor is clearly seen in the series of sketches from the French film (Figure 109). Judging from the duration of the cycle, the monitor in this case, moved with a speed corresponding to that mentioned for series K1-No. 2. The foot rested its entire plantar surface on the substratum, but at the end of retraction the position became digitigrade as in all lizards (Figure 83, frame 174; Figure 104, a; in Figure 108, it is not shown). The entire foot was stretched in almost a straight line. In some sketches made from the French film and not given here, it could be clearly seen that lifting the foot from the ground took place as a result of aventral flexion of the hand. Even the position was fixed when in the proximal portions of the limb retraction had already started and a large section of the hand had already formed a clear angle with the forearm by keeping the plantar surface upward and slightly medially, almost parallel to the substrate, and only the ends of the phalanges did not lose contact with the soil and formed a sharp angle with the entire hand, moving forward. After disconnection of the hand in the first half of the restoration period (Figure 104, b; Figure 109, frames 67 and 68) retain the same position of the plantar surface positioned dorsally, but afterwards, together with the protraction and supination of the humerus, also starts the extension of the hands. The plantar surface is directed behind, but its preaxial border below (Figure 109, frame 70; Figure 104, c). The hand continues to revolve and extend, assumes the normal contact position (Figure 109, frames 72 and 74). There is almost no flexion at the below during the restoration period; the entire foot is carried in a horizontal position with a wide arc described by the distal end. This makes it possible to complete the complex revolution of the hand without touching the ground, which is important in relation to the low degree of upper arm abduction. However, as shown in Figure 109, frames 70 and 72, the claws often create characteristic lines on the substratum (Hoogerwerf, 1958, p. 137, photo).

In landing, the hand touches with the axis of finger IV parallel to the direction of movement. During limb retraction, revolutions of the hand are not observed. At the beginning of the propulsive period, the hand continues to extend (Figure 109, frames 52 to 74). At the same time, the entire limb flexes strongly at the elbow. The upper arm moves strictly in a horizontal plane by which monitors clearly differ from all other lizards in which the trajectory of displacement of the elbow presents quite a wide ellipse. The forearm acts specifically in a vertical plane.

In plate-tailed geckos (Figure 103, b) and toad-headed lizard (Figure 85, frame 27; Figure 87, frames 14 and 15), the forefoot touches the substrate with its entire plantar surface. However, during its fastest movement, toad-headed lizards touch the soil only with the fingers. At the time of propulsion,

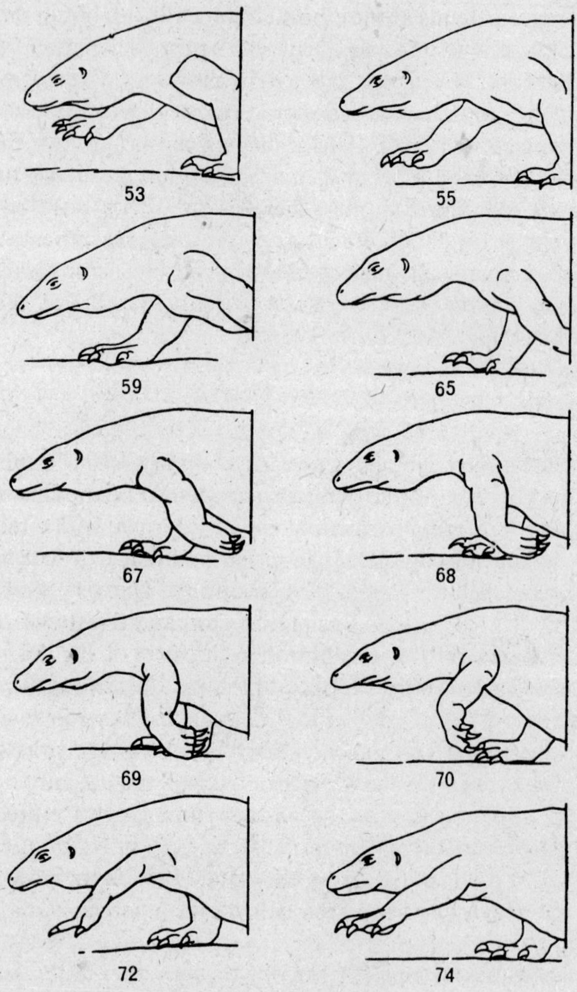

Figure 109. The right forefoot in the locomotion of the Komodo monitor (from motion pictures).

Figures—*number of frames; film speed, 24 frames per second.*

the hand actively flexes (Figure 108, c). After disconnection, the hand retains a flexed position for some time in plate-tailed geckos (Figure 103, c and d) and in toad-headed lizards (Figure 85, frame 30; Figure 106, c). In the latter, the foot is already bent at the beginning of transport (Figure 94, frames 3 to 6). Before landing, it extends at the elbow (Figure 108, c), but in the beginning of propulsion, it is again somewhat bent. The propulsion itself corresponds to a strong extension. The upper arm, as in monitors, is carried forward in a horizontal plane, but during retraction the degree of adduction increases (Figure 94, frames 12 to 14). The ability of the upper arm in toad-headed lizard to assume almost a vertical position in some rest postures is widely known (Figure 108, a and d). In other lizards such a position is never retained for long; possibly, this is associated with the absence of a special muscle, occurring only in toad-headed lizards, m. supracoracoideus accessorius which is considered by us as a functional parallel of the m. supraspinatus in mammals (Sukhanov, 1961).

* * *

Lizards have five inherent gaits but they use them in different degrees in different forms. The important gaits are seen to be the slow trot-like walk (during locomotion without much speed), slow trot with predominance of hind limbs (during slightly increased speed) and fast trot with predominance of hind limbs (in instances of fast locomotion). The very slow walk is used during the slowing down period prior to a stop and the slow trot with predominance of forelimbs during locomotion in the form of a trot with a particular low speed but it is not related to the subsequent following stop. Geckos use all five gaits irrespective of the fact that they do not develop a very high speed. Barbs are, perhaps, similar to geckos, but the fast trot is characteristic of them to a considerable degree. The Komodo monitor moves only by a slow trot-like walk and sometimes during speed by a slow trot with predominance of hind limbs. However, the desert monitor may possibly also use fast trot with predominance of hind limbs. In essence, the latter is the only gait of toad-headed lizards which just prior to a halt utilize a similar variant of the slow trot.

The index characterizing rhythm of action of hind limbs with an increase of speed sharply decreases but only up to a limit, after which change stops. In the forelimbs, rhythms change to a considerably less degree. All this is related to the difference in the paces of reduction of support time and transport time. The support time for the hind limbs changes significantly more than that for the forelimbs, but again only up to a limit. Transport time of limbs during a speed increase remains almost unchanged. The rhythm of locomotion varies widely in lizards. The largest range of change is characteristically seen in plate-tailed geckos (usually from 50 to —11 %), the smallest change, in toad-headed lizards (5 to —8 %) which is related to the limitation of its ability for slow movement. An speed increase in four-paced movement of lizards, also of salamanders, causes a closeness between the rhythm of locomotion and the rhythm of the trot. But unlike salamanders, lizards are capable of the trot and are potentially able to increase their locomotion without changing rhythm. The index characterizing the rhythm of locomotion, during the movement by a trot, has a tendency to deviate from the rhythm of the trot (0%) both in the positive direction (four-paced movement in a diagonal sequence), as well as in the negative (four-paced movement in the lateral sequence) but limits of variation, as a rule, do not exceed ±10%. It is consequently necessary to accept these as the limits of the trot. The higher the speed, the more likely that negative rhythms of locomotion will appear which, apparently, are related to a particular advantage of movement in a lateral sequence during fast motion. This throws light on the origin of trot and similarly amble where the same phenomenon is observed.

As a rule, movement in lizards takes place with some degree of predominance of either fore or hind limbs. The latter is more characteristic for lizards. The role of the forelimbs in locomotion is increased only during very slow movement. Predominance of hind limbs is only partially conditioned by their greater length compared to the forelimbs, as it grows with an increase of speed even in those forms where the limbs are almost equal. Respectively, the bipedal run of lizards, their speediest gait, is characterized by an extreme degree of predominance of hind limbs (100%). Possibly, the difference in length of fore and hind limbs inherent to the majority of reptiles, is caused by an adaptation not only to fast running, but seems also to be the result of their capability for the trot in general, as in this instance, the appearance of predominance is useful during fast movement, also during slow, where it effectively reduces the duration of the non-locomotory quadrupodal stages of the cycle.

With increased speed, the duration of the cycle has a tendency to reduce only up to a known limit which is established by the physiological and biomechanical specialities of the animal. Its size depends upon the size of the animal, particularly in the larger forms. Dependents of the duration of cycle (t) from speed of locomotion (v) are expressed in the following formulas: $t=a+m/v$, where a is the lower limit of cycle reduction, by m, the size of the glenoacetabular distance of the given animal. A change in cycle duration for similar sized scincogeckonomorphs (plate-tailed gecko, retinal barb, long-legged scink) is expressed factually by one curve, dffering from that of toad-headed lizard, though the latter are almost of the same size. This is apparently related to the different directions that specialization took in scincogeckonomorphs and iguanomorphs. A speed change in toad-headed lizard is more responsible for quicker limb movement than an increase in length of step. In scincogeckonomorphs, the ratio of both factors during fast locomotion is reversed, but during slow, the role of frequency is increased.

Increased speed causes particular changes in regard to the duration of separate stages of the cycle. The duration of diagonal support during increased speed is increased, but with the change to a fast trot, it again starts to decrease. Quadrupodal stages are decreased to zero, but their place is taken by stages of free flight. A change from the slow trot with predominance of hind limbs to fast trot, may lead to the appearance in the cycle of short stages, not usually present in the locomotion of animals, for example, a stage of support on only two hind limbs.

CHAPTER VIII

GENERAL CONCLUSIONS

1. It is necessary to differentiate the methods of locomotion, to characterize the biomechanic of animal locomotion, and to document the forms of locomotion or gaits which reflect the coordinative activity of the central nervous system.

2. The suggested method is a diagrammatic presentation of gaits combining the positive aspects of earlier methods. The support plans for all stages of a cycle are added by special lines, two upwards and two downwards, on which the proportional times of support and transport of limbs are shaded. The action of the left limbs are registered on the upper lines; of the right limbs, on the lower; of the forelimbs, on the inside; of the hind limbs, on the outside. This new method enables one to compare gaits clearly, stressing the main point that either they are different or similar.

3. Symmetrical or assymetrical gaits of terrestrial vertebrates are based on two different types of limb coordination. The type of coordination is determined first by the sequence of similar limb movements (only fore or only hind) and in connection with this, the rhythm of locomotion is characterized as intracyclic or intercyclic for symmetrical and asymmetrical types

respectively.

4. The symmetrical gaits are based on sequences wherein the movement of the forefoot follows a similar movement of its diagonal hind foot (symmetrical-diagonal sequence); or the converse (symmetrical-lateral). In all asymmetrical gaits after the sequences of action of both forelimbs, similarly and subsequently, the hind limbs enter into action one after the other. In asymmetrical-diagonal gaits, the diagonal hind limb follows after the second forelimb, but in asymmetrical-lateral, the ipsilateral hind limb.

5. Only two main factors determine the substance of each symmetrical gait: the rhythm of limb action and the rhythm of locomotion. The first is determined by the ratio of support time to transport time of the limb in the cycle. It has been shown that a speed increase is completed only with a change of the ratio of support/transport: as support time grows relatively, transport time decreases. Thus, each level of speed should correspond to its own significant rhythm of limb action. The rhythm of locomotion is the specific sequence at the time of similar movements for all four limbs. This rhythm is expressed by the ratio of the interval between movements of the limbs of one diagonal to the duration of half locomotory cycle (in percents), or by the ratio of the interval between the movement on one foot of the same-sided, and on the other hand, of diagonally placed limbs (in absolute numbers).

6. Thus, each symmetrical gait is a function of speed entering in the form of the rhythm of limb action and the rhythm of locomotion and, as such, may be expressed as a diagrammatic system (Figure 6) of coordination (abscissa, rhythm of locomotion; odinate, rhythm of limb action). Theoretically, it is more convenient to conduct calculations on conditional norms of gaits in which all the stages of a cycle are equal, and hence, support time, transport time, and all the remaining time intervals may be expressed by a simple number of stages.

7. Five main rhythms of locomotion have been separated: rhythm of trot (0%), half-trot (25%), walk (50%), half-amble (75%) and amble (100%); respective to these are the five main forms of symmetrical locomotion: trot, trot-like walk, walk, amble-like walk, and amble, with different grades on the speed in each (fast to slow in each, except the walk which is separated into very slow, normal, and fast walks). These general types of gaits identified initially by the activity of the central nervous system, are necessarily differentiated from particular or morphological types, similar to the external variant of symmetrical gaits, etc.

8. The mechanism of nervous control functions differently for the trot, walk, and amble. In the first, it provides a simultaneous forward movement of the diagonal limb pair; in the second, consecutive limb movements of one diagonal with an interval in one half-period of the wave, passing over the body (hind limb after forelimb); and in the third, it leads to leaving the hind leg behind its diagonal foreleg throughout the whole period.

9. Symmetrical locomotion should be considered as a single system of interrelated changes, opposite to the pole occupied by trot and amble. The evolutionary beginning for terrestrial vertebrates' movement by the walk (very slow) is based on the mechanism already found in fish. The trot and amble appear only as a result of a long and gradual evolution of terrestrial vertebrates during adaptation to locomotion at progressively higher speeds. Evolutionarily, they were preceded by the appearance of the slow trot-like walk and slow amble-like walk. In the evolution of animals, the trot appeared much earlier than the amble and the faster from of the walk earlier than the very slow walk; in connection with the limitations placed on amphibians and sauropsids, the forms of the walk were inherited from fishes by the primitive position of limbs. The transference of limbs in the parasagittal plane during the change to mammals, made it possible to possess all variations of symmetrical and asymmetrical locomotion. Movement by the symmetrical-lateral sequence was the latest adaptation of vertebrates and came to them via the trot.

10. The locomotion of amphibian-sauropsidian line of lower tetrapods developed strictly as three symmetrical gaits. Salamanders move only by the very slow and slow trot-like walk, though with an increase of speed, the rhythm of locomotion has a tendency to become closer to the rhythm of trot. The real trot apparently seems to be an historical achievement of reptiles. Slow locomotion in lizards occurs in two main forms (slow trot-like walk and slow trot with predominance of hind limbs and, rarely, of forelimbs). Slowing of motion with a following stop passes through the first form and further through the very slow walk in all forms, except agamids, repeating occasionally in the reverse order the sequence of appearance of symmetrical gaits: very slow walk—slow trot-like walk—slow trot—fast trot.

11. The ability to move with greater speed by the fast trot with predominance of hind limbs developed independently in such systematically distant groups of lizards as scincogeckonomorphs and iguanomorphs. However, the latter in the course of adaptation to fast movement, completely lost the ability to move slowly in the majority of cases. On the other hand, scincogeckonomorphs not only retained this ability, but in addition to the slow trot-like walk formed external variants of the slow trot: for some fast movements with predominance of hind limbs; for the slowest with predominance of forelimbs. Thus, scincogeckonomorphs are rare examples in nature of the phenomenon, adaptation particularly to slow movement, including also several morphological features in association with the reduction of the functional length of the hind limbs.

12. Fast trot with predominance of hind limbs finds its basis in the bipedalism of lizards (first mentioned for lizards of our fauna). Both forms of movement are similar in principles; also, in lizards during movement within a certain range of speeds, change from one to the other does not cause any signi-

ficant additional efforts. There are many justifications for thinking that the fast trot with predominance of hind limbs also formed the basis for the change to bipedalism in archosaurus; at the time the latter appeared, it already existed (Permian and Triassic periods).

13. Asymmetrical locomotion of lower tetrapods (frogs, sea turtles, turtles, pterosaurs, and birds) developed only during a complete change in habitat (change from land to water or to air), in the root of changing conditions of equilibrium. Several of its forms differ characteristically from the real asymmetrical locomotion of mammals.

BIBLIOGRAPHY

ABEL, O., 1912, Grundzuge der Paleobiologie der Wirbeltiere. Stuttgart.

ABEL, O., 1935. Vorzeitliche Lebensspuren. Jena.

ANDERSON, P.K., 1954. Studies in Ecology of the Narrow-mouthed Toad. *Microhyla carolinensis carolinensis*. Tulane Stud. Zool., **2**, 2: 15-46.

ANNANDALE, N., 1902. Bipedal Locomotion in Lizards. Nature, **66**, 1719: 577.

ANNANDALE, N., 1919. Some Frogs from Streams in the Bombay Presidency, Rec. Indian Museum. **16**: 121-125.

ASHTON, E.H. and C.E. OXNARD, 1964. Locomotor Patterns in Primates. Proc. Zool. Soc. London, **142**: 1-28.

BAIRD, D., 1952. Revision of the Pennsylvanian and Permian Footprints of *Limnopus, Allopus* and *Baropus*. J. Paleontol., **26**, 5: 832-840.

BARBOUR, TH., 1934. Reptiles and Amphibians: Their Habits and Adaptations. Boston and New York.

BARBOUR, TH., 1943. Defense Posture of *Varanus gouldi*. Copeia, **1**: 56-57.

BARCLAY, O.R., 1946. The Mechanics of Amphibian Locomotion. J. Exper. Biol., **23**, 2: 177-203.

BARCLAY, O. R., 1953. Some Aspects of the Mechanics of Mammalian Locomotion. J. Exper. Biol., **30**, 1: 116-120.

BARRETT, C., 1931. The Gippsland Watr Lizard. Victorian Naturalist, **47**, 10: 162-165.

BARRETT, C., 1950. Reptiles of Australia. Sydney.

BARTH, R., 1962. Observacoes Sobre a grande tertaruga marinha, *Chelonia mydas* L., Feitas n Ilha de Trinadade. An. Acad. Brasil. cienc., **34**, 3: 405-409.

BARTHOLOMEW, G.A., Jr., and G.R. GARY, 1954. Locomotion in Pocket Mice. J. Mammal., **35**, 3: 386-392.

BARTHOLOMEW, G.A., Jr. and H.H. CASWELL, 1951. Locomotion in Kangaroo Rats and Its Adaptive Significance, J. Mammal., **32**, 2: 155-168.

BARWICK, R.E., 1961. Illustrations of the New Zealand Frog Fauna, Tuatara, **8**, 3: 95-98.

BELKIN, D.A., 1961. The Running Speeds of the Lizards *Dipsosaurus dorsalis* and *Callisaurus draconoides,* Copeia, **2**: 223-224.

BERGOUNIOUX, F.M., 1955. Testudinata, *Traite de Paleontologia*. 5, *Amphibiens, Reptiles, Oiseaux*. Paris, 487-544.

BERNSHTEIN, N.A., 1926. Obshchaya biomekhanika (General Biomechanics).

Moscow.

BERNSHTEIN, N.A., 1927. Issledovanie po biodinamike khod'by i bega, V sb. Vopr. dinamiki mostov (Studies on the Biodynamics of Walking and Running, in Problems of the Dynamics of Elevation). Tr. Nauchno-tekhn. komit. NKPS, Moscow: 63: 51-76.

BERNSHTEIN, N.A., 1935. Issledovaniya po biodinamike lokomotsii (Studies on the biodynamics of Locomotion). Moscow and Leningrad.

BERNSHTEIN, N.A., 1940. Issledovanie biodinamiki bega vydayushikhsya masterov, V sb. Issl. po biodinam. khod'by, bega i pryzhka (Studies on the Boidynamics of Running for Leading Master Sportsmen, in Studies of the Biodynamics of Walking, Running and Jumping). Moscow, 131-223.

BERNSHTEIN, N.A., 1946. Fiziologiya tsentral'noi nervnoi sistemy, V kn. Fiziol. cheloveka. Pod. red. M.E., Marshaka (Pshysiology of the Central Nervous System, in Physiology of Man. Ed. M.E. Marshak). Moscow, 237-271.

BERNSHTEIN, N.A., 1947. O postroenii dvizhenii (On the Structure of Movements). Moscow.

BICKEL, A., 1897. Ueber den Einfluss der sensibelen Nerven und der Labyrinthe auf die Bewegungen der Thiere. Pflug. Arch. Ges. Physiol., **67**: 299-344.

BICKEL, A., 1900. Beitrage zur Ruckenmarksphysiologie der Frosches. Arch. Physiol., 485-493.

BIEDERMANN, W., 1909. Beitrage zur Kenntniss der Reflexfuntion des Ruckenmarkes. Arch. Ges. Physiol., **80**: 408-469.

BLAIR, A.P., 1950. Skittering Locomotion in *Acris crepitans*. Copiea, **4**: 237.

BOCK, W., 1952. Triassic Reptilian Tracks and Trends of Locomotive Evolution. J. Paleontol., **26**, 3: 395-433.

BOKER, H., 1935. Einfuhrung in die vergleichende biologische Anatomie der Wirbeltiere. 1, Jena.

BORELLI, A., 1681. De Motu Animalium, Roma.

BOURDELLE, E., 1934. Les Allures de la giraffe, en particulier le galop. Bull. Museum nat. histoire natur. Paris: ser. 2, **6**: 329-339.

BRADY, L.F., 1935. Notes on the Geology of Northern Arizona. Museum Notes, Museum Northern Arizona, **8**: 9-12.

BRAUNE, W., and O. FISCHER, 1898-1903. Der Gang des Mensche. 1-6. Leipzig.

BREM, A.E., 1939. Zhizhn' Zhivotnykh: III. Ryby, Zemnovodnye, presmykayushchiesya (Life of Animals: III. Fishes, Amphibians and Reptiles). Moscow.

BRUL, E.L. du., 1962. The General Phenomenon of Bipedalism. Amer. Zoologist **2**, 2: 205-208.

BURT, C.E., 1931. A Study of the Teiid Lizards of the Genus *Cnemidophorus* with Special Reference to Their Phylogenetic Relationships. Bull U.S. Nat. Museum, **154**: 1-286.

CASAMIQUELA, R.M., 1964. Estudios icnologicos: Problemas y metodos de la icnologia con aplication al estudio de pisadas mesozoicas (*Reptilia*, *Mammalia*) de la Patagonia. Buenos Aires.

CATE, J., TEN., 1928. Contribution a la physiologie de la moelle epiniere chez *Triton cristatus*. Arch. neerl. physiol., **12**: 213-253.

CHABANAUD, P., 1949. Skittering Locomotion of the African Frog. *Rana occipitalis*. Copeia, 5: 288.

CHEPELYUGINA, M.F., 1950. O roli efferentastii postroenii dvigatel'nykh aktov (On the Role of Efferentive Construction of Movement Acts). Moscow: Avtoref Kand. diss.

CLIBURN, J.W., 1957. Leaping Ability of the Glass Lizard. Herpetologica, **13**, 1: 24.

COGHILL, G.E., 1929. Anatomy and the Problem of Behavior. Cambridge.

COPE, E.D., 1875. On the *Batrachia* and *Reptilia* of Costa Rica. J. Acad. Natur. Sci. (Philadelphia), **8**: 93-154.

COTT, H.B., 1926. Observations on the Life-habits of Some Batrachians and Repeptiles from the Lower Amazon and a Note on Some Mammals from Marajo Island. Proc. Zool. Soc., **2**: 1159-1178.

COTT, H.B., 1961. Scientific Results of an Inquiry into the Ecology and Economic Status of the Nile Crocodile (*Crocodilus niloticus*) in Uganda and Northern Rhodesia. Trans. Zool. Soc. London, **29**, 4: 211-356.

COWLES, R.B., 1941. Observations on the Winter Activities of Desert Reptiles, Ecology, **22**, 2: 125-140.

COWLES, R.B., 1946. Swimming Ability of the Alligator Lizard (*Gerrhonotus multi-carinatus webbii*). Copeia 2: 105.

CROIX, P.M., de la, 1928, Sobre la evolucion del galope de carrera y la consecutiva de la forma. An. Soc. cient. (Argentina), 106: 317-331.

CROIX, P.M., de la, 1929 a. Filogenia de las locomociones cuadrupedal y bipedal en los vertebrados y evolution de la forma consecutiva de la evolution de la locomocion An. Soc. cient. (Argentina), 108: 383-406.

CROIX, P.M., de la, 1929b. On the Subject of the Observations Made in the Zoological Station of the 'San Francisco Mountain' on Bipedal Rat Movements. An. Soc. cient. (Argentina), **109**: 144-146.

CROIX, P.M., de la, 1929c. Los andares cuadrupedales y bipedales del hombre y del mono. Semana medica, **48**: 5-12.

CROIX, P.M., de la, 1930a. Andares irregulares o transitorios su papel en la evolution. Physis, Rev. Soc. Argentina cienc. natur., **10**: 99-108.

CROIX, P.M., de la, 1930b. La marche quadrupedale du chimpanze et de l'homme. An. Soc. cient. (Argentina), **110**: 393-398.

CROIX, P.M., de la, 1931. Repetition des impressions cinesthesiques on l'evolution des allures. An. Soc. cient. (Argentina), **111**: 352.

CROIX, P.M., de la, 1932a. Evolucion del galope transverso. An. Soc. cient. (Argentina), **113**: 150.

CROIX, P.M., de la, 1932b. Les deux formes du galop pithecoide. An. Soc. cient. (Argentina), **113**: 150.

CROIX, P.M., de la, 1932c. Parallele entre l'evolution locomotrice des vertebres et celle des articules. An. Soc. cient. (Argentina), **114**: 143.

CROIX, P.M., de la, 1933a. Evolution de la Locomocion terrestre en los vertebrados. Rev. med. y veterinarn., **15-19**: 2-6.

CROIX, P.M., de la, 1933b. El andar cuadrupedal de los ninos. Semana medica, **1**: 3.

CROIX, P.M., de la, 1933c. Des retours de l'evolution et la relativite des theories. An. Soc. cient. (Argentina), **116**: 225-239.

CROIX, P.M., de la, 1934. El shock y su papel en la herencia. Semana medica, **27**: 5-23.

CROIX, P.M., de la , 1936. The Evolution of Locomotion in Mammals. J. Mammal., **17**, 1: 51-54.

CROIX, P.M., de la, 1940. Como termina la evolucion de los andares reptilianos, La Plata. Vol. 3 of Kraglievich L. Obras de Geologia y Paleontologia. 923-928.

DAGG, A.I., 1960. Gaits of the Giraffe and Okapi. J. Mammal., **41**, 2: 282.

DAGG, A.I., 1962. The Role of the Neck in the Movements of the Giraffe. J. Mammals., **43**, 1: 88-97.

DAVIDSON, T., 1963. Bullfrog Ballet Filmed in Flight. Nat Geogr. Mag., **123**, 6: 790-799.

DECHASEAUX, C., 1959. Les adaptations des vertebres marins et le mystere de leur origines: II. Physiologie-signification des resemblances. Nature, **3295**: 493-497.

DENBURGH, J., van, 1922. The Reptiles of Western North America: I. Lizards. San Francisco.

DERANIAGALA, P.E.P., 1930. The Testudinata of Ceylon, Ceylon J. Sci., B. **16**: 43-88.

DITMARS, R.L., 1933. Reptiles of the World. New York.

DOLLO, L., 1905, Les allures des iguanodons, d'apres les empreintes des pieds et de la queue. Bull. scient. France Belgique, **40**: 1-12.

DU BRUL, E.L., 1962. The General Phenomenon of Bipedalism, Amer. Zoologist, **2**, 2: 205-208.

DUEDEREN, 1903. Methods of Evolution. Cited in Essex. 1927.

DUNN, E.R., 1928. Results of the Douglas Burden Expedition to the Island of Komodo: IV. Frogs from the East Indies. Amer. Museum Novitates, **315**: 1-9.

DYURST, Y., 1936. E'kster'er loshadi (Exterior of Horses) Leningrad.

ELFTMAN, H., 1934. A Cinematic Study of the Distribution of Pressure in the Ruman Foot. Anat. Rec., **59**: 481-487.

ELFTMAN, H., 1940. The Work Done by Muscles in Running. Amer. J. Physiol., **129**: 672-684.

ESSEX, R., 1927. Studies in Reptilian Degeneration. Proc. Zool. Soc. London, 879-945.

EVANS, F.G., 1946. The Anatomy and Function of the Foreleg in Salamander Locomotion, Anat. Rec., **95**, 3: 257-281.

FABER, J., 1956. The Development and Coordination of Larval Limb Movements in *Triturus taeniatus* and *Ambystoma mexicanum,* Arch. neerl. zool., **2**, 4: 498-517.

FITZSIMONS, V.F., 1943. The Lizards of South Africa. Pretoria.

FLETCHER, H.O., 1959. A Giant Marine Reptile from the Cretaceous Rocks of Queensland. Austral. Museum Mag., **13**: 47-49.

FOKIN, I.M., 1963. Osobennosti bega tushkanchikov (Peculiarities of Running in Jerboa). Byull. Mosk. Obshch. ispyt. Prirody. otd. biol. **68**, 5: 22-28.

GADOW, H.F., 1901. Amphibia and Reptiles. London.

GAMBARYAN, P.P., 1955. Biomekhanika rikoshetiruyushchgo pryzhka u gryzunov (Biomechanics of the Ricocheting Jump in Rodents). Zool. zh., **34**, 3: 621-630.

GAMBARYAN, P.P., 1964. Morfofunktsional'nyi analiz myshts konechnostei tapira (*Tapirus americanus*) (Morphofunctional Analysis of Limb Muscles in *Tapirus americanus*). Zool. sb. Zool. inst. AN ArmSSR, **13**: 5-50.

GAMBARYAN, P.P., 1967. Proiskhozhdenie mnogobraziya allyurov u mlekopitayushchikh (Origin of Diversity of Allures in Mammlas). Zh. obshch. biol. **28**, 3: 289-305.

GAMBARYAN, P.P., 1968. Beg melkopitayushchikh (Prisposobitel'nye osobennosti organov dvizheniya) [Running in Mammals (Adaptive Capacity of the Organs of Locomotion)]. Leningrad: Avtoref. Dokt. diss.

GANS, C., 1961. A Bullfrog and Its Prey: A Look at the Biomechanics of Jumping. Natur. History, **70**, 2: 26-37.

GANS, C., 1962. Terrestrial Locomotion without Limbs. Amer. Zoologist **2**, 2: 167-182.

GANS, C., 1966a. Locomotion without Limbs: Diverse Mechanisms Propel Snakes on Land, *Natur. History,* **75**, 2: 11-17.

GANS, C., 1966b. Locomotion without Limbs. II. Smooth surfaces Pose Special Problems. *Natur. History*, **75**, 3: 36-41.

GANS, C. and T.S. PARSONS, 1966. On the Origin of the Jumping Mechanism in Frogs. Evolution, **20**, 1: 92-99.

GESSE, R., 1913. Telo zhivotnykh kak samostoyatel'nyi organizm (Animal Body as an Independent Organism). St. Petersburg.

GILMORE, C.W., 1927. Fossil Footprints from the Grand Canyon: Second Contribution. Smithson. Misc. Collect., **80**, 3: 1-78.

GLAESNER, L., 1925. Normentafeln zur Entwicklungsgaschichte des geneinen Wassermolchs (*Molge vulgaris*). Vol. 14 of Normentafeln zur Entwicklungsgeschichte der Wirbeltiere by F. Keibel. Jena.

GNAEDINGER, L.M., and C.A. REED, 1948. Contribution to the Natural History of the Plethodont Salamander *Ensatina eschscholtzii*, Copeia. **8**: 187-196.

GOIFFON and VINCENT. 1779. Memoire artificielle des principes relatifs a la fide le representation des animaux tant en peinture, qu'en sculpture: I. Partie concernant le cheval Alfort.

GOUBAUX, A. and G. BARRIER, 1884. De l'exterieur du cheval. Paris.

GRAHAM, BROWN T., 1912a. The Intrinsic Factors in the Act of Progression in the Mammal. Proc. Roy, Soc. London, B, **84**: 308-319.

GRAHAM, BROWN T., 1912b. The Factors in Rhythmic activity of the Neıvous System. Proc. Roy. Soc. London. B, **85**: 278-289.

GRAHAM, BROWN T., 1913. The Phenomenon of 'Narcosis Progression' in Mammals. Proc. Roy. Soc. London. B, **86**: 140-146.

GRAY, J., 1933. Studies in Animal Locomotion: I. The Movement of Fish with Special Reference to the Eel. J. Exper. Biol., **10**, 1: 88-104.

GRAY, J., 1936a. Studies in Animal Locomotion: IV. The Neuromuscular Mechanism of Swimming in the Eel. J. Exper. Biol., **13**, 2: 170-180.

GRAY, J., 1936b. Studies in Animal Locomotion: V. Resistance Reflexes in the Eel. J. Exper. Biol., **13**, 2: 181-191.

GRAY, J., 1939a. Aspects of Animal Locomotion. Proc. Roy. Soc. London, B, **128**: 26-62.

GRAY, J., 1939b. Studies in Animal Locomotion: VIII. The Kinetics of Locomotion of *Nereis diversicolor*. J. Exper. Biol., **16**, 9: 17.

GRAY, J., 1944. Studies in the Mechanics of the Tetrapod Skeleton. J. Exper. Biol., **20**, 2: 88-116.

Gray J., 1946. The Mechanism of Locomotion in Snakes. J. Exper. Biol., **23**, 2: 101-120.

GRAY, J., 1950. The Role of Peripheral Sense Organs duridg Locomotion in the Vertebrates, Physiological Mechanisms in Animal Behavior. Sympos. Soc. Exper. Biol. Cambridge, **4**: 112-126.

GRAY, J., 1953. How Animals Move. Cambridge.

GRAY, J., 1961. General Principles of Vertebrate Locomotion, Sympos. Zool. Soc. London: 5. Vertebrate Locomotion, 1-11.

GRAY, J. and H.W. LISSMANN, 1938. Studies in Animal Locomotion: VII. Locomotory Reflexes in the Earthworm. J. Exper. Biol., **15**, 4: 506-517.

GRAY, J., 1940a. The Effect of De-afferentation upon the Locomotory Activity of Amphibian Limbs. J. Exper Biol., **17**, 2: 227-236.

GRAY, J., 1940b. Ambulatory Reflexes in Spinal Amphibian, J. Exper. Biol., **17**, 2: 237-251.

GRAY, J., 1946a. Further Observations on the Effect of De-afferentation on the Locomotory Activity of Amphibian Limbs. J. Exper. Biol., **23**, 2: 121-132.

GRAY, J., 1946b. The Coordination of Limb Movements in the Amphibia. J. Exper. Biol., **23**, 2: 133-142.

GRAY, J., 1950. The Kinetics of Locomotion of the Grass Snake. J. Exper. Biol., **26**, 4: 354-367.

GRAY, J. and R.J. PUMPHREY, 1938. The Mechanism of Locomotion in the Leech (*Hirudo medicinalis*). J. Exper. Biol., **15**, 3: 408-430.

GRAY, J. and A. SAND, 1936a. The Locomotory Rhythm of the Dogfish (*Scyllium canicula*). J. Exper. Biol., **13**, 2: 200-209.

GRAY, J., 1936b. Spinal Reflexes of the Dogfish, *Scyllium canicula,* J. Exper. Biol., **13**, 2: 210-217.

GREEN, E.E., 1903. Bipedal Locomotion of a Ceylonese Lizard. J. Bombay Natur. History Soc., **14**: 817.

GREGORY, W.K., 1912. Notes on the Principles of Quadrupedal Locomotion and on the Mechanism of the Limbs in Hoofed Animals. Ann. N.Y. Acad. Sci., **22**: 267-292.

GREGORY, W.K., 1937. The Bridge-that-walks. Natur. History, **39**: 33-48.

GREGORY, W.K., 1951. Evolution Emerging: A Survey of Changing Patterns from Primeval Life to Man. N.Y.: 1,2.

GREGORY, W.K. and C.L. CAMP, 1918. Studies in Comparative Myology and Osteology: III. Notes on the Origin and Evolution of Certain Adaptations for Forward Locomotion in the Pectoral and Pelvic Girdles of Reptiles and Mammals. Bull. Amer. Museum Natur. History, **38**, 3: 447-563.

GRIFFITHS, I., 1963. The Phylogeny of the Salientia. Biol. Revs. **38**, 2: 241-292.

GROFAN, J.W., 1951. The Gaits of Horses. J. Amer. Vet. Med. Assoc., **119**, 893: 112-117.

GUBO, A. and G. BARRE, 1901. E'kster'er loshchadi (Exterior of Horses). Orel.

GUPTA, B.B., 1964. Locomotion and Some Postures in the Indian Hedgehogs, Zool. polon., **14**: 1-2 and 71-74. (facsimile).

GYURST, U., 1936. Ekster'er loshchadi (Exterior of Horses). Leningrad.

HATT, R.G., 1932. The Vertebral Columns of Ricochetal Rodents. Bull. Amer. Museum Natur. History, **63**, 6: 599-738.

HAUGHTON, S., 1873. Principles of Animal Mechanics. London.

HAY, O.P., 1910. On the Manner of Locomotion of the Dinosaurs, Especially *Diplodocus*, with Remarks on the Origin of the Birds. Proc. Washington Acad. Sci., **12**: 1-25.

HERING, H.E., 1893. Ueber die nach Durchschneidung der hinteren Wurzeln auftretende Bewegungslosigkeit des Ruchenmarksfrosches. Pflug. Arch. ges. Physiol., **54**, 10-12: 614-636.

HERING, H.E., 1897. Ueber Bewegungsstorungen nach centripetaler Lahmung. Arch. exper. Pathol. Pharmakol., **38**, 3-4: 266-283.

HEYLER, D. and J. LESSERTISSEUR, 1963. Pistes de tetrapodes permiens dans la region de Lodeve (Herault). Mem. Museum nat. histoire natur., C, ii, **2**: 9-222.

HILDEBRAND, M., 1959. Motions of the Running Cheetah and Horse, J. Mammal., **40**, 4: 481-495.

HILDEBRAND, M., 1960. How Animals Run. Scient. Amer., **202**, 5: 148-157.

HILDEBRAND, M., 1961. Further Studies on the Locomotion of the Cheetah. J. Mammal., **42**, 1: 84-91.

HILDEBRAND, M., 1962. Walking Running and Jumping. Amer. Zoologist, **2**, 2: 151-155.

HILDEBRAND, M., 1963. The Use of Motion Pictures for the Functional Analysis of Vertebrate Locomotion. Proc. XVI Internat. Congr. Zool., **3**: 263-268.

HILDEBRAND, M., 1966. Analysis of the Symmetrical Gaits of Tetrapods. Folia biotheoret., **13**, 6: 9-22.

HIRSH, W., 1931. Zur physiologischen Mechanik des Froschsprunges, **Zs.** vergleich. Pnysiol., **15**: 1-49.

HIRTH, H.F., 1963. The Ecology of two Lizards on a Tropical Beach. Ecol. Monogr., **33**, 2: 83-112.

HOBSON, E.S., 1965. Observations on Diving in the Galapagos Marine Iguana, *Amblyrhyncnus cristatus* (Bell). Copeia. **2**: 249-250.

HOLMES, S.J., 1096. The Biology of the Frog. New York.

HOOGERWERF, A., 1958. The Indonesian Giant, Natur. History, **67**, 3: 136-141.

HOWELL, A.B., 1932. The Saltatorial Rodent *Dipodomys*: Functional and Comparative Anatomy of Its Muscular and Osseous Systems, Proc. Amer. Acad. Arts Sci., **67**, 10: 377-536.

HOWELL, A.B., 1944. Speed in Animals, Chicago.

HOYT, I.S.Y., 1941. High Speed Attained by *Cnemidophorus sexlineatus,* Copeia, 1: 180.

HUDSON, R.G., 1952. Observations on Cricket Frog Locomotion. Copeia, 1: 185.

HUENE, F., VON, 1908. Die Dinosaurier der europaischen Trias-Formation. Geol. und palaeontol. Abhandl., Suppl., 1: 419.

HUENE, F., VON, 1913. Beobachtungen uber die Bewegungsart der Extremitaten bei Krokodilen. Biol. Cbl., **33**, 8: 468-472.

INGER, R.F., 1962. On the Terrestrial Origin of Frogs, Copeia, 4: 835-836.

JANSON, H.S., 1953. Skittering Locomotion in the Frog *Hyla cinerea cinerea.* Copeia, 1: 62.

KALIN, J., 1959. Filmvorfuhrungen: Uber die Lokomotion der Crocodiliden. Verhandle. Dtsch. zool. Ges., 1958: 335-337.

KALIN, J. and L. KNUSEL, 1944, Uber die Lokomotion der Crocodiliden, Rev. suisse zool., **51**: 389-393.

KAS'YANENKO, V.G., 1947. Apparat dvizheniya i opory loshadi (Funktsional'nyi analiz) [Locomotion Aparatus and Supports of a Horse Functional Analysis)]. Kiev.

KLINGEL, H., 1965. Uber das Flugverhalten von *Draco volans* (*Agamidae*) und verwandten Arten. Zool. Anz., **175**, 4/6: 273-281.

KORN, H., 1929. Fossile Gasblasenbahnen aus dem Thuringer Palaozoikum, eine neue Deutung von *Dictyodora*. Zs. Naturwiss, **82**, 2: 25.

KOTIKOVA, E.A., 1939. Biomekhanika fizicheskikh uprazhnenii (Biomechanics of Physical Exercises). Leningrad.

KRASNIKOV, A.S., 1957. E'kster'er loshadi (Exterior of Horses). Moscow.

KUHN, O. 1958. Die Fahrten der vorzeitlichen Amphibien und Reptilien. Bamberg.

LECOQ, F., 1843. Traite de l'exterieur de cheval, et des principaux animaux domestiques. Paris.

LENOBLE DU TEIL, J., 1877. Locomotion quadrupede etudies sur le cheval. J. Haras: 224.

LESSERTISSEUR, J., 1955. Traces fossiles d'activite animale et leur sigification paleobiologique. Mem. Soc. geol. France (n.s.) 34: **4**, 74: 1-150 (fascimile).

LILIENSTERN, H.R., VON, 1939. Fahrten und Spuren im Chirotherien-Sandstein von Sudthuringen. Fortschr. Geol. Palaontol., **12**, 40: 293-387.

LISSMANN, H.W., 1946a. The Neruological Basis of the Locomotory Rhythm in the Spinal Dogfish (*Scyllium canicula, Acanthias vulgaris*): I. Reflex Behavior. J. Exper. Biol. **23**, 2: 143-161.

LISSMANN, H.W., 1946b. The Neurological Basis of the Locomotory Rhythm in the Spinal Dogfish (*Scyllium canicula, Acantias vulgaris*): II. The Effect of De-afferentation. J. Exper. Biol., **23**, 2: 162-176.

LOEB, J., 1894. Beitrage zur Gehirnphysiologie der wurmer, Arch. ges. Physiol., **56**: 268.

LOTZE, F., 1928. Die Tambacher-Sphaerodactylum-Fahrten. Palaontol. Zs., **9**, 4: 170-175.

LOVERIDGE, A., 1934. Australian Reptiles in the Museum of Comparative Zoology, Bull. Museum Compar. Zool. (Cambridge, Massachusetts), **77**, 6: 243-283.

LOVERIDGE, A., 1945. Reptiles of the Pacific World, New York.

LUCHSINGER, B., 1880. Ueber gekzeuzte Reflexe, Pflug. Arch. ges. Physiol., **22**: 179-180.

LYDEKKER, R., 1912. Reptiles, In: Reptiles, Amphibia, Fishes, and Lowar Chordata. London, 1-156.

MAHENDRA, B.C., 1941. Contribution to the Bionomics, Anatomy, Reproduction and Development of the Indian House-Gecko, *Hemidactylus flaviviridis* Ruppell: II. The Problem of Locomotion. Proc. Indian Acad. Sci.,

B, **13**, 5: 288-306.

MANTER, J.T., 1938. The Dynamics of Quadrupedal Walking. J. Exper. Biol., **15**, 4: 522-540.

MANTER, J.T., 1940. The Mechanics of Swimming in the Alligator. J. Exper. Zool., **83**, 3: 345-358.

MAREI, E., 1875. Mekhanika zhivotnogo organizma. Peredvizhenie po zemle i vozdukhu (Mechanics of Animal Organism: Movement on Land and in the Air). St. Petersburg.

MAREY, E., 1873. La machine animale: Locomotion terrestre et aerienne. Paris.

MAREY, E., 1878. La methode graphique dans les sciences experimentales, et particulierement en physiologie et en medicine. Paris.

MAREY, E., 1884. Development de la methode graphique par l'emploi de la photographie. Paris.

MAREY, E., 1894. Le Mouvement. Paris.

MAREY, E., 1901. Locomotion animale, Traite de physique biologique by C.G. Arsonval and E. Marey. 1: 229-287. Paris.

MERTENS, R., 1959. Fallschirmspringer und Gleitflieger unter den Amphibien und Reptilien. Natur und Volk, **89**, 9/10: 338-346.

MERTENS, R., 1960a. Schwimmunfahige Wasserschildkroten, Natur und Volk, **90**, 4: 127-133.

MERTENS, R., 1960b. The World of Amphibians and Reptiles. New York.

MERTENS, R., 1960c. Falschirmspringer und Gleitflieger nuter den Amphibien und Reptilien. Der Flug der Tiere by H. Schmidt *et al.* Frankfurt am Main.

MINER, R.W., 1925. The Pectoral Limbs of *Eryops* and other Primitive Tetrapods. Bull. Amer. Museum Natur, History, **51**, 7: 145-312.

MOODIE, R.L., 1929. Vertebrate Footprints from the Red Beds of Texas. Amer. J. Sci., **5**, 17: 352-368.

MOSAUER, W., 1932a. Uber die Ortsbewegung der Schlangen: Eine Kritik und Erganzung der Arbeit Wiedemann's. Zool. Jahrb., Abt. allgem. Zool. Physiol. Tiere, **52**: 191-215.

MOSAUER, W., 1932b. Adaptive Convergence in the Sand Reptiles of the Sahara and California: A Study in Structure and Behavior. Copeia, 2: 72-78.

MOSAUER, W., 1935. The Reptiles of a Sand Dune Area and Its Surroundings in the Colorado Desert, California: A Study in Habitat Preference. Ecology, **16**, 1: 13-27.

MOSAUER, W. and K. WALLIS, 1928. Beitrage zur Kenntnis der Reptilien fauna von Tunesien: I. Uber die Sanspuren einiger Kleintiere der Sahara und ihre Deutung aus dem Bewegungsmechanismus. Zool. Anz., **79**: 195-207.

MUYBRIDGE, E., 1887. Animal Locomotion. Philadelphia. Republished in 1957 as Animal in Motion, New York.

NAUCK, E.T., 1924. Die Beziehungen zwischen Beckenstellung and Gliedmassenstelung bei tetrapoden Vertebraten. Morph. Jahrb. **53**: 1-47.

NEVO, E., 1964. Population Studies of Anurans from the Lower Cretaceous of Makhtesh Ramon, Israel. Doct. Diss. Jerusalem. Cited by Gans and Parsons, 1966.

NEWCASTLE, P.G., 1657. La methode et l'evention nouvelle de dresser les chevaux. Anvers. Cited by Muybridge, 1957.

NOPCSA, F., VON, 1926. Osteologia reptillium fossilium et recentium, In: Fossilium Catalogus: I. Animalia, pars 27.

NOPCSA, F., 1931. Osteologia reptilium fossilium et recentium, In: Fossilium Catalogus: I. Animalia, pars 50.

NORRIS, K.S., 1951. The Lizard that Swims in the Sand. Natur. History, **60**, 9: 404-407.

NURSALL, J.R., 1958. A Method of Analysis of the Swimming of Fish. Copeia, 2: 136-141.

OLIVER, J.A., 1951. 'Gliding' in Amphibians and Reptiles, with a Remark on Arboreal Adaptation in the Lizard *Anolis c. carolinensis* Voigt. Amer. Naturalist, **35**: 171-176.

OLIVER, J.A., 1955. The Natural History of North American Amphibians and Reptiles. Princeton.

OLIVER, J.A., 1959. The Matamata: Surely all Turtles Can Swim...? Animal Kingdom, **62**: 167-170.

ORR, R.T., 1961. Vertebrate Biology. Philadelphia.

OSBORN, H.F., 1917. Skeletal Adaptations of *Ornitholestes, Struthiomimus, Tyrannosaurus*. Bull. Amer. Museum Natur. History, **35**: 733-771.

OTTOVEI, S.V., 1959. Peredvizhenie zhivotnykh, sb. Novoe v fiziol. domashnykh zhivotnykh (Animal Movement, In Advances in the Physiology of Domestic Animals). Moscow and Leningrad: **2**: 265-313.

PEABODY, F.E., 1948. Reptile and Amphibian Trackways from the Lower Triassic Moenkopi Formation of Arizona and Utah. Univ. Calif. Publs., Bull, Dept. Geol. Sci., **27**, 8: 295-468.

PEABODY, F.E., 1959. Trackways of Living and Fossil Salamanders. Univ. Calif. Publs. Zool., **63**, 1: 1-72.

PETIT, G., 1928. Sur le *Chalarodon madagascariensis* Peters. Bull. Soc. Zool., (France), **53**: 401-405.

PETTIGREW, J.B., 1873. Animal Locomotion. London.

PHILLIPSON, M., 1903. Contribution a l'etude des reflexes locomoteurs. C.r. Acad. Sci., **136**: 61-62.

POPOVA, T., 1935. Biodinamicheskii analiz gruzeinoi khod'by, V. sb. Issl. po biodinam. lokomotsii. Pod red. N.A. Bernshteina (Bio-dynamical Analysis of Walk under Pressure, in Studies on the Biodynamics of Locomotion. Ed. N.A. Bernstein). Moscow and Leningrad, 23-180.

RAABE, C., 1870. Theorie raisonnee de l'ecole de cavalier. Paris.

RAND, A.S., 1952. Jumping Ability of Certain Anurans, with Notes on Endurance. Copeia, 1: 15-20.

REED, C.A., 1956. Temporary Bipedal Locomotion in the Lizard *Agama caucasica* in Iraq. Herpetologica, **12**: 128.

REED, C.A., 1957. Non-swimming Water Turtles in Iraq. Copeia **1**: 51.

RIPER, W., VAN, 1952. The Tyrant's Tiny Cousin, Natur, History, **61**, 4: 173-175.

ROMER, A.S., 1922. The Locomotor Apparatus of Certain Primitive and Mammal-like Reptiles, Bull. Amer. Museum Natur, History, **46**, 10: 517-606.

ROMER, A.S., 1956. Osteology of the Reptiles. Chicago.

ROMER, J.D., 1951. Surface Locomotion of Certain Frogs (*Rana*) and the Occurrence of *R. taipehensis* Van Denburg in India. J. Bombay Natur. History Soc., **50**: 414-415.

ROOS, P.J., 1964, Lateral Bending in Newt Locomotion. Proc. Koninkl. nederl. akad. wetenschap., C, **67**, 4: 223-232.

ROSE, H.T., 1902. Bipedal Locomotion of Lizards, Nature, **66**, 1718: 551.

ROSE, W., 1950. The Reptiles and Amphibians of Southern Africa. Cape Town.

ROSE, W., 1954. The Jumping Powers of Frogs. Herpetologica, **10**: 183.

SAVILE, D.B.O., 1962. Gliding and Flight in the Vertebrates. Amer. Zoologist, **2**, 2: 161-166.

SAVILLE-KENT, W., 1895. Observations of the Frilled Lizard, *Chlamydosaurus kingi,* Proc. Zool. Soc. London, 712-719.

SAVILLE-KENT, W., 1897. Bipedal Locomotion in Lizards. Nature, **56**: 271.

SAVILLE-KENT, W., 1898. Bipedal Locomotion in Lizards. Nature, **57**: 341-365.

SAVILLE-KENT, W., 1899. Bipedal Locomotion among Existing Lizards. Proc. IV Internat. Congr. Zool., 168-169.

SAVILLE-KENT, W., 1902. Bipedal Locomotion in Lizards, Nature, **66**: 630.

SCHAEFFER, R., 1941. The Morphological and Functional Evolution of the Tarsus in Amphibians and Reptiles. Bull. Amer. Museum Natur. History, **78**, 6: 395-472.

SCHMALHAUSEN, I.I., 1964. Proiskhozhdenie nazemnykh pozvonochnykh (Origin of Terrestrial Vertebrates). Moscow.

SCHMIDT, K.P., and R. INGER, 1957. Living Reptiles of the World. New York.

SEPP, E.K., 1959. Istoriya razvitiya nervnoi sistemy pozvonochnykh (History of the Development of the Nervous System in Vertebrates). Moscow.

SHERRINGTON, C.S., 1910. Flexion-reflex of the Limb. Crossed Extension-reflex, and Reflex Stepping and Standing, J. Physiol., **40**: 28-121.

SHERRINGTON, C.S., 1913. Further Observations of the Production of Reflex Stepping by Combination of Reflex Excitation with Reflex Inhibition. J. Physiol., **47**: 196-214.

SHULEIKIN, V.V., 1934. Vneshnyaya i vnutrenyaya dinamika ryby (External and Internal Dynamics of Fishes), Izv. AN SSSR, ser 7, otd. mat. estestv. nauk, **8**: 1151-1186.

SLIJPER, E.J., 1941. De Voortbewegingsorganen, Leerboek der verglijkende ontleedkunde van de vertebraten. Ihle J.E. W. (rd). 2 dr, Utrecht: 95-222.

SLIJPER, E.J., 1946. Comparative Biologic-anatomical Investigations on the Vertebral Column and Spinal Musculature of Mammals. Verhandl. Koninkl. nederl. akad. Wetenschap., sect. II, **42**, 5: 1-128.

SMITH, F., 1912. A Manual of Veterinary Physiology. London.

SMITH, H.M., 1947. Occurrence of a Caudivagant Mechanism in Salamanders. Natur, History Misc., **8**: 1-2.

SMITH, H.M., 1946. Handbook of Lizards. Ithaca, New York.

SMITH, J.M., 1952. The Importance of the Nervous System in the Evolution of Animal Flight, Evolution, **6**, 1: 127-129.

SMITH, M.A., 1935. The Fauna of British India: Reptilia and Amphibia. II. Sauria. London.

SNYDER, C.D., 1907. Locomotion in *Batrachospes* with Severed Nerve Cord. Biol. Bull., **7**: 280-288.

SYNDER, R.C., 1949. Bipedal Locomotion of the Lizard *Basiliscus basiliscus*. Copeia, 2: 129-137.

SNYDER, R.C., 1952. Quadrupedal and Bipedal Locomotion of the Lizard. Copeia, 1: 64-70.

SNYDER, R.C., 1954. The Anatomy and Function of the Pelvic Girdle and Hindlimb in Lizard Locomotion. Amer. J. Anat., **95**, 1: 1-46.

SNYDER, R.C., 1962. Adaptations for Bipedal Locomotion of Lizards. Amer. Zoologist, **2**, 2: 191-203.

SOERGEL, W., 1925. Die Fahrten der Chirotheria. Eine palaeobiologische Studies. Jena.

STEBBINS, R.C., 1944. Some Aspects of the Ecology of the Iguanid Genus *Uma*. Eclol. Monogr., **14**, 3: 311-332.

STEBBINS, R.C., 1947. Tail and Foot Action in the Locomotion of *hydromates playcephalus*. Copeia, 1: 1-5.

STEINER, J., 1885. Die Funktion des Centralnervensystems und ihre Phylogenese. Braunschweig.

STILLMAN, J.D.B., 1882. The Horse in Motion as Shown by Instantaneous Photography. Boston.

STIRLING, E.C., 1912. Observations on the Habits of the Large Central Australian Monitor (*Varanus giganteus*) with a Note on the 'Fat Bodies' of This Species. Trans. Proc. Roy. Soc. South Australia, **36**: 26-33.

STOKELY, P.S. and J.F. BERBERIAN, 1953. On the Jumping Ability of Frogs, Copeia, 1: 187.

SUKHANOV, V.B., 1957. Nekotorye osobennosti glubokoi tazobedrennoi muskulatury *Lacertilia* (Some Peculiarities of the Deep Pectoral Musculature in *Lacertilia*). Sb. nauchn. stud. rabot. MGU (Biol), 7-13.

SUKHANOV, V.B., 1961. Nekotorye voprosy filogenii i sistemy *Lacertilia* (s. *sauria*) [Some Problems of Phylogeny and Systems in *Lacertilia* (s. *sauria*)], Zool. zh., **40**, 1: 73-83.

SUKHANOV, V.B., 1963. Formy peredvizheniya (pokhodki) nazemnykh pozvonochnykh: K teoriyu lokomotsii i evolyutsii ee form [Forms of Movement (Slow Walk) of Terrestrial Vertebrates: the Theory of Locomotion and the Evolution of Its Forms]. Byull. Mosk. obshch. ispyt. prirody. otd. biol., **68**, 5: 136-137.

SUKHANOV, V.B., 1964a. Podklass Testudinats, V kn. Osnovy Paleontologii Zemnovodnye, presmykayushchiesya i ptitsy (Subclass Testudinata, in Principles of Paleontology: Amphibians, Reptiles and Birds). Moscow. 354-438.

SUKHANOV, V.B., 1964b. Lokomotsiya yashcherits i ee mesto v obshchei sistemy lokomotsii nazemnykh pozvonochnykh. V sb. Vopr. gerpetol. (Locomotion in Lizards and Its Place in the General System of Locomotionin Terrestrial Vertebrates, in Problems of Herpetology). Leningrad. 67-69.

SUKHANOV, V.B., 1967a. Materialy po lokomotsii nazemnykh pozvonochnykh: I. Obshchaya klassifikatsiya simmetrichnykh pokhodok (Material on the Locomotion of Terrestrial Vertebrates: I. General Classification of Symmetrical Movements). Byull. Mosk. obshch. ispyt. prirody. otd. biol., **72**, 2: 118-135.

SUKHANOV, V.B., 1967b. Obshchaya sistema simmetrichnoi lokomotsii nazemnykh pozvonochnykh i osobennosti peredvizheniya nizshchikh tetrapod (General System of Symmetrical Locomotion in Tettestrial Vertebrates and Peculiarities of Movements of Lower Tetrapods). Moscow. Dokt. diss.

SUKHANOV, V.B., 1968a. E'volyutsiya dvizhenii u pozvonochnykh zhivotnykh (Evolution of Movement in Vertebrate Animals). Nauka i zhizn', **7**: 58-59, and 3-4 pages of colored illustrations.

SUKHANOV, V.B., 1968b. Materialy po lokomotsii nazemnykh pozvonochnykh: II. Pokhodki yashcherits i nekotorye osobennosti lokomotsii nizshchikh tetrapod (Material on the Locomotion of Terrestrial Vertebrates: II. Walk in Lizards and Some Peculiarities of Locomotion of Lower Tetrapods). Byull. Mosk. obshch. ispyt. prirody. otd. biol., **73**, 6.

SVIHLA, A., and R.D. SVIHLA, 1952. Bipedal Locomotion in the Iguana (*Iguana tuberculata*), Copeia, 2: 119.

SWANSON, P.L., 1950. The Iguana *Iguana iguana iguana*. Herpetologica, **6**: 187-193.

TATARINOV, L.P., 1953. O roli uslovii zhizni v filogeneze zemnovodnykh (On the Role of Conditions of Life in the Phylogenesis of Amphibians). Moscow: Kand. diss.

TAYLOR, E.H., 1963. The Lizards of Thailand. Kansas Univ. Sci. Bull., **44**, 14: 687:1077.

TAYLOR, E.H., and H.M. SMITH, 1945. Summary of the Collections of Amphibians Made in Mexico. Proc. U.S. Nat. Museum, **95**, 3185 : 521.-613.

TERENT'EV, P.V., 1961. Gerpetologiya: Uchenie o zemnovodnykh i presmykayushchikhsya (Herpetology: Concept of Amphibians and Reptiles). Moscow.

TIWARI, K.K., 1961. The Eggs and Flight of the Gecko *Ptychozoon kuhli* Stejneger from Car Nicobar. J. Bombay Nat. Hist. Soc., **58**: 523-527.

TSILMAN, O., 1930. Chastnoe uchenie o dvizhenii, V kn. Rukovodstvo sravnitel'noi fiziologii domashnykh zhivotnykh, V. Ellenberger i.A. Sheinert (Particular Study of Movement, in Manual on Comparative Physiology of Domestic Animals by V. Ellenberger and A. Sheinert). Moscow and Leningrad, 399-420.

URBAN, E.K., 1964. A Comparative Study of Locomotion in Some Teiid Lizards. Diss. Abstrs, **25**, 6: 3769.

URBAN, E.K., 1965. Quantitative Study of Locomotion in Teiid Lizards. Animal Behavior, **13**, 4: 513-529.

USPENSKII, V.D., 1953. Anatomo-fiziologicheskii analiz konechnostei v allyure i ego prakticheskoe znachenie (Anatomical-physiological Analysis of Limbs in Allure and Its Practical Significance). Tr. Saratovsk. zoovet. inst., **4**: 109-115.

VANZOLINI, P.E., 1961. Notes bionomicas sobre *Dracaena quianensis* po para (*Sauria*, *Teiidae*). Paps. Dept. zool. Secretar. agric, S. Paulo, **14**, 25: 237-241.

VERMEL', YU., 1931. E'skizy o faktorakh napravlyayushchikh evolyutsiyu (An Outline of Factors Directing Evolution). Tr. inst. zool. MGU, **4**, 3: 1-126.

VIS, C.W., de, 1884. Myology of *Chlamydosaurus kingi.*, Proc. Linnena Soc. N.S. Wales, 300-320.

WATSON, D.M.S., 1917. The Evolution of the Tetrapod Shoulder Girdle and Fore-limb. J. Anat., **52**: 1-63.

WATSON, D.M.S., 1926. The Evolution and Origin of the Amphibia. Philos. Trans. Roy. Soc., B, **214**: 189-257.

WATSON, D.M.S., 1951. Paleontology and Modern Biology. New Haven.

WEBB, R.G., 1962. North American Recent Soft-shelled Turtles (Family *Trionychidae*). Univ. Kansas Publs. Museum Natur. History, **13**: 429-611.

WEBER, E. and W. WEBER, 1836. Mechanik der menschlichen Gewerkzeuge. Gottingen.

WEISS, P., 1936. A Study of Motor Coordination and Tonus in De-afferented Limbs of Amphibia. Amer. J. Physiol., **115**: 461:475.

WEISS, P., 1941a. Does Sensory Control Play a Constructive Role in the

Development of Motor Coordination? Schweiz. med. Wochenschr., **71**, 12: 106-407.

WEISS, P., 1941b. Self-differentiation of the Basic Patterns of Coordination, Compar. Psychol. Monogr., **88**, 17: 4.

WERMEL, J., 1934. Die Extremitaten-proportionen und der Schprung bei den Salientia. Zs. Anat. Entwicklungsgesch, **103**: 645-659.

WHITING, H.P., 1961. Pelvic Girdle in Amphibian Locomotion, Sympos. Zool. Soc. London, 5, Vertebrate Locomotion, 43-57.

WILFARTH, H.M., 1949. Die Lebensweise der Dinosaurier. Stuttgart.

WOODS, G.T., 1945. Rate of Travel of the Wood Turtle. Copeia, 1: 49.

WYNMALEN, H., 1954. The Horse in Action. New York.

YAKOVLEV, A.A., 1951. Allyury kak pokazateli polzovatel'nykh kachestv loshchadei (Allures as an Index of the Exploitational Qualities of Horses). Moscow. Doct. diss.

ZAKHIDOV, T., 1938. Biologiya reptilii Yuzhnykh Kyzylkumov i khrebta Nura-Tau (Biology of Reptiles of the South Kyzylkums and Nura-Tau Peak). Tr. Sredneaziatsk. gos. univ. zool., **8**a, 54: 1-50.

ZAVARZIN, A.A., 1941. Ocherki po evolyutsionnoi gistologii nervnoi sistemy (Notes on Evolutional Histology of the Nervous System). Moscow.